Prentice Hall

MATHEMATICS

Course 2

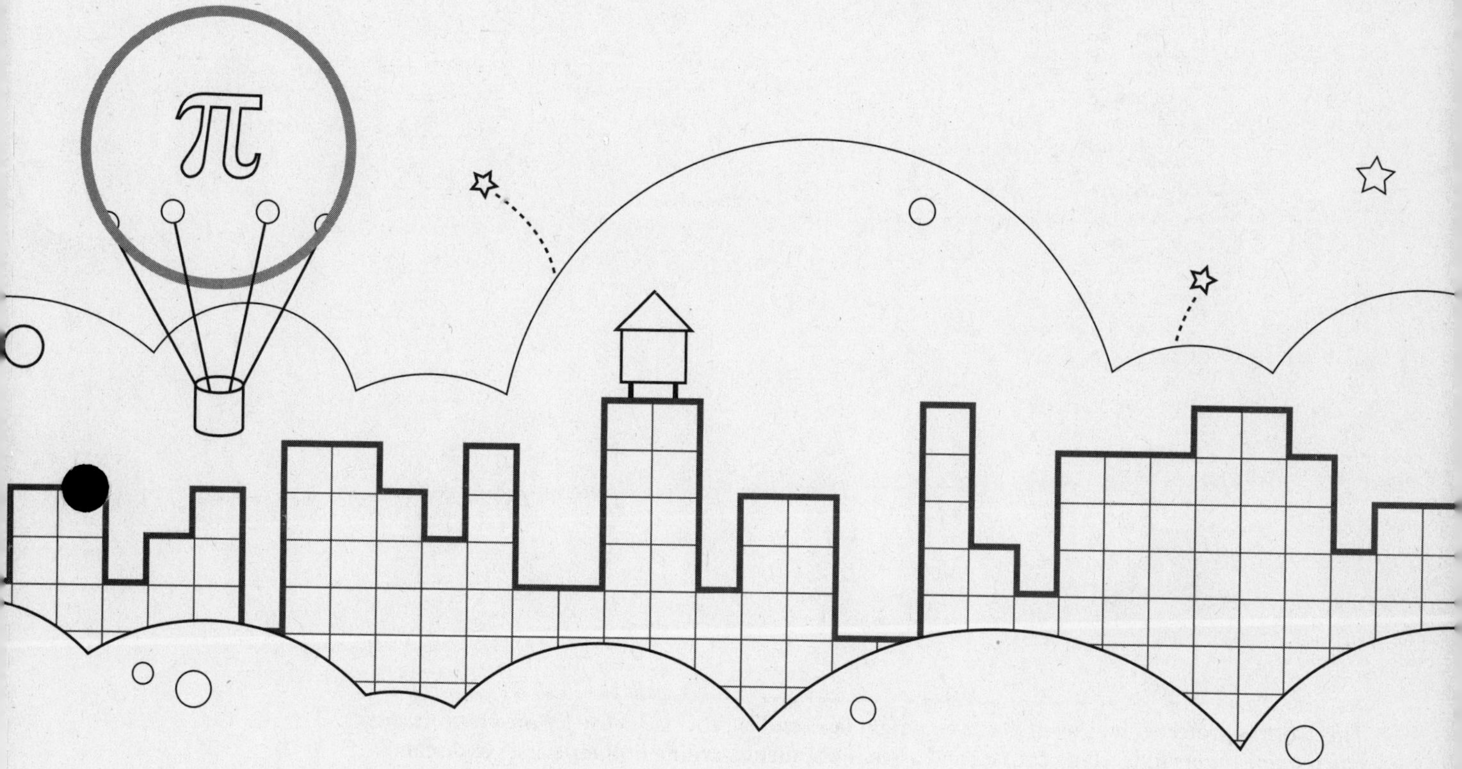

ALL-IN-ONE

Teaching Resources

CHAPTERS 9–12

Boston, Massachusetts • Chandler, Arizona • Glenview, Illinois • Upper Saddle River, New Jersey

ISBN-13: 978-0-13-372130-0
ISBN-10: 0-13-372130-2

2 3 4 5 6 7 8 9 10 V012 13 12 11 10

All-In-One Teaching Resources

Chapters 1–4

Chapters 5–8

Chapters 9–12

To the Teacher:

During the school year, you use several sources to help create your daily lesson plans. In Prentice Hall's *All-In-One Teaching Resources*, these lesson and chapter based sources are organized for you so that you can plan easily and effectively.

The *All-In-One Teaching Resources* are split into 3 volumes — Chapters 1–4, Chapters 5–8, and Chapters 9–12 — in the same order as the student edition chapters. Inside, you'll find several resources to support and extend every lesson:

- Practice (regular and adapted)
- Guided Problem Solving
- Reteaching
- Enrichment
- Activity Labs
- Daily Puzzles

Additional resources have been designed to support and assess every chapter:

- Vocabulary and Study Skills support
- Checkpoint Quizzes
- Chapter Projects
- Chapter Tests (regular and below level)
- Alternative Assessment
- Cumulative Review

To assist you in effective lesson planning, a special 2-page detail showing each resource page is included in each volume. All resources have been aligned either to a particular lesson, as review, or as assessment material.

At the end of each book, you will also find all of the answers for the chapters in that volume.

How To Read

Chapter

Lessons

Chapter 1: Whole Numbers and Decimals

Lesson	1-1	1-2	1-3	1-4	1-5	1-6	1-7	1-8	1-9		Review	Assess
For Each Lesson												
Practice (regular)	1	9	17	25	35	43	51	59	67			
Practice (adapted)	3	11	19	27	37	45	53	61	69			
Reteaching	5	13	21	29	39	47	55	63	71			
Guided Problem Solving	2	10	18	26	36	44	52	60	68			
Enrichment	6	14	22	30	40	48	56	64	72			
Activity Lab	4	12	20	28	38	46	54	62	70			
Daily Puzzle	8	16	23	33	42	50	57	65	74			
For Each Chapter												
Vocabulary and Study Skills												
Graphic Organizer	7											
Reading Comprehension		15										
Math Symbols					41							
Visual Vocabulary Practice						49						
Vocabulary Check				31								
Vocabulary Review/Puzzle											73	
Chapter Project											75	
Checkpoint Quizzes												79
Chapter Test (regular)												81
Chapter Test (below level)												83
Alternative Assessment												85
Cumulative Review											87	

Resource Types

Page References

Contents Chart

Chapter 9: Algebra: Patterns and Rules

Chapter 10: Algebra: Graphing in the Coordinate Plane

Contents Chart (continued)

Chapter 11: Displaying and Analyzing Data

Lesson	11-1	11-2	11-3	11-4	11-5	11-6	11-7				Review	Assess
For Each Lesson												
Practice (regular)	153	161	169	177	185	193	201					
Practice (adapted)	155	163	171	179	187	195	203					
Reteaching	157	165	173	181	189	197	205					
Guided Problem Solving	154	162	170	178	186	194	202					
Enrichment	158	166	174	182	190	198	206					
Activity Lab	156	164	172	180	188	196	204					
Daily Puzzle	160	167	176	184	191	199	211					
For Each Chapter												
Vocabulary and Study Skills												
Graphic Organizer	159											
Reading Comprehension			175									
Math Symbols				183								
Visual Vocabulary Practice							209					
Vocabulary Check							207					
Vocabulary Review/Puzzle											210	
Chapter Project											212	
Checkpoint Quizzes												216
Chapter Test (regular)												217
Chapter Test (below level)												219
Alternative Assessment												221
Cumulative Review											223	

Chapter 12: Using Probability

Lesson	12-1	12-2	12-3	12-4	12-5	12-6					Review	Assess
For Each Lesson												
Practice (regular)	225	233	241	249	257	265						
Practice (adapted)	227	235	243	251	259	267						
Reteaching	229	237	245	253	261	269						
Guided Problem Solving	226	234	242	250	258	266						
Enrichment	230	238	246	254	262	270						
Activity Lab	228	236	244	252	260	268						
Daily Puzzle	232	240	247	255	264	275						
For Each Chapter												
Vocabulary and Study Skills												
Graphic Organizer	231											
Reading Comprehension		239										
Math Symbols					263							
Visual Vocabulary Practice						273						
Vocabulary Check						271						
Vocabulary Review/Puzzle											274	
Chapter Project											276	
Checkpoint Quizzes												280
Chapter Test (regular)												281
Chapter Test (below level)												283
Alternative Assessment												285
Cumulative Review											287	

Name ______________________ Class ______________ Date ______________

Practice 9-1

Patterns and Graphs

1. The table shows the costs of packages containing writable CDs. Graph the data in the table.

Number of CDs	10	20	50	100	200
Cost ($)	10	15	25	40	75

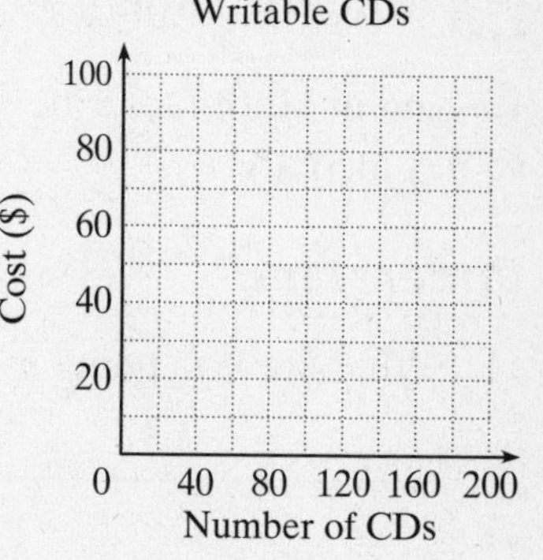

The graph shows the 2005 median income of some year-round workers and the number of years of school. The trend line is shown. Use this graph for Exercises 2–3.

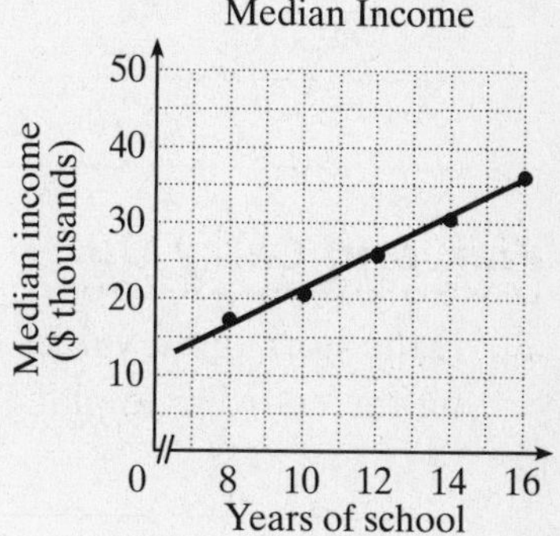

2. Predict the median income for the workers who have spent 20 years in school.

____

3. Do you think you can use this graph to predict the median salary for workers who have spent less than 8 years in school? Explain.

____

____

The table shows average monthly temperatures in degrees Fahrenheit for American cities in January and July. Use this information for Exercises 4–5.

City	Seattle	Boise	Chicago	LA	New York	Anchorage
Jan.	39.1	29.9	21.4	56.0	31.8	13.0
Jul.	64.8	74.6	73.0	69.0	76.4	58.1

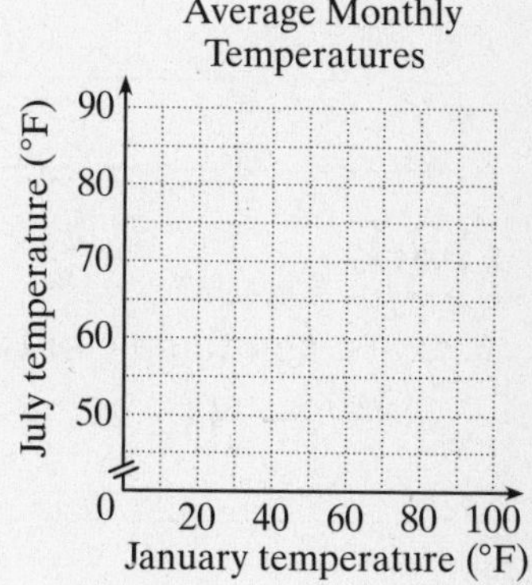

4. Graph the data in the table.

5. Use your graph to estimate the July temperature of a city whose average January temperature is 10°F.

____

Name _______________ Class _______________ Date _______________

9-1 • Guided Problem Solving

GPS Student Page 439, Exercise 13:

Writing in Math Describe what a graph looks like when both sets of values increase.

Understand

1. What are you being asked to do?

____

____

2. What does the phrase *both sets of values* mean?

____

____

Plan and Carry Out

3. If the horizontal values increase, or get bigger, where are the points on the coordinate plane?

____

4. If the vertical values increase, or get bigger, where are the points on the coordinate plane?

____

5. Describe what a graph looks like when both sets of values increase.

____

____

Check

6. Give an example of two quantities that would have this relationship.

____

____

Solve Another Problem

7. Describe what a graph looks like when only the vertical values decrease.

____

____

Name ______________________ Class ______________ Date ______________

Practice 9-1

Patterns and Graphs

1. The table shows prices of packages containing writable CDs. Graph the data in the table.

Number of CDs	10	20	50	100	200
Cost ($)	10	15	25	40	75

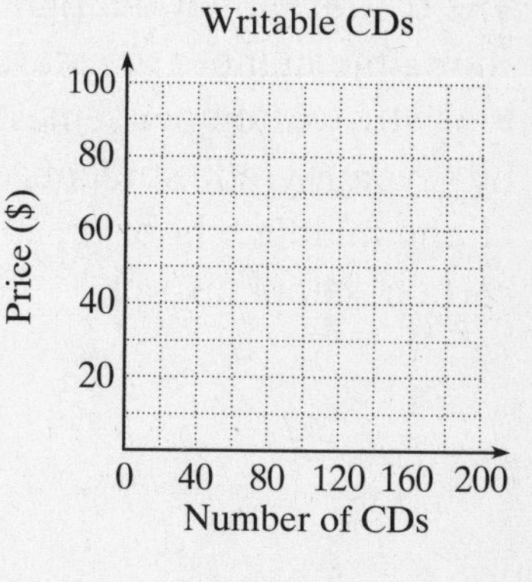

2. The graph shows the 2005 median income of some year-round workers and the number of years of school. The trend line is shown. Do you think you can use this graph to predict the median salary for workers who have spent less than 8 years in school? Explain.

____

____

____

____

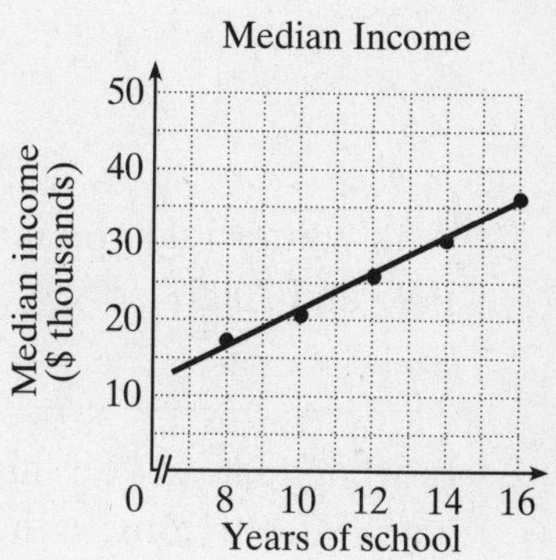

The table shows average monthly temperatures in degrees Fahrenheit for American cities in January and July. Use this information for Exercises 3–4.

City	Seattle	Boise	Chicago	LA	New York	Anchorage
Jan.	39.1	29.9	21.4	56.0	31.8	13.0
Jul.	64.8	74.6	73.0	69.0	76.4	58.1

3. Graph the data in the table.

4. Use your graph to estimate the July temperature of a city whose average January temperature is 10°F.

____

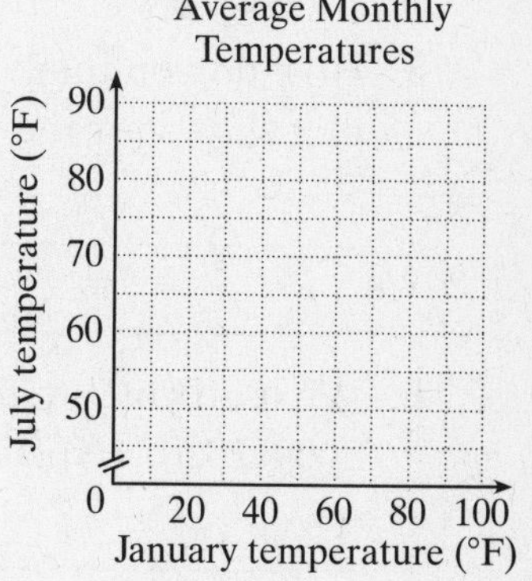

Name ________________________ Class ________________ Date ________________

Activity Lab 9-1

Patterns and Graphs

The scatter plot at the right shows the number of essays typically written per semester by seventh-grade students at all the middle schools in a certain school district.

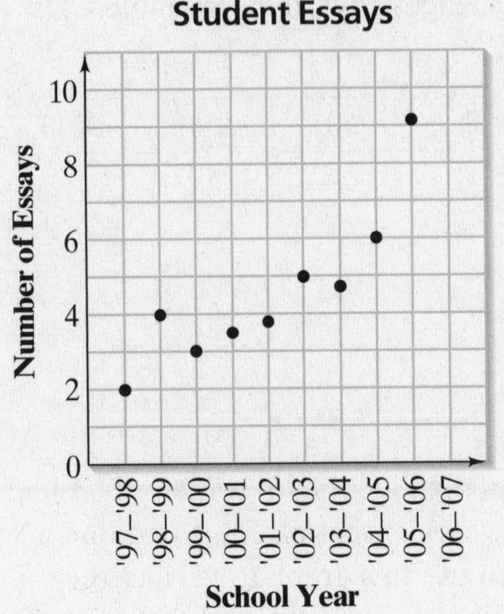

1. What pattern do you notice over the eight-year period between 1997 and 2005?

____

2. In what year do you think that more teachers began to emphasize writing in their classes? Explain.

____

3. Suppose that during the 2007–2008 school year, the schools received news that they had a three-year grant to pay for a specialist to teach students to write in all subject areas.

   a. How do you think the grant will affect the value the scatter plot shows for the year 2008–2009?

   ____

   ____

   b. What do you predict might happen to the pattern for the year 2009–2010? Explain.

   ____

   ____

4. Suppose that during the three years that the specialist was in the school system, she trained all of the middle school teachers to use writing in their subject areas. What pattern might this show for the school years 2010–2011 and 2011–2012? Explain.

____

____

Reteaching 9-1

Patterns and Graphs

Graphs can help you visualize the relationship between data. A graph includes two scales, one on the horizontal axis and one on the vertical axis. An interval is the distance between the values on a scale.

Graph the data in the table.

Hours Worked	Money Earned
5	$41.25
6	$49.50
7	$57.75
8	$66.00
9	$74.25

Step 1 Choose the scales and intervals.

Graph the data in the first column on the horizontal axis. Graph the data in the second column on the vertical axis.

Choose the interval for the scale on the horizontal axis. The greatest number of hours worked is 9. If each interval is 1 hour, then the number of intervals is $9 \div 1 = 9$.

Choose the interval for the scale on the vertical axis. The greatest amount of money earned is $74.25. If each interval is $5, then the number of intervals is $74.25 \div 5 = 14.85$, or 15 intervals.

Step 2 Draw the graph and plot the data. Estimate the position of data points that fall between intervals.

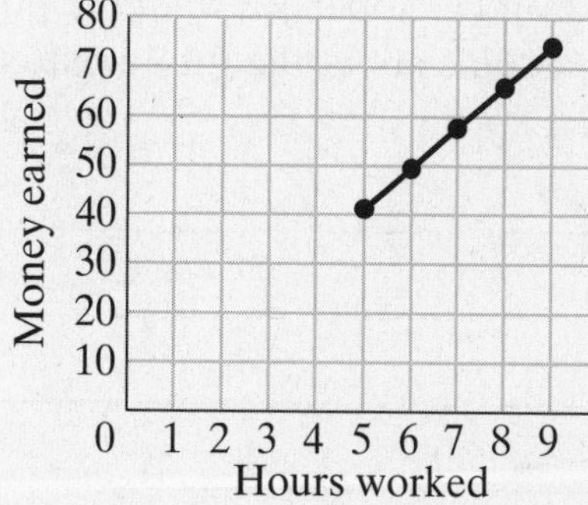

Graph the data in each table.

1.

Hours	Miles Run
2	10
2.8	14
3.2	16
3.6	18

2.

Gallons of Gas	Miles Driven
0.5	13
1.5	39
2.5	65
3	78

Name ______________________ Class ______________ Date ____________

Enrichment 9-1

Patterns and Graphs

Patterns in Data

Bookends is a three-year-old chain of bookstores. The scatter plot at the right shows the average price of one share of Bookends stock for January through June of 2006.

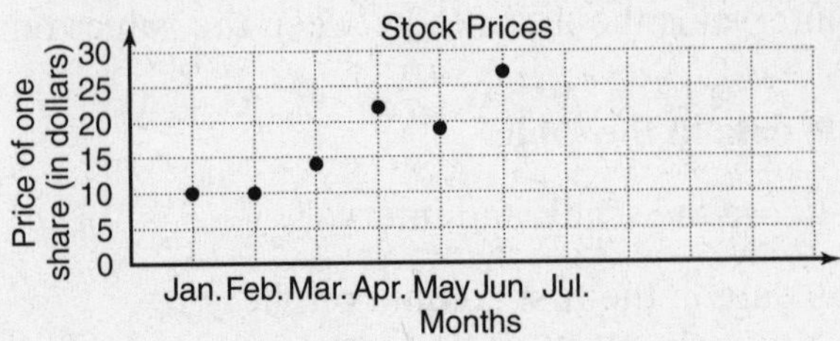

1. Draw a line for the stock prices for January through June. Label it *Trend 1*. Based on this pattern, what would you expect the average price to be in July? Explain.

____

____

2. Suppose the average stock price for July was \$16, August \$17, September \$22, and October \$25. Plot the points on the graph. What can you assume about the future pattern of stock prices for this company? Explain.

____

____

____

____

3. When a 2-for-1 stock split occurs, each stock owner owns twice as many shares of stock as before the split, but each share is worth half as much. In this way, a company can keep its stock affordable. Suppose you learn that Bookends had a 2-for-1 stock split in July.

   a. How would that change your prediction of the future pattern of its stock prices? Explain.

   ____

   ____

   ____

   b. Draw a line on the graph above to show your new prediction. Label it *Trend 2*. How does it compare with the trend line you drew in Exercise 1?

   ____

   ____

Name ________________ Class ____________ Date ____________

9A: Graphic Organizer

For use before Lesson 9-1

Study Skill Many skills build on each other, particularly in mathematics. Before you begin a new lesson, do a quick review of the material you covered in earlier lessons. Make sure you ask for help when there are concepts you did not understand or do not remember.

Write your answers.

1. What is the chapter title?

   ____

2. How many lessons are there in this chapter?

   ____

3. What is the topic of the Test-Taking Strategies page?

   ____

4. Complete the graphic organizer below as you work through the chapter.
   - In the center, write the title of the chapter.
   - When you begin a lesson, write the lesson name in a rectangle.
   - When you complete a lesson, write a skill or key concept in a circle linked to that lesson block.
   - When you complete the chapter, use this graphic organizer to help you review.

Name ______________________ Class ______________ Date ______________

Puzzle 9-1

Patterns and Graphs

Analyze the shapes on the grid to find the pattern. Then complete the missing section in the center.

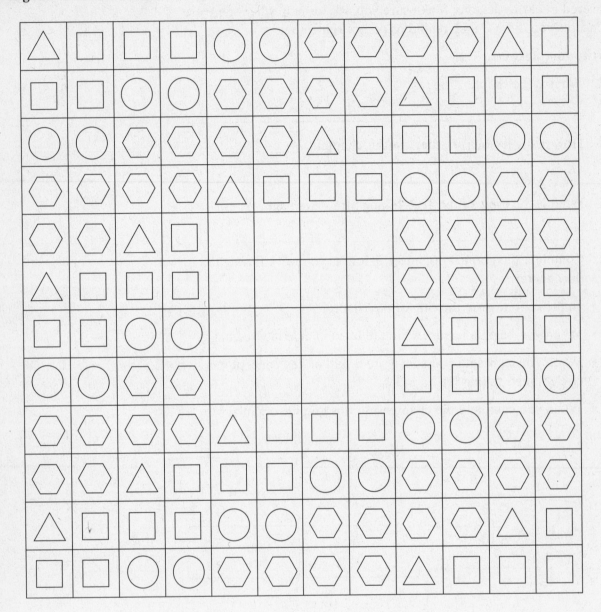

Name ______________________ Class ______________ Date ______________

Practice 9-2

Number Sequences

Identify each sequence as *arithmetic, geometric,* or *neither.* Write a rule for each sequence.

1. 2, 6, 18, 54, . . .

2. 5, −10, 20, −40, . . .

3. 3, 5, 7, 9, . . .

4. 5, 6, 8, 11, 15, . . .

5. 1, 2, 6, 24, . . .

6. 17, 16, 15, 14, . . .

7. 50, −50, 50, −50, . . .

8. 1, 2, 4, 5, 10, 11, 22, . . .

Find the next three terms in each sequence.

9. 15, −14, 13, −12, . . .

10. 243, 81, 27, . . .

11. 5, 12, 26, . . .

12. 2, 5, 9, 14, . . .

Write the first five terms in the sequence described by the rule. Identify the sequence as *arithmetic, geometric,* or *neither.*

13. Start with 2 and multiply by −3 repeatedly.

14. Start with 27 and add −9 repeatedly.

15. Start with 18 and multiply by 0.1, then by 0.2, then by 0.3, and so on.

Name ______________________ Class ______________ Date ______________

9-2 • Guided Problem Solving

GPS Student Page 444, Exercise 21:

Running Mario can run a mile in 9 min. After 4 months of training, he hopes to run a mile in 8 min. His time decreases by 15 s each month. What would you tell Mario about his conjecture?

Understand

1. What is a conjecture?

____

____

2. What is Mario's conjecture?

____

____

3. What are you being asked to do?

____

Plan and Carry Out

4. After 1 month of training, how fast can Mario run a mile?

____

5. After 2 months of training, how fast can Mario run a mile? After 3 months? After 4 months?

____

6. Is Mario's conjecture valid?

____

Check

7. How could you have worked the problem another way?

____

____

Solve Another Problem

8. Linda can walk a mile in 12 min. After 6 months of training, she hopes to walk a mile in 10 min 30 s. Her time decreases by 10 s each month. What would you tell Linda about her conjecture?

____

____

Name ______________________ Class ______________ Date ______________

Practice 9-2

Number Sequences

Identify each sequence as *arithmetic, geometric,* or *neither.* Write a rule for each sequence.

1. 2, 6, 18, 54, . . .

2. 5, −10, 20, −40, . . .

3. 3, 5, 7, 9, . . .

4. 5, 6, 8, 11, 15, . . .

5. 1, 2, 6, 24, . . .

6. 17, 16, 15, 14, . . .

Find the next three terms in each sequence.

7. 15, −14, 13, −12, . . .

8. 243, 81, 27, . . .

Write the first five terms in the sequence described by the rule. Identify the sequence as *arithmetic, geometric,* or *neither.*

9. Start with 2 and multiply by −3 repeatedly.

10. Start with 27 and add −9 repeatedly.

Name ____________________ Class ______________ Date ______________

Activity Lab 9-2

Number Sequences

Count the squares in the grids below.

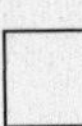

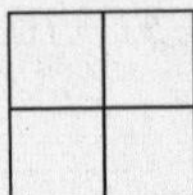

<u>1 square</u>	<u>5 squares</u>	<u>14 squares</u>
1×1 square	one 2×2 square four 1×1 squares	one 3×3 square four 2×2 squares nine 1×1 squares

1. Now find the total number of squares in this 4×4 grid.

   ____________ 4×4 square

   ____________ 3×3 squares

   ____________ 2×2 squares

   ____________ 1×1 squares

   Total number of squares ____________

2. What pattern do you see for the numbers of smaller squares?

   ____

   ____

3. Continue the pattern. List the squares in a 5×5 grid.

   ____

   ____

4. Continue the pattern. List the squares in a 6×6 grid.

   ____

   ____

5. Continue the pattern. List the squares in a 10×10 grid.

   ____

   ____

Name ____________________ Class ____________ Date ____________

Reteaching 9-2

Number Sequences

A set of numbers that follows a pattern forms a **sequence.** The numbers 2, 4, 6, 8, . . . form a sequence. The three dots ". . ." tell you that the pattern continues. The numbers 2, 4, 6, 8, and so on are the **terms** of the sequence.

Arithmetic Sequence

Add the same number to each term to get the next term. In the sequence 2, 4, 6, 8, . . . , you add 2 to each term to get the next term.

Write a rule to describe this sequence, and find the next three terms.
5, 10, 15, 20, . . .

5 → +5 → 10 → +5 → 15 → +5 → 20

Start with 5 and add 5 repeatedly.

To find the next three terms, add 5.

$20 + 5 = 25$

$25 + 5 = 30$

$30 + 5 = 35$

The next three terms are 25, 30, and 35.

Geometric Sequence

Multiply each term by the same number to get the next term. In the sequence 1, 4, 16, 64, . . . , you multiply each term by 4 to get the next term.

Write a rule to describe this sequence, and find the next three terms.
2 , 4, 8, 16, . . .

2 → ×2 → 4 → ×2 → 8 → ×2 → 16

Start with 2 and multiply by 2 repeatedly.

To find the next three terms, multiply by 2.

$16 \times 2 = 32$

$32 \times 2 = 64$

$64 \times 2 = 128$

The next three terms are 32, 64, and 128.

Write a rule for each arithmetic sequence. Then find the next three terms.

1. 4, 7, 10, 13, . . .

____

____

____

2. 2, 4, 6, 8, . . .

____

____

____

3. 20, 35, 50, . . .

____

____

____

Write a rule for each geometric sequence. Then find the next three terms.

4. 5, 25, 125, 625, . . .

____

____

____

____

5. 7, 49, 343, 2,401, . . .

____

____

____

____

6. 0.3, 0.9, 2.7, 8.1, . . .

____

____

____

____

Name ______________________ Class ______________ Date ______________

Enrichment 9-2

Number Sequences

Patterns in Data

In 1202, Leonardo Fibonacci, an Italian mathematician, described a mathematical sequence that is named after him, the *Fibonacci Sequence.*

The first ten numbers in the sequence are given below.

1 1 2 3 5 8 13 21 34 55

1. How are the first two terms related to the third term?

____

2. How are the second and third terms related to the fourth term?

____

3. How are the third and fourth terms related to the fifth term?

____

4. What general rule can you make for finding each successive term?

____

Additional patterns can be found in the *Fibonacci Sequence.*

5. Complete the table for the given three consecutive terms of the sequence. Then choose two additional sets of three consecutive terms of the sequence and complete the table for them.

Consecutive terms	Product of first and third terms	Square of second term
1, 2, 3	3	4
2, 3, 5		

6. What pattern do you notice in the numbers in the second and third columns for each set of consecutive terms? Explain.

____

____

7. Is the smaller number always in the same column? Explain.

____

____

Name ______________________ Class ______________ Date ______________

Puzzle 9-2

Number Sequences

Describe the pattern for each sequence, then give the next three terms and indicate whether each sequence is *arithmetic, geometric, both,* or *neither*. To solve the puzzle, write the letter of each sequence above its next term.

	Sequence	Pattern	Next three terms	Arithmetic, geometric, both, or neither?
A	3, 8, 13, 18,...			
N	20, 10, 5, 2.5,...			
A	0.1, –1, 10, –100,...			
N	1, 7, 19, 43,...			
A	1, 4, 9, 16, 25,...			
T	–8, –8, –8, –8,...			
I	12, 5, –2, –9,...			
Z	1, 0, –2, –6, –14,...			

Mount Kilimanjaro, the highest mountain in Africa, is located in the country of

____ ____ ____ ____ ____ ____ ____ ____.

–8 1,000 91 –30 23 1.25 –16 36

Name ______________________ Class ______________ Date ______________

Practice 9-3

Patterns and Tables

Complete each table.

1.

Time (h)	1	2	3	4	7
Distance cycled (mi)	8	16	24	32	

2.

Time (min)	1	2	3	4	7
Distance from surface of water (yd)	−3	−2	−1	0	

Write a variable expression to describe the rule for each sequence. Then find the 100th term.

3. 35, 36, 37, . . .

   Expression: ____________

   100th term: ____________

4. 8, 10, 12, 14, . . .

   Expression: ____________

   100th term: ____________

Find the values of the missing entries in each table.

5.

m	4	6		10
n	24	26	28	

6.

p	2		10	14
q	1	13	25	

7. A pattern of squares is shown. 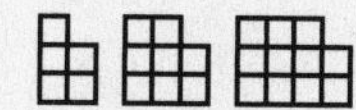

   a. Sketch the 4th and 5th figure in this pattern. ____________

   b. Make a table comparing the figure number to the number of squares. Write an expression for the number of squares in the *n*th figure.

   c. How many squares would there be in the 80th figure? ____________

Write a variable expression to describe the rule for each sequence. Then find the 20th term.

8. 6, 12, 18, 24, . . .

   Expression: ____________

   20th term: ____________

9. 3, 6, 9, 12, . . .

   Expression: ____________

   20th term: ____________

10. One month's average price for ground beef is $2.39 per pound. Using this relationship, make a table that shows the price for 1, 2, 3, and 4 pounds of ground beef.

Name ______________________ Class ______________ Date ______________

9-3 • Guided Problem Solving

GPS Student Page 448, Exercise 20:

Music The table shows costs for violin lessons. Complete the table.

Time (h)	0.5	1	1.5	2
Cost ($)	12.50			

Understand

1. In which row is the cost of a violin lesson?

____

2. What information is given in the first column of the table?

____

3. What are you being asked to do?

____

Plan and Carry Out

4. How much is a 0.5-hour lesson? ____________
5. What is the relationship between 0.5 and 1? ____________
6. Use the same relationship you found in Step 5 to find the cost of a 1-hour lesson. ____________
7. What amount should you add to the answer in Step 6 to find the cost of a 1.5-hour lesson? ____________
8. How much does a 1.5-hour lesson cost? ____________
9. How much does a 2-hour lesson cost? ____________

Check

10. Explain how you could use multiplication in this problem.

____

____

____

Solve Another Problem

11. The table shows costs for math tutoring. Complete the table.

Time (h)	0.5	1	1.5	2
Cost ($)	15.75			

Name ____________________ Class ____________ Date ____________

Practice 9-3

Patterns and Tables

Complete each table.

1.

Time (h)	1	2	3	4	7
Distance cycled (mi)	8	16	24	32	

2.

Time (min)	1	2	3	4	7
Distance from surface of water (yd)	−3	−2	−1	0	

Write a variable expression to describe the rule for each sequence. Then find the 100th term.

3. 35, 36, 37, . . .

   Expression: ____________

   100th term: ____________

4. 8, 10, 12, 14, . . .

   Expression: ____________

   100th term: ____________

Find the values of the missing entries in each table.

5.

m	4	6		10
n	24	26	28	

6.

p	2		10	14
q	1	13	25	

7. A pattern of squares is shown.

   a. Sketch the 4th and 5th figures in this pattern. ____________

   b. Make a table comparing the figure number to the number of squares.

Write a variable expression to describe the rule for each sequence. Then find the 20th term.

8. 6, 12, 18, 24, . . .

   Expression: ____________

   20th term: ____________

9. 3, 6, 9, 12, . . .

   Expression: ____________

   20th term: ____________

Name ______________________ Class ______________ Date ______________

Activity Lab 9-3

Patterns and Tables

An Italian mathematician, Leonardo Fibonacci, discovered this interesting number pattern around A.D. 1200. The numbers in the pattern are called Fibonacci numbers and appear quite frequently in nature.

Use the diagram of the tree to help you complete the table.

Year	Number of branches
First	1
Second	1
Third	2
Fourth	
Fifth	
Sixth	
Seventh	

1. Choose any two consecutive years and add the number of branches. What do you notice about the sum? Repeat using two other consecutive numbers. Does the same thing occur?

____

____

2. If the tree continues to grow at the same rate, what would be the number of branches for the eighth year? The ninth year? The tenth year?

____

3. Find the missing numbers for this number pattern:

   1, 1, 2, 3, n, n, 13, n, 34, n, n, n, 233 . . .

____

Name ______________________ Class ______________ Date ______________

Reteaching 9-3

Patterns and Tables

A table can help you write a variable expression that describes a sequence.

Give the next two terms in this sequence: 6, 12, 18, 24, 30, . . .

Term number	1	2	3	4	5
Term	6	12	18	24	30

The rule is *"multiply the term number by 6."* A variable expression is $n \cdot 6$, or $6n$.

So the next two terms will be 36 and 42.

Give the next two terms in this sequence: 4, 8, 12, 16, 20, . . .

1. What will you multiply the term number by to find the corresponding term?

   ____

2. Let n = term number. Write an expression that shows this relationship.

   ____

3. How will you find the sixth term in the sequence? the seventh term?

   ____

4. What are the sixth and seventh terms?

   ____

Let *n* equal the term number. Circle the expression that gives the rule for each sequence.

5. 2, 5, 8, 11, 14, . . . $2n - 1$ $3n - 1$ $3n + 1$
6. 1, 4, 9, 16, 25, 36, . . . $n + 5$ n^2 $n^2 - 1$
7. 5, 10, 15, 20, 25, . . . $5n$ n^5 $n + 5$

Name ______________________ Class ______________ Date ______________

Enrichment 9-3

Visual Thinking

Which of these figures do you think will have the greatest area? The greatest perimeter? The least area? The least perimeter? Record your estimates inside each figure.

1.

2.

3.

4.

5.

Measure each figure to the nearest centimeter and complete the table.

Exercise	Length (cm)	Width (cm)	Area (cm^2)	Perimeter (cm)
1				
2				
3				
4				
5				

Record the exercise number(s) of the figure(s) with the

6. greatest area ______________________

7. greatest perimeter ______________________

8. least area ______________________

9. least perimeter ______________________

Name ____________________ Class ____________ Date ____________

9B: Reading Comprehension

For use after Lesson 9-3

Study Skill Use tables when you need to organize complex information. The columns and rows allow you to display different types of information in a way that is easy to read. Make sure you include appropriate headings.

Use the table below to answer the questions.

Top-Grossing Movies for the Weekend

Movie	Weekend Box Office Receipts (in millions)	Total Receipts (in millions)	Percent Change from Last Week	Weeks Movie Has Played
Movie A	$19.2	$62.3	−38%	2
Movie B	$16.2	16.2	New	1
Movie C	$14.0	$255.1	−33%	4
Movie D	$11.0	11.0	New	1
Movie E	$10.3	$370.4	−28%	6

1. What information does the table display?

   ____

2. What is the greatest number in the table?

   ____

3. What does a negative value in the Percent Change column indicate?

   ____

4. Why does Movie B have no value in the Percent Change column?

   ____

5. Which movie has been shown for six weeks?

   ____

6. Which movie had the greatest box office receipts for the weekend?

   ____

7. Movie E grossed a total of $370.4 million dollars in 6 weeks. What was the average amount of money it grossed per week?

   ____

8. **High-Use Academic Words** What does it mean to *organize*, as mentioned in the study skill at the top of the page?

   a. to exclude

   b. to arrange

Name ______________________ Class ______________ Date ______________

Puzzle 9-3

Find the missing values in each table.

1.

x	y
2	
4	24
	36
8	48
10	
12	72

2.

x	y
2	180
3	270
4	
5	
7	630
	1,080

3.

x	y
5	−7
7	−5
9	−3
	0
13	
	5

4.

x	y
10	
20	−60
30	−90
	−180
70	−210
	−270

5.

x	y
4	48
8	52
	54
16	60
20	
	69

6.

x	y
2	54
3	
5	135
7	189
10	
	2,727

The famous mathematician Pierre de Fermat was born in the seventeenth century. Discover the year he was born by finding the sum of the missing values above.

____ ____ ____ ____

Name ____________________ Class ____________ Date ____________

Practice 9-4

Function Rules

Use each function rule. Find y for $x = 1, 2, 3,$ and 4.

1. $y = 2x$ ________

2. $y = x + 4$ ________

3. $y = x^2 - 1$ ________

4. $y = -2x$ ________

5. $y = 3x + 1$ ________

6. $y = 8 - 3x$ ________

7. $y = 6 + 4x$ ________

8. $y = x - 5$ ________

9. $y = 2x + 7$ ________

Write a rule for the function represented by each table.

10.

x	y
1	6
2	7
3	8
4	9

____

11.

x	y
1	4
2	8
3	12
4	16

____

12.

x	y
1	−6
2	−9
3	−12
4	−15

____

13.

x	y
1	5
2	7
3	9
4	11

____

14.

x	y
1	4
2	7
3	10
4	13

____

15.

x	y
1	−1
2	−3
3	−5
4	−7

____

16. A typist types 45 words per minute.

a. Write a function rule to represent the relationship between the number of typed words and the time in which they are typed. ________

b. How many words can the typist type in 25 minutes? ________

c. How long would it take the typist to type 20,025 words? ________

Name ______________________ Class ______________ Date ______________

9-4 • Guided Problem Solving

GPS Student Page 454, Exercise 21:

Money Suppose you put $.50 in a piggy bank on July 1, $1.00 on July 2, $1.50 on July 3, and so on. Use *n* to represent the date. Write a function rule for the amount you put in for any date in July.

Understand

1. What is a function rule?

____

____

2. What are you being asked to do?

____

____

Plan and Carry Out

3. What are the inputs? ______________________

4. What are the outputs? ______________________

5. What variable represents the inputs? ______________________

6. What is the relationship between the amount of money you put in the piggy bank on the first day and number of the day, July 1? July 2?

____

7. What do you do to *n* to figure out how much money to put in the piggy bank? ______________________

8. Write a function rule for the amount, *a*, you put in for *any* date in July. ______________________

Check

9. Check that your rule works with days July 1, 2, and 3.

____

Solve Another Problem

10. Suppose your parents paid you $.10 on December 1, $.20 on December 2, $.30 on December 3, and so on. Use *n* to represent the date. Write a function rule for the amount your parents will pay you for any date in December.

____

Name ______________________ Class ______________ Date ______________

Practice 9-4

Function Rules

Use each function rule. Find y for $x = 1, 2, 3,$ and 4.

1. $y = 2x$ ______________
2. $y = x + 4$ ______________
3. $y = x^2 - 1$ ______________
4. $y = -2x$ ______________
5. $y = 3x + 1$ ______________
6. $y = 8 - 3x$ ______________

Write a rule for the function represented by each table.

7.

x	y
1	6
2	7
3	8
4	9

____

8.

x	y
1	4
2	8
3	12
4	16

____

9.

x	y
1	5
2	7
3	9
4	11

____

10.

x	y
1	4
2	7
3	10
4	13

____

11. A typist types 45 words per minute.
    a. Write a function rule to represent the relationship between the number of typed words and the time in which they are typed. ______________
    b. How many words can the typist type in 25 minutes? ______________

Name ______________________ Class ______________ Date ______________

Activity Lab 9-4

Function Rules

1. Study Table 1 and Table 2. Write a rule for the function represented in each table, then use the rules to fill in the missing values.

Table 1

Rule: __________

x	y
0	0
1	2
2	4
3	6
4	
5	
6	
7	
10	
100	
1000	

Table 2

Rule: __________

x	y
0	1
1	3
2	5
3	7
4	
5	
6	
7	
10	
100	
1000	

2. Notice that all of the y-values in Table 1 are even integers. Explain why this is true.

____

3. In Table 2, all of the y-values are odd integers. Why?

____

4. Find an input value for the rule used in Table 1 that will produce an odd output value.

____

5. For Table 2, what input values will give y-values that are NOT positive odd integers?

____

6. Use what you know about the multiplication and addition of integers to write a function rule that will produce both odd and even integers as output values for the input values given in the table at the right.

____

____

x	y
0	
1	
2	
3	
4	
5	

Name ______________________ Class ______________ Date ______________

Reteaching 9-4

Function Rules

The function table shows the relationship between inputs and outputs.
A function rule for this table is:

output = 4 · input

Input	Output
1	4
2	8
3	12

You can use the function rule $y = 2x + 3$ to find y when $x = 0, 1, 2,$ and 3.
Replace x with 0, 1, 2, and 3.

x	$y = 2x + 3$
0	$2(0) + 3 = 3$
1	$2(1) + 3 = 5$
2	$2(2) + 3 = 7$
3	$2(3) + 3 = 9$

Write input/output function rules for each table of values.

1.

Input	Output
3	6
4	8
5	10
6	12

____

2.

Input	Output
1	45
2	90
3	135
4	180

____

Make a table for the function represented by each rule.
Find y when $x = 0, 1, 2,$ and 3.

3. $y = 10x$

x	y
0	
1	
2	
3	

4. $y = x - 4$

x	y
0	
1	
2	
3	

5. $y = 3x - 1$

x	y
0	
1	
2	
3	

6. A printer can print 9 black-and-white pages per minute.

   a. Write a function rule to represent the relationship between the number of black-and-white printed pages and the time it takes to print them. ______________________

   b. How many black-and-white pages can be printed in 15 minutes? ______________________

   c. How long would it take to print a 75-page black-and-white report? ______________________

Name ______________________ Class ______________ Date ______________

Enrichment 9-4

Function Rules

Decision Making

Many banks have different types of checking accounts available. The type of account you open depends upon how many checks you write each month and how much money you plan to keep in your account.

Here are the charges from one bank:

Basic Account	\$5 per month, plus \$0.10 per check
Student Account	\$0.20 per check for the first 10 checks each month, \$1 per check for each check over 10
\$1,000 Minimum Balance Account	\$0.10 per check

1. Make a graph that shows the monthly fees related to the number of checks written for each type of account.

Checking Account Fees

Fees (dollars): 0, 5, 10, 15, 20

Number of Checks Written per Month: 0, 5, 10, 15, 20, 25

Key Basic —— Student - - - - \$1,000 ....

2. Suppose you are a student who writes about 5 checks per month.

a. Which account will you open?

____

b. About how much will your monthly fees be?

____

3. Suppose you are a student who writes 20 checks per month.

a. Which account will you open?

____

b. How much will your monthly fees be?

____

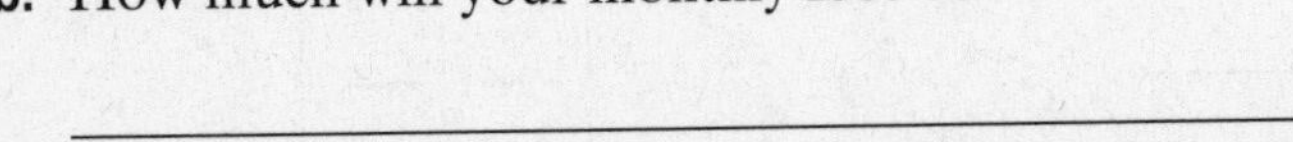

c. Suppose you have \$1,000 earning 4.8% interest each year. Should you open the \$1,000 minimum balance checking account instead of the basic account? Explain. If so, how much money will you save?

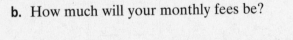

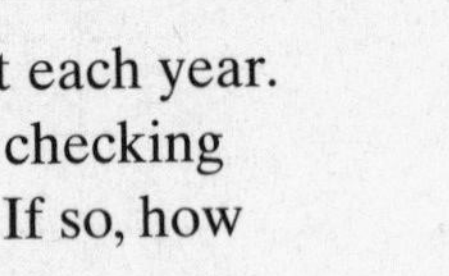

____

____

____

____

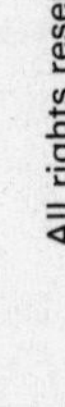

Name ______________________ Class ______________ Date ______________

9C: Reading/Writing Math Symbols

For use after Lesson 9-4

Study Skill Using mathematical symbols is a great way to take notes more quickly. Other symbols are helpful as well, such as these: @ (at), w/ (with), # (number), and = (equal).

Write each mathematical statement in words.

1. $x \leq 3$

____

____

2. $MN = 3$

____

____

3. $y = 3x$

____

____

4. $(4 + (-7)) = -3$

____

____

5. $4:5 = 8:10$

____

____

6. $\triangle EFG \cong \triangle KLM$

____

____

7. $x > 3$

____

____

8. $\overline{MN} \cong \overline{AB}$

____

____

9. $60\% = \frac{60}{100}$

____

____

10. $5^2 = 25$

____

____

11. $\triangle EFG \sim \triangle KLM$

____

____

12. $\sqrt{17} \approx 4$

____

____

13. $y = x + 4$

____

____

14. $\frac{3}{5} \neq \frac{4}{6}$

____

____

Name ________________ Class ________________ Date ________________

Puzzle 9-4

Function Rules

Matching Functions

Match the function with the real-life situation.

FUNCTION		*SITUATION*
1. $f(x) = 0.020x + 78$	______	B. A 50 cm spring will stretch $\frac{1}{4}$ the weight in kg attached to it.
2. $f(x) = 35$	______	D. A parking garage charges \$3 plus \$1.50 per hour.
3. $f(x) = 95x + 15$	______	O. A phone company charges \$0.20 per message unit plus a base charge of \$78.
4. $f(x) = 4x$	______	R. A car rental agency charges \$38 for one day plus \$0.22 per mile.
5. $f(x) = 38 + 0.22x$	______	I. A taxi company charges \$2 for the first mile plus \$0.85 each additional mile.
6. $f(x) = 0.25x + 12$	______	C. A firewood supplier charges \$95 per cord plus a \$15 delivery charge.
7. $f(x) = \frac{1}{4}x$	______	M. A water department charges \$0.25 per kiloliter plus a fixed charge of \$12.
8. $f(x) = 78x + 20$	______	N. An airport taxi charges \$35 to take someone to the airport
9. $f(x) = 3 + 1.5x$	______	G. A plumber charges \$20 to make a house call plus \$78 an hour.
10. $f(x) = 2 + 0.85(x - 1)$	______	K. A recipe calls for 4 tablespoons of oatmeal for one dozen cookies.

Write the letter of each correct answer above the exercise numbers in the letter code below to answer the question:

What is the state bird of Arkansas?

___	___	___	___	___	___	___	___	___	___	___
6	1	3	4	10	2	8	7	10	5	9

Name ______________________ Class ______________ Date ______________

Practice 9-5

Using Tables, Rules, and Graphs

The graph at the right shows the relationship between distance and time for a car driven at a constant speed.

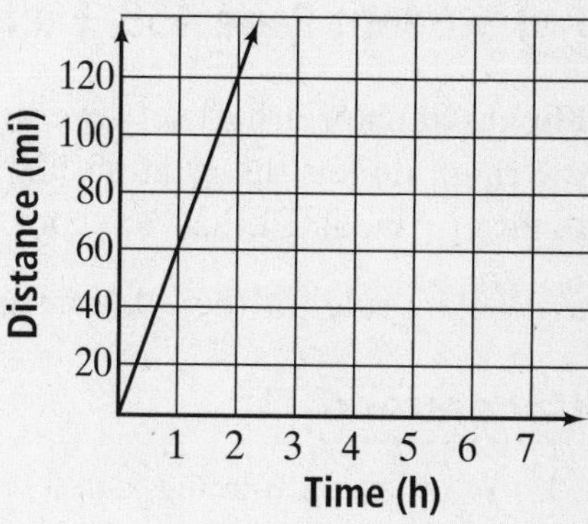

1. What is the speed? ______________
2. Is this a function relationship? ______________
3. If this is a function, write a rule to represent it.

   ____

4. Make a table for the function, listing six input/output pairs.

Graph each function. Use input values of 1, 2, 3, 4, and 5.

5. $y = -\frac{1}{2}x$

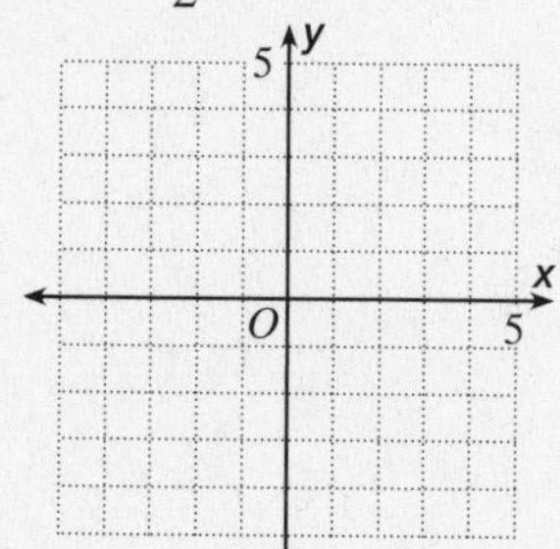

6. $y = -2x + 4$

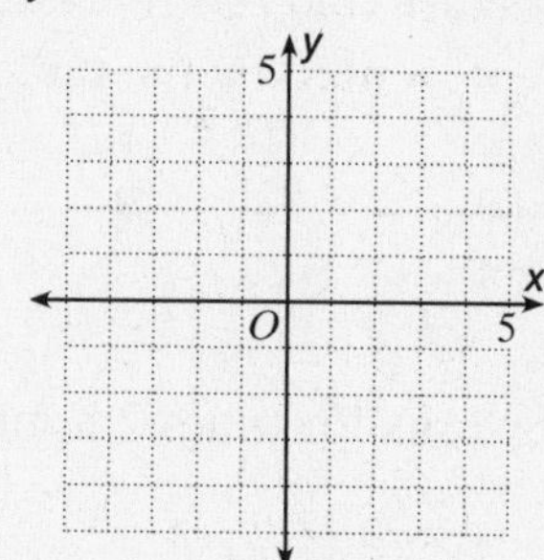

7. The relationship between the amount of time a zebra runs at maximum speed and the distance it covers is shown.

Time (min)	3	6	9	12	15
Distance (mi)	2	4	6	8	10

   a. Write an equation to describe this relationship.

   ____

   b. Use the equation to find the distance the zebra would travel in 48 minutes.

   ____

Name ______________________ Class ______________ Date ____________

9-5 • Guided Problem Solving

GPS Student Page 459, Exercise 20a:

Flight Amelia Earhart set several flight speed records. The table at the right models the relationship between distance and time for a flight at Amelia Earhart's record speed.

Amelia Earhart's Flight

Time (h)	Distance (mi)
2	362
4	724
6	1,086
8	1,448

a. Write a rule for the relationship represented by the table.

Understand

1. What are you being asked to do?

____

____

Plan and Carry Out

2. How many miles did Earhart travel in 2 h?

____

3. How many miles did Earhart travel in 1 h?

____

4. What are the inputs? What are the outputs?

____

5. Use d to represent distance and t to represent time. Write a rule for the relationship represented by the table.

____

Check

6. Check that your rule works for times 2 hours, 4 hours, and 6 hours.

____

Solve Another Problem

7. On February 20, 1962, John Glenn flew the *Friendship 7* spacecraft on the first manned orbital mission of the United States. He completed three orbits around the earth, reaching a maximum orbital velocity of approximately 17,500 miles per hour. Write a rule for the relationship of Glenn's distance d and time t at this speed.

____

Name ______________________ Class ______________ Date ______________

Practice 9-5

Using Tables, Rules, and Graphs

The graph at the right shows the relationship between distance and time for a car driven at a constant speed.

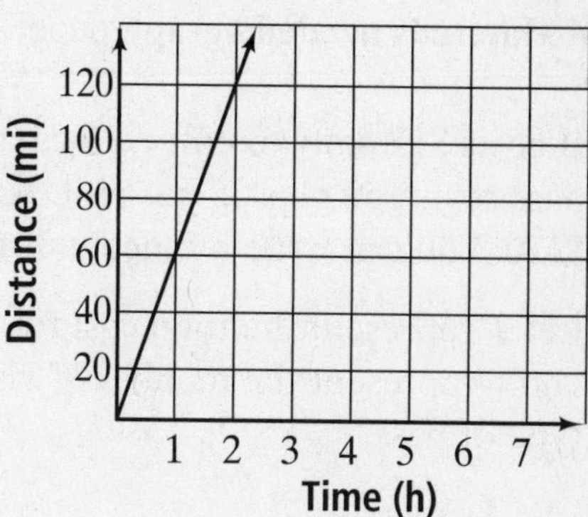

1. Is this a function relationship?

   ____

2. If this is a function, write a rule to represent it.

   ____

3. Make a table for the function, listing six input/output pairs.

Graph the function. Use input values of 1, 2, 3, 4, and 5.

4. $y = -2x + 4$

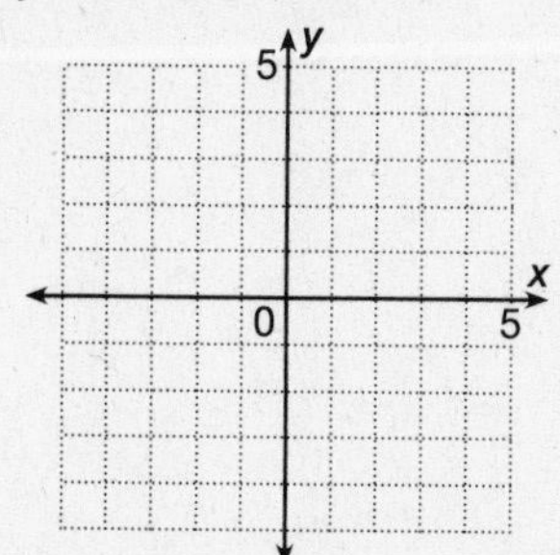

5. The relationship between the amount of time a zebra runs at maximum speed and the distance it covers is shown.

Time (min)	3	6	9	12	15
Distance (mi)	2	4	6	8	10

   a. Write an equation to describe this relationship.

   ____

   b. Use the equation to find the distance the zebra would travel in 48 minutes.

   ____

Name ______________________ Class ______________ Date ______________

Activity Lab 9-5

Using Tables, Rules, and Graphs

Materials needed: graph paper

It costs \$15 daily to enter a local amusement park. A frequent visitor pass costs \$50 plus \$5 per visit. A season pass for unlimited visits costs \$120. You can write a function for each option.

Let T represent the total cost for admission to the park for the season and v represent the number of visits. Write the function rules for each type of pass.

1. Daily pass: $T = 15v$
2. Frequent visitor pass: $T =$ ______________
3. Season pass: $T =$ ______________
4. Using the functions, complete the tables below:

Daily Pass

Number of Visits	Total Cost
1	
2	
4	
10	
20	

Frequent Visitor Pass

Number of Visits	Total Cost
1	
2	
4	
10	
20	

Season Pass

Number of Visits	Total Cost
1	
2	
4	
10	
20	

5. On a sheet of graph paper, create a graph to show the relationship between the number of visits (input) and the total cost (output) for each type of pass. Include information about each type of pass in your graph.
6. If you go to the park 4 times, which plan would you choose? Explain.

____

____

7. How much will you save by buying a frequent visitor pass if you go to the park 8 times?

____

8. How many visits do you have to make in order to save money by buying the frequent visitor pass rather than the daily pass?

____

9. How many visits do you have to make in order to save money by buying the season pass rather than the frequent visitor pass?

____

Name ________________ Class ________________ Date ________________

Reteaching 9-5

Using Tables, Rules, and Graphs

If you ride a bicycle at 12 mph, the distance you ride is a **function** of time. For each input value (time), there is exactly one output value (distance).

- You can represent the relationship between time and distance with a table.

Input (hours)	1	2	3	4
Output (miles)	12	24	36	48

- You can represent the relationship, or function, with a rule.

  output = 12 · input
  distance = 12 · time

- You can represent the relationship, or function, with a graph.

① Graph the points from the table.
(1, 12), (2, 24), (3, 36), (4, 48)

② Draw a line through the points.

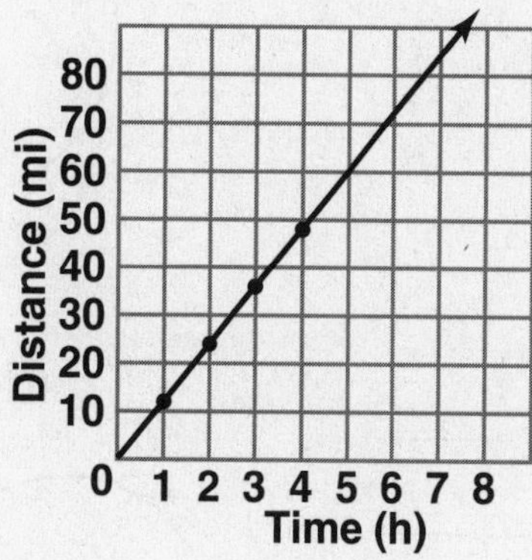

Graph the equation $y = -2x$.

1. Complete the table of values for the equation $y = -2x$. Then write each pair of values as ordered pairs.

Table of values **Ordered pairs**

x	y		Ordered pairs
−2		→	________
0		→	________
1		→	________
3		→	________
4		→	________
		→	________

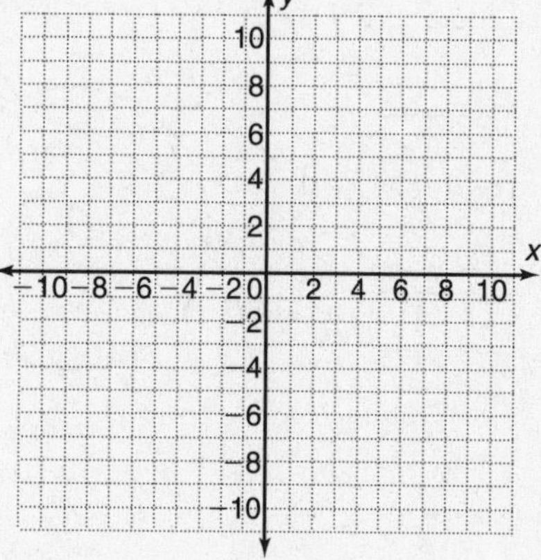

2. Plot the points on the coordinate grid. Then connect the points.

Name ______________________ Class ______________ Date ______________

Enrichment 9-5

Using Tables, Rules, and Graphs

Visual Thinking

The letter in each circle represents a digit from 1 to 9. Where two circles intersect and a number is given, the number is the sum of the values of the letters in those two circles. Find the value of each letter. *Hint:* There are two circles labeled A and two labeled E. The value of a letter is the same each time it occurs in the puzzle.

Example

Possible values of x and y:
$x = 1, y = 4; x = 4, y = 1;$
$x = 2, y = 3; x = 3, y = 2$

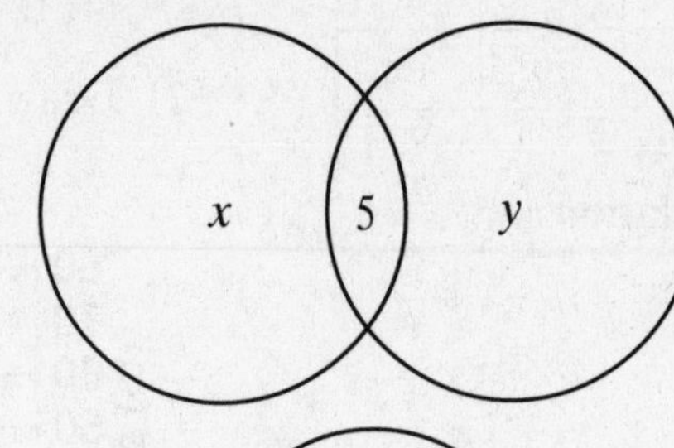

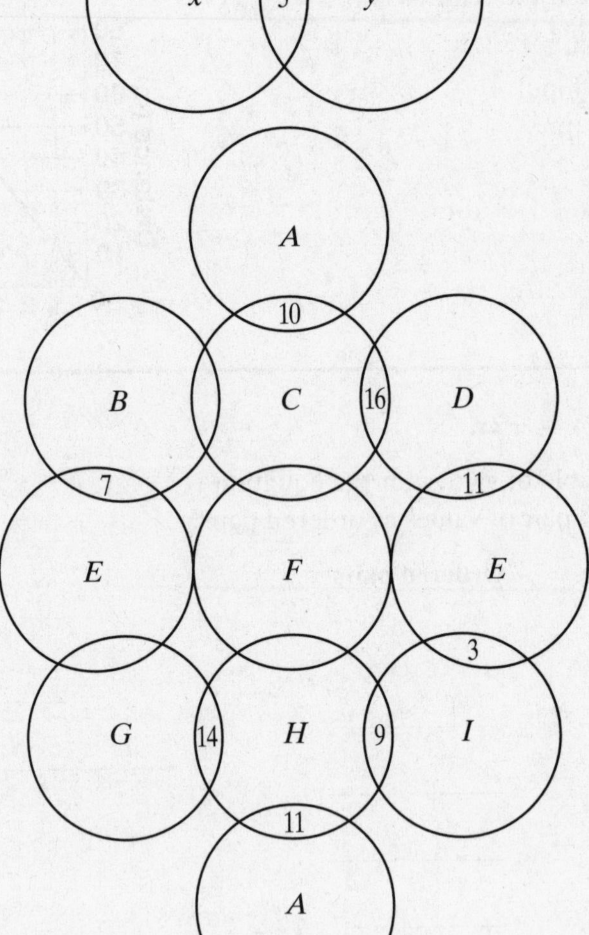

1. $A =$ ______
2. $B =$ ______
3. $C =$ ______
4. $D =$ ______
5. $E =$ ______
6. $F =$ ______
7. $G =$ ______
8. $H =$ ______
9. $I =$ ______

10. Write at least six expressions using the variables above that show values equal to 12. For example, $D - A + G = 12$.

____

____

____

Name ______________________ Class ______________ Date ______________

9D: Visual Vocabulary Practice

For use after Lesson 9-5

High-Use Academic Words

Study Skill When you feel you're getting frustrated, take a break.

Concept List

name	classify	acronym
measure	rule	symbolize
dimensions	abbreviate	property

Write the concept that best describes each exercise. Choose from the concept list above.

1. $a + b = b + a$ ____________	**2.** 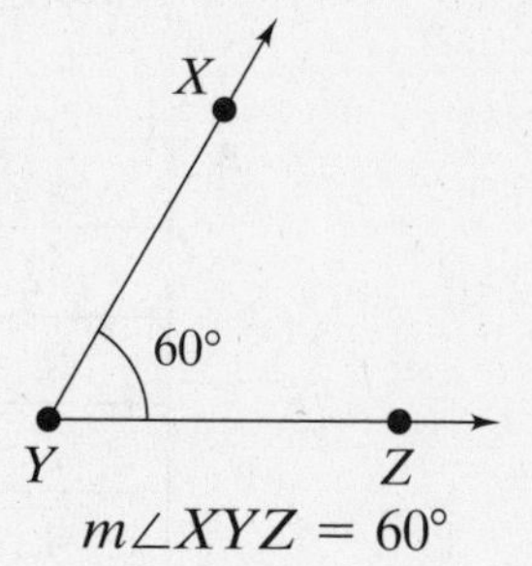 $m\angle XYZ = 60°$ ____________	**3.** Trapezoids, rectangles, and parallelograms are all quadrilaterals; circles and octagons are not. ____________
4. $l \times w \times h$ ____________	**5.** Write oz for ounces. ____________	**6.** is equal to $=$ is similar to $\sim$ is congruent to $\cong$ ____________
7. 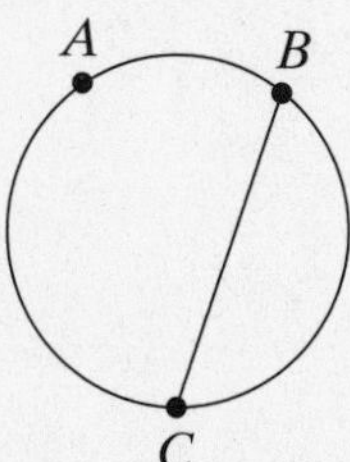 Three arcs are $\overset{\frown}{AB}$, $\overset{\frown}{ABC}$, and $\overset{\frown}{BC}$. ____________	**8.** $f(x) = 2x + 1$ ____________	**9.** Write GCF for greatest common factor. ____________

Name ______________________ Class ______________ Date ______________

Puzzle 9-5

Using Tables, Rules, and Graphs

The graphs for the exercises below combine to form an image. To discover the design, write a rule for each table, and then graph the solution to each exercise on the single grid at the bottom of the page.

1.

x	y
−2	−1
0	0
2	1
4	2

Rule: ______

2.

x	y
−1	2
0	2
2	2
4	2

Rule: ______

3.

x	y
0	5
1	2
2	−1
3	−4

Rule: ______

4.

x	y
−2	1
0	0
2	−1
4	−2

Rule: ______

5.

x	y
−3	−4
−2	−1
−1	2
0	5

Rule: ______

6.

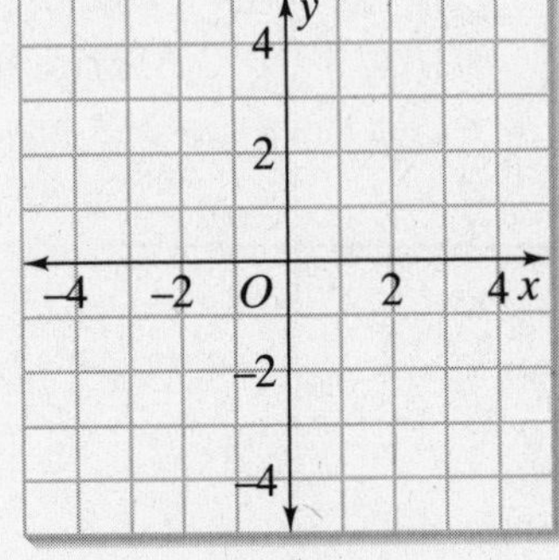

Name ______________________ Class ______________ Date ______________

Practice 9-6

Interpreting Graphs

Graphs I through VI represent one of the six situations described below. Match each graph with the situation that describes it.

I.

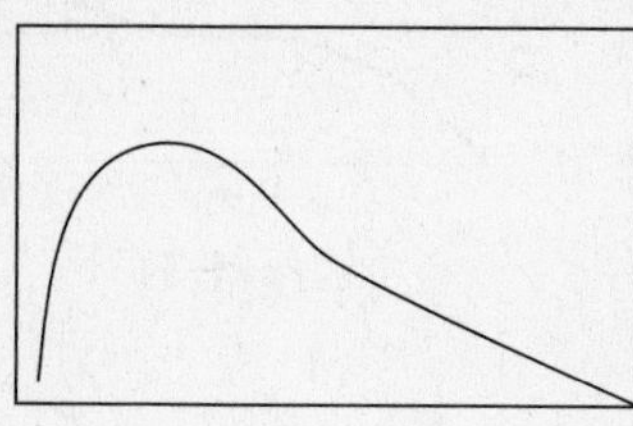

II.

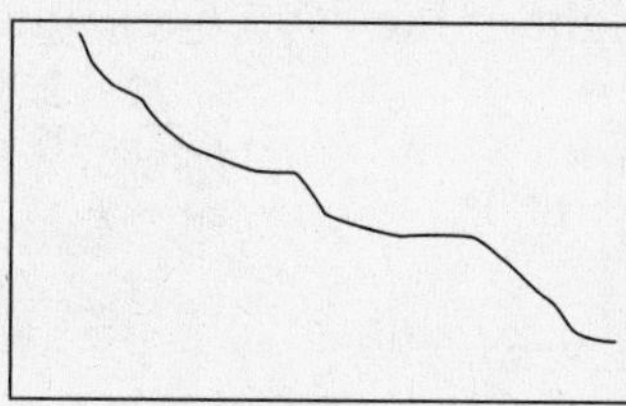

III.

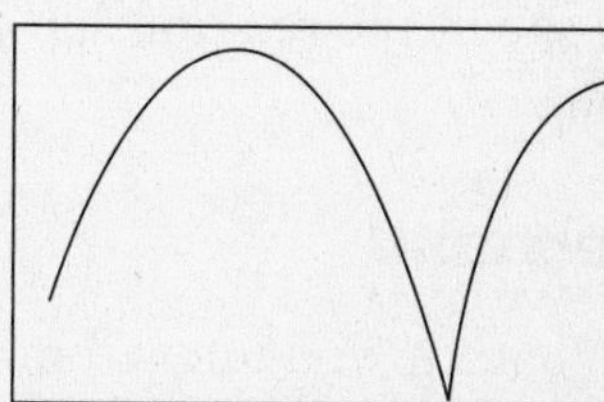

IV.

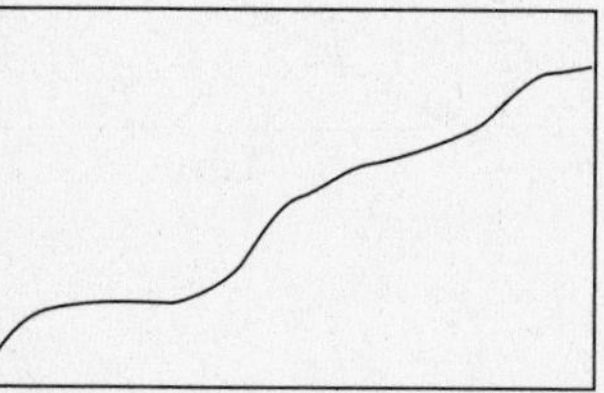

V.

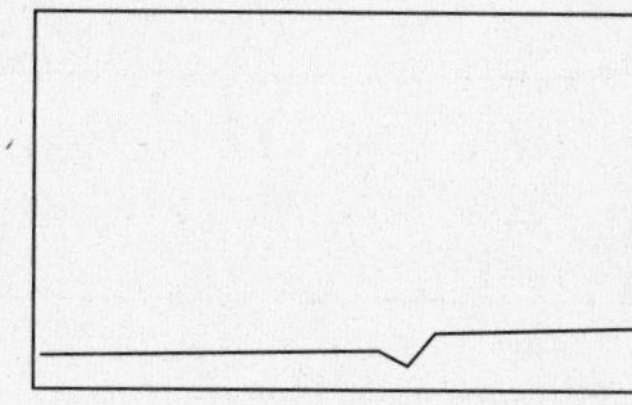

VI.

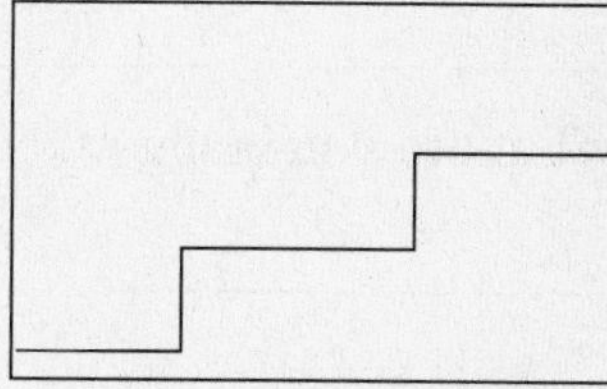

1. temperature as the weather changes from rainy to snowy ________
2. number of fish caught per hour on a bad fishing day ________
3. total rainfall during a rainy day ________
4. speed of a car starting from a stop sign and then approaching a stoplight ________
5. height of a cricket as it jumps ________
6. total amount of money spent over time during a trip to the mall ________

Sketch a graph for each situation.

7. The speed of a runner in a 1-mi race.

8. The height above ground of the air valve on a tire of a bicycle ridden on flat ground. (You can model this using a coin.)

9-6 • Guided Problem Solving

GPS Student Page 464, Exercise 10:

Suppose you steadily pour sand into the bowl below. Which graph better shows the relationship of the height of the sand over time? Explain.

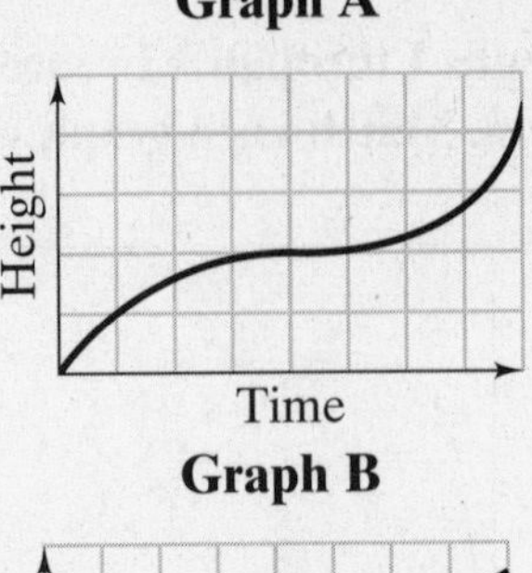

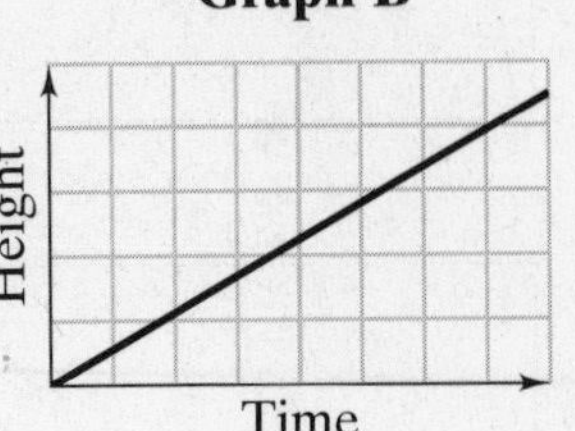

Understand

1. What can you infer from the word *steadily*?

____

____

2. What are you being asked to do?

____

____

Plan and Carry Out

3. Describe the shape of the bowl.

____

4. How is the bowl different from a cylinder?

____

5. Will the height of the sand increase at a constant rate?

____

6. Which graph better shows the relationship of the height of the sand with the amount you have poured?

____

Check

7. Explain your reasoning for Step 6.

____

____

Solve Another Problem

8. Suppose you are steadily pouring sand into the bowl at the right. Which graph above better shows the relationship of the height of the sand over time? Explain.

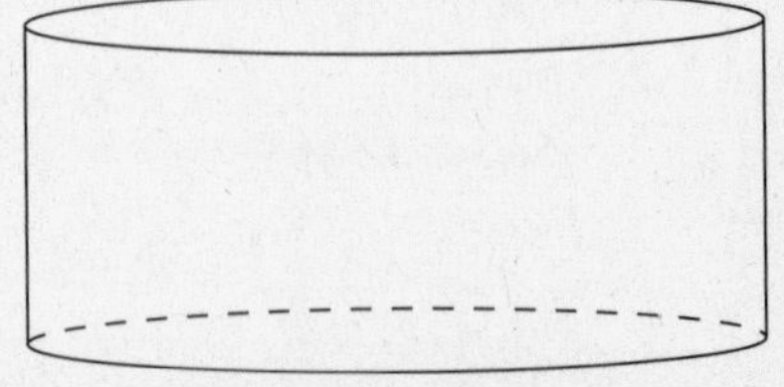

____

____

Name ______________________ Class ______________ Date ______________

Practice 9-6

Interpreting Graphs

Graphs I through IV each represent one of the six situations described below. Match each graph with the situation that describes it.

I.

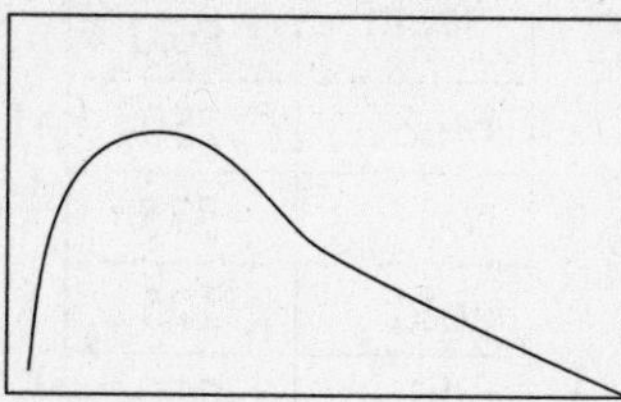

II.

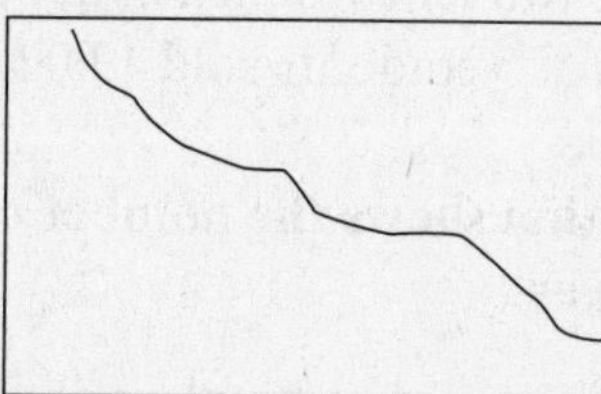

III.

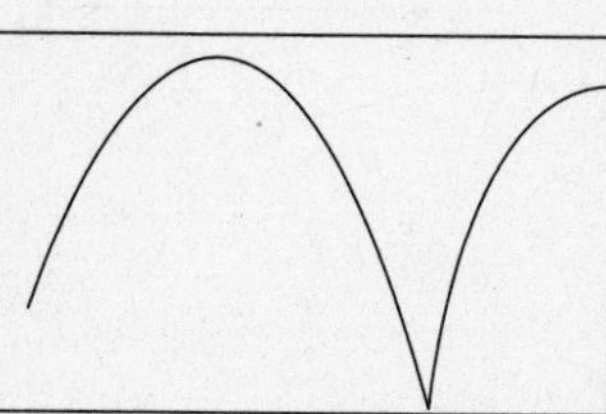

IV.

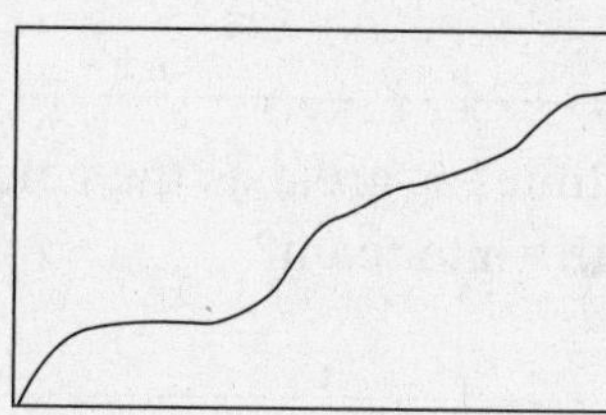

1. temperature as the weather changes from rainy to snowy __________
2. total rainfall during a rainy day __________
3. speed of a car starting from a stop sign and then approaching a stoplight __________
4. height of a cricket as it jumps __________

Sketch a graph for each situation.

5. The speed of a runner in a 1-mi race.
6. The height above ground of the air valve on a tire of a bicycle ridden on flat ground. (You can model this using a coin.)

Name ______________________ Class ______________ Date ______________

Activity Lab 9-6

Interpreting Graphs

Visual Thinking

The 20 members of the Student Council sold t-shirts as a school fundraiser. Four teams of 5 students sold 1,000 t-shirts at $6.50 each.

Team	Number Sold
blue	250
red	375
gold	125
white	250

Construct a bar graph that shows the number of shirts sold by each team. Use unbroken axes.

1. Which team sold the greatest number of shirts?

____

2. About how many times as great as the gold team was the number of shirts sold by the white team?

____

3. Change your graph so there is a break in one axis. Also change the scale. Make your new graph give the impression that the white team sold about three times as many shirts as the gold team. What scale did you use for the number sold?

____

4. About how times as great as the gold team was the number of shirts sold by the red team?

____

5. About how many times as great as the gold team does the number of shirts sold by the red team seem based on your second graph?

____

6. What bar graph would members of the red team prefer?

____

Construct a line graph that compares the number of shirts sold and the amount of money raised. Show data for 100, 200, 300, . . . 1,000 shirts sold.

7. What scale did you use for "Money Raised"?

____

8. What unbroken scale could you use for "shirts sold" to give the impression that the money raised would increase more rapidly with each shirt sold than your first graph?

____

9. Which line graph would members of the gold team prefer?

____

Name ______________________ Class ______________ Date ______________

Reteaching 9-6

Interpreting Graphs

You can describe a situation shown by a graph.

- An airplane ascends to its cruising altitude of 20,000 ft in 20 min. After 50 min it begins its descent into Atlanta. The descent takes 15 min.

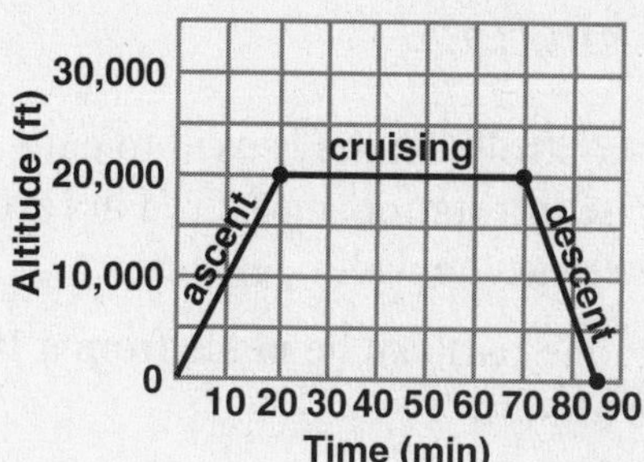

The graph at the right shows time and altitude for the airplane trip. Each part of the trip is labeled.

You can sketch a graph to describe a situation.

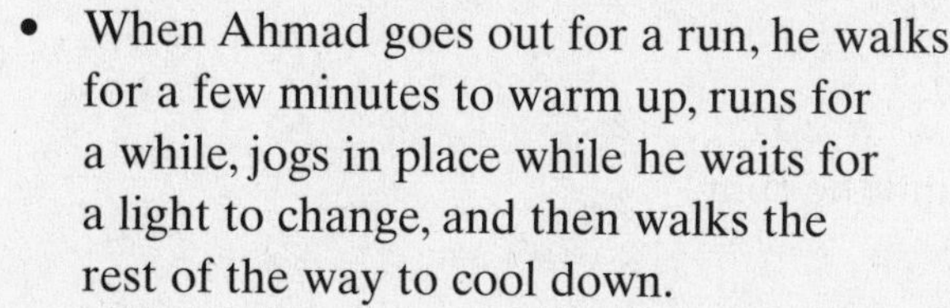

- When Ahmad goes out for a run, he walks for a few minutes to warm up, runs for a while, jogs in place while he waits for a light to change, and then walks the rest of the way to cool down.

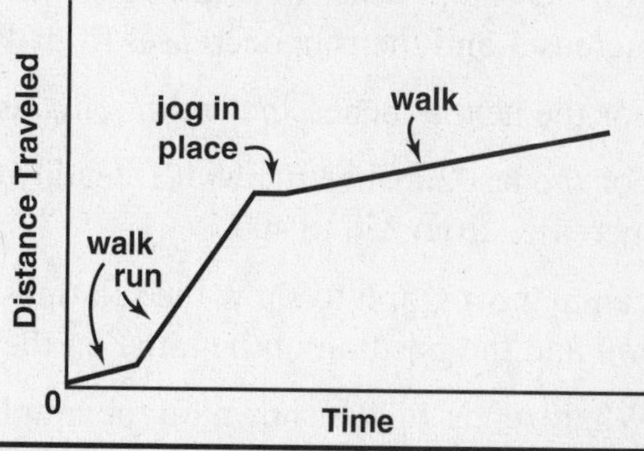

The graph at the right shows the distance Ahmad travels and each type of movement.

Match each graph with its situation.

A.

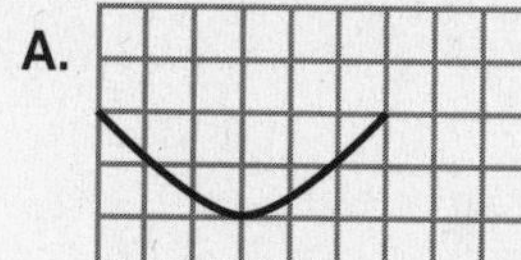

B.

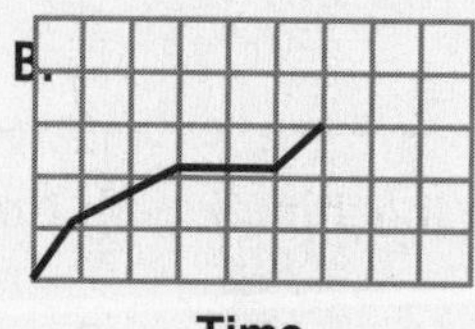

C.

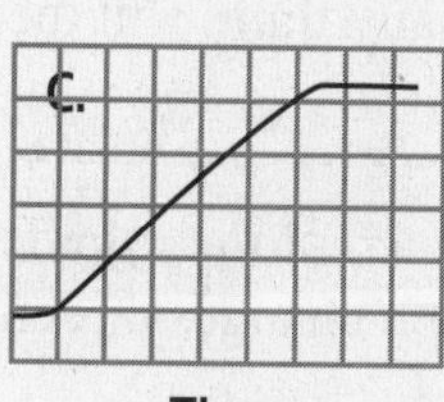

1. A car travels at 10 mph for 5 min, 50 mph for 27 min, and then is stopped for 10 min.

   ____

2. Total rainfall over a 24-hour period

   ____

3. Water level in a bay

   ____

Sketch a graph for the situation. Include labels.

4. You walk to a park, visit with a friend for few minutes, and then jog home.

5. You climb up a ladder, then climb down the ladder.

Name ______________________ Class ______________ Date ______________

Enrichment 9-6

Interpreting Graphs

Critical Thinking

A computer-controlled lathe is used to cut various objects as they rotate. The rate of rotation, measured in revolutions per minute (rpm), increases as the width decreases.

For example, one part can be made from a 10-inch-long cylinder. It is made as follows.

- For the first 3 inches of length, the width of the part steadily increases and the rpm decreases from 400 to 250.
- For the next 5 inches, the width remains the same.
- For the last 2 inches, the width steadily decreases and the rpm increases from 250 to 400.

You can make a graph to show the relationship between the rate of rotation and the position of the lathe on the cylinder.

1. What trends will be shown on the graph?

____

2. How many times will the graph change direction?

____

3. How much of the cylinder will have been machined each time the graph changes direction?

____

4. Between what measurements will the graph be increasing?

____

5. Between what measurements will the graph remain constant?

____

6. Between what measurements will the graph be decreasing?

7. Make a graph to represent the given information.

8. Suppose the finished part comes to a point on both ends. Draw a diagram of its side view below.

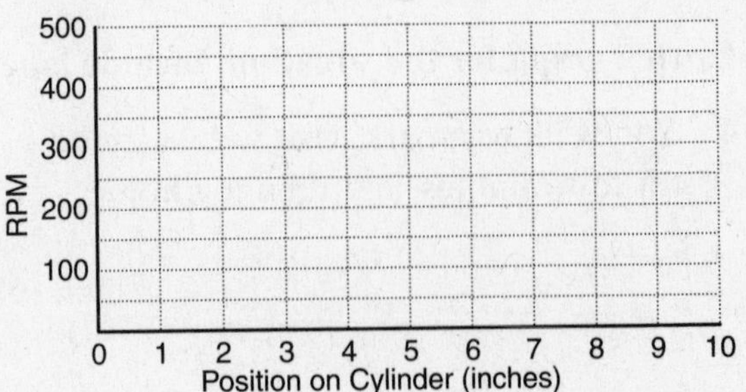

Name ______________________ Class ______________ Date ______________

Puzzle 9-6

Interpreting Graphs

Match each exercise description with the graph that best relates to the given scenario. When you have finished, write the letter of the graph above the exercise number in the letter code at the bottom of the page.

1. The number of leaves on a tree from the summer of 2001 to the summer of 2003.
2. The temperature of a cup of hot tea when left in a cool room for two hours.
3. During a long road trip you drive all morning, take a one-hour break for lunch, and then continue driving for the rest of the afternoon. Find a graph relating the distance from your home and the time of day.
4. A large cone-shaped vessel is being filled with water at a constant rate. The bottom of the vessel is the base of the cone. Find the graph that shows the depth of the water over time.
5. A volleyball is hit high above the net, and falls to the ground on the other side. Which graph shows the height of the ball on the vertical axis?
6. Every morning you walk to school at a constant speed. Today, you did not have to stop during your trip. Find the graph showing your distance from the school during your walk.

N.

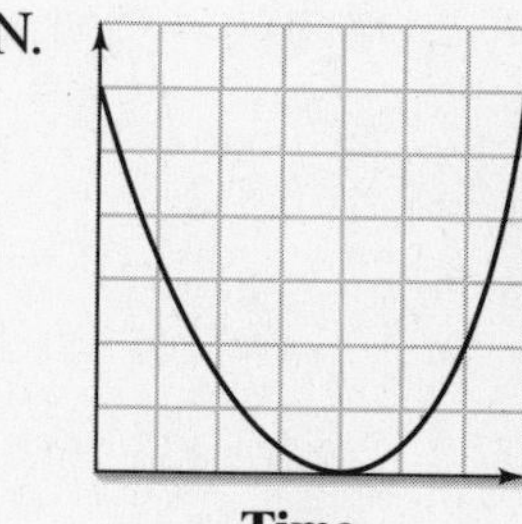

L.

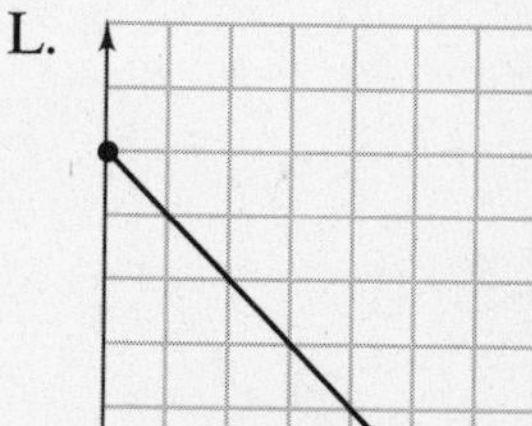

M.

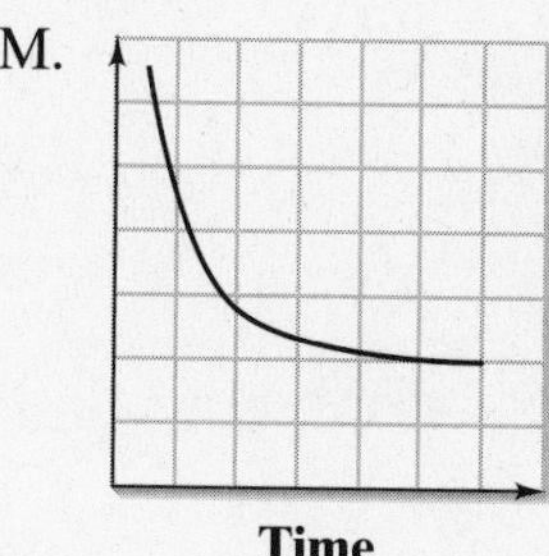

B.

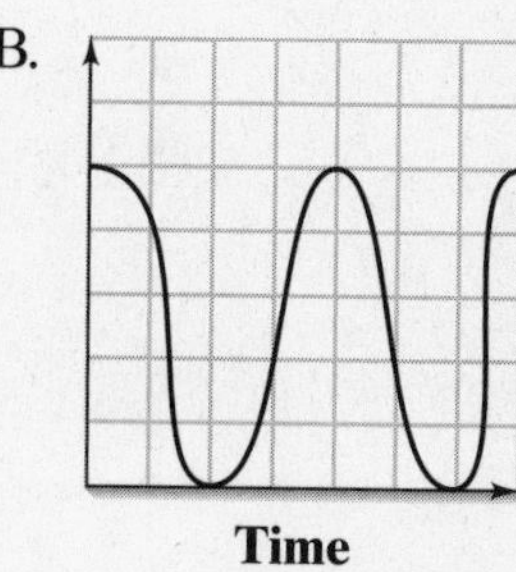

T.

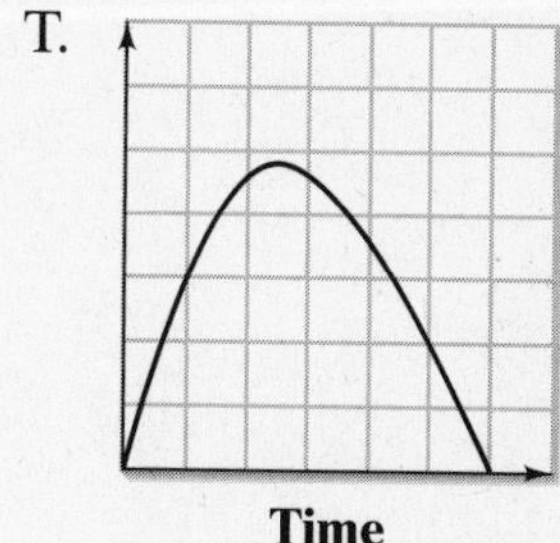

R.

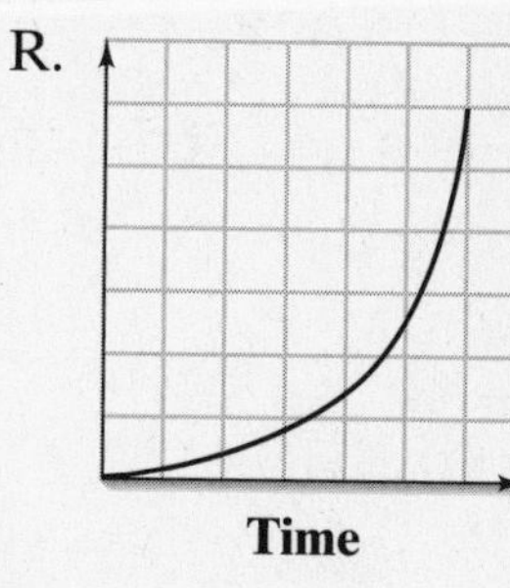

S.

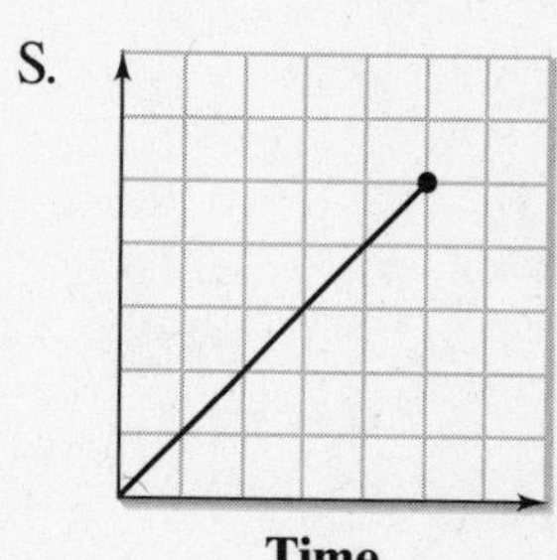

E.

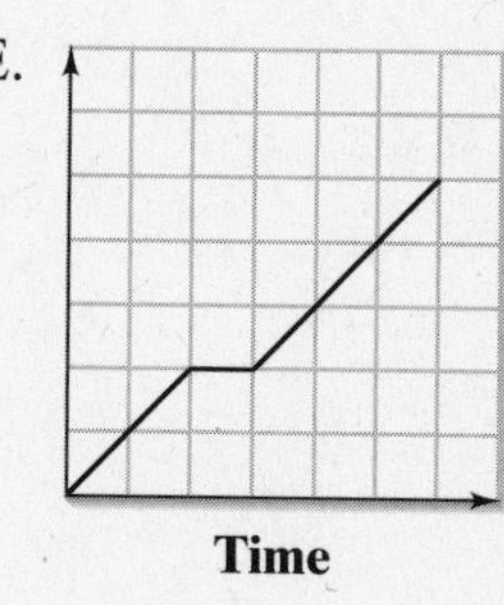

What is the highest point of elevation in the state of Colorado?

___ ___. ___ ___ ___ ___ ___ ___

2 5 3 6 1 3 4 5

Name ______________________ Class ______________ Date ______________

Practice 9-7

Simple and Compound Interest

Graph the total *simple* interest earned for each account over 5 years.

1. $1,300 at 6.9%

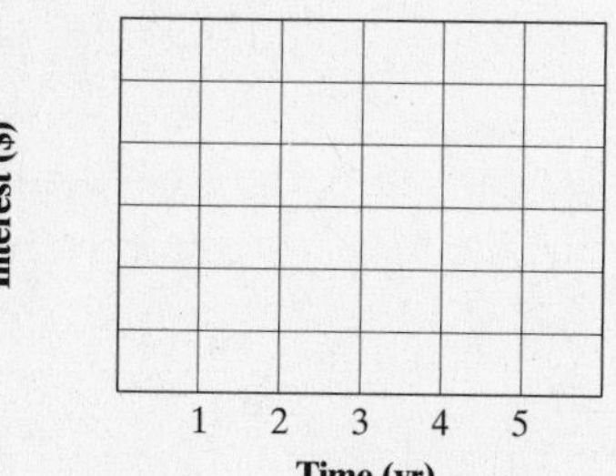

2. $11,500 at 12.50%

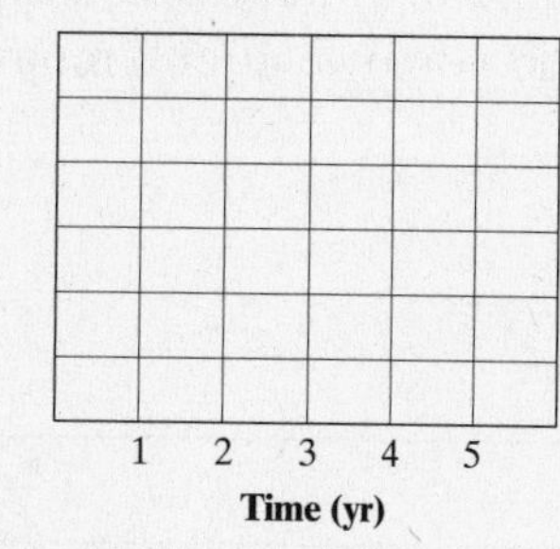

3. $450 at 3%

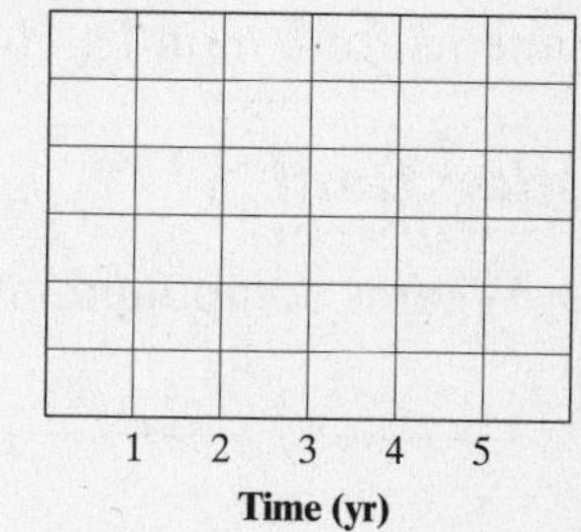

Find the simple interest earned in each account.

4. $2,000 at 4% for 6 months ______________

5. $10,000 at 10% for 2 years ______________

6. $500 at 3% for 3 months ______________

7. $25,000 at 4.25% for 5 years ______________

Find the balance in each *compound* interest account.

8. $800 principal
6% interest rate
9 years
____

9. $5,200 principal
5% interest rate
4 years
____

10. $3,500 principal
4.5% interest rate
10 years
____

Solve.

11. You borrow $600. You pay 5% interest compounded annually. How much do you owe at the end of 4 years?
____

12. You deposit $2,000 in an account that pays 6% interest compounded annually. How much money is in the account at the end of 12 years?
____

13. You invest $5,000 in an account earning simple interest. The balance after 6 years is $6,200. What is the interest rate?
____

Name ______________________ Class ______________ Date ______________

9-7 • Guided Problem Solving

GPS Student Page 470, Exercise 21:

You borrow \$500 at 18% annual compound interest. You make no payments for 6 months. How much do you owe after 6 months?

Understand

1. What is compound interest?

____

____

2. What are you being asked to do?

____

Plan and Carry Out

3. What is the formula for compound interest? ______________
4. What is the original principal? ______________
5. What is the interest rate? ______________
6. How much time in years has passed since the money was borrowed? ______________
7. Substitute the values into the formula.

____

8. How much do you owe after 6 months? ______________

Check

9. Find the total simple interest on the account after six months. Add the simple interest to the principal. How should this number compare to your answer?

____

____

____

Solve Another Problem

10. You borrow \$1,050 at 16% annual compound interest. You make no payments for 9 months. How much do you owe after 9 months?

____

Name ______________________ Class ______________ Date ______________

Practice 9-7

Simple and Compound Interest

Graph the total *simple* interest earned for each account over 5 years.

1. $1,300 at 6.9%

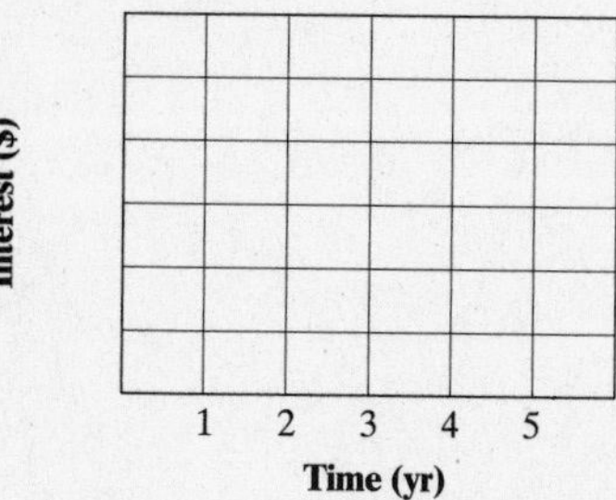

2. $11,500 at 12.50%

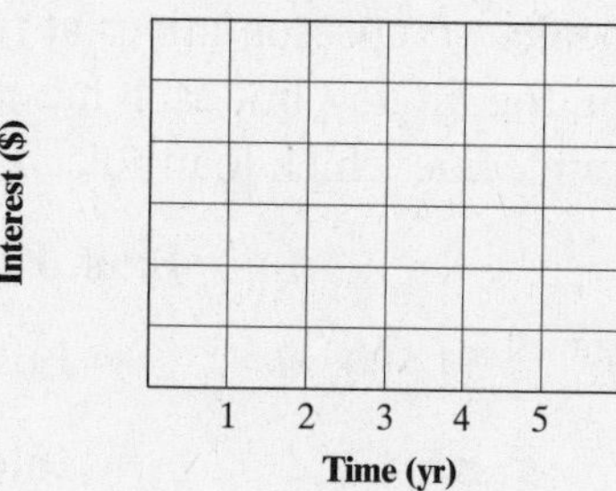

Find the simple interest earned in each account.

3. $2,000 at 4% for 6 months

____

4. $10,000 at 10% for 2 years

____

5. $500 at 3% for 3 months

____

6. $25,000 at 4.25% for 5 years

____

Find the balance in each *compound* interest account.

7. $800 principal
   6% interest rate
   9 years

____

8. $5,200 principal
   5% interest rate
   4 years

____

Solve.

9. You borrow $600. You pay 5% interest compounded annually. How much do you owe at the end of 4 years?

____

____

10. You deposit $2,000 in an account that pays 6% interest compounded annually. How much money is in the account at the end of 12 years?

____

____

Name ______________________ Class ______________ Date ______________

Activity Lab 9-7

Simple and Compound Interest

Lucien needs $1,500 to repair his automobile, and he is considering borrowing money from a bank. He has determined that he will be able to pay back the loan in 2 years with extra money earned from his summer job. He speaks to representatives at two banks. Both banks offer to lend Lucien the money, but each has a different interest rate option. Help Lucien decide which loan to accept.

Bank A

- Loan amount: $1,500
- Interest rate: 8.5%
- "Interest will be calculated using a simple interest rate formula"

Bank B

- Loan amount: $1,500
- Interest rate: 8%
- "It is Bank B's policy to calculate all loan interest owed using a compound interest formula."

1. Which bank do you predict will be a better choice? Why?

____

2. If Lucien accepts the loan from Bank A, how much interest will he pay after two years?

____

3. What is the total amount of money that he will have to repay to Bank A after two years?

____

4. If Lucien chooses Bank B, what will be the total balance owed after two years?

____

5. Which bank should Lucien choose? How does this compare with your prediction?

____

6. Lucien has decided to reduce the number of hours worked per summer. Given this adjustment, he has determined that it will now take three years to repay the loan. Re-calculate the loan amounts including interest for each bank assuming the loan will be repaid after three years.

____

7. If the term of the loan is three years, which bank is the better option?

____

8. What can you conclude about choosing interest rates, and the differences between compound and simple interest?

____

Name ______________________ Class ______________ Date ______________

Reteaching 9-7

Simple and Compound Interest

When you deposit money in a bank, the bank pays interest. **Simple interest** is interest paid only on the amount you deposited, called the **principal. Compound interest** is paid on the original principal and on any interest that has been left in the account.

Simple Interest

To find simple interest, use this formula.

Interest = principal · rate · time in years

$I = p \cdot r \cdot t$

Find the simple interest on $1,800 invested at 5% annual interest for 3 years.

$I = p \cdot r \cdot t$
$= 1{,}800 \cdot 0.05 \cdot 3$ ← **Use 0.05 for 5%.**
$= 270$

The interest is $270. (The balance will be $1,800 + $270, or $2,070.)

Compound Interest

To find compound interest, use this formula.

Balance = principal · (1 + rate)$^{\text{time in years}}$

$B = p \cdot (1 + r)^t$

You put $1,800 in the bank. The interest rate is 5% compounded annually. How much will be in the account after 3 years?

$B = p \cdot (1 + r)^t$
$= 1{,}800(1 + 0.05)^3$ ← **Use 0.05 for 5%.**
$= 1{,}800 \cdot (1.05)^3$
$\approx 2{,}083.73$

The balance is $2,083.73.

Find the simple interest earned by each account.

1. $800 principal
4% interest rate
5 years
$I = p \cdot r \cdot t$
= ________ · ________ · ________
= ________

2. $800 principal
3% interest
4 years
____

3. $1,900 principal
4.5% interest
20 years
____

4. $20,000 principal
3.5% interest
15 years
____

Find the balance of each account earning compound interest.

5. $600 principal, 6% interest rate, 3 years
$B = p(1 + r)^t$
= ________ (1 + ________)^3
= ________

6. $9,000 principal, 5% interest rate, 4 years
$B = p(1 + r)^t$
= ________ (1 + ________)—
= ________

Name ______________________ Class ______________ Date ______________

Enrichment 9-7

Simple and Compound Interest

Critical Thinking

Solve each problem by writing an equation.

1. You have \$3,200 to invest. You decide to put some of your money in a money market fund that makes 8% simple interest and the rest in a bond that makes 5% interest. How much did you invest in each account if after 1 year you earned \$220 in interest?

   ____

2. You have 2 options for saving \$12,000 in a bank. You can put it in a savings account that earns 6% simple interest for 1 year or in another account that earns 2% compound interest for 3 years. Which account earns you the most interest?

   ____

3. Your parents invested \$5,000 in one account for 6 years and \$3,000 in another account for 4 years. If the \$5,000 account earned \$1,080 more in simple interest and both accounts have the same interest rate, what is the interest rate?

   ____

4. Your grandparents invest \$4,200 in an account for 3 years that earns 2.5% compound interest. Your aunt earns the same amount of interest as your grandparents, but invests \$3,500 in an account for 2 years earning compound interest. What is the interest rate on your aunt's account?

   ____

5. Your uncle has \$2,500 to invest at 3.2% compound interest, but he can only invest it for 6 months. Write an equation using the formula for compound interest to show the balance.

   ____

6. If an exponent of 2 means you "square" the base, what does an exponent of the multiplicative inverse of 2, or $\frac{1}{2}$, mean?

   ____

7. Simplify the equation you wrote in exercise 5 to find the balance.

   ____

8. Suppose you deposit \$12,000 in a bank account that pays 2.75% interest compounded annually. What is your balance after 6 months?

   ____

Name ______________________ Class ______________ Date ______________

9E: Vocabulary Check

For use after Lesson 9-7

Study Skill Strengthen your vocabulary. Use these pages and add cues and summaries by applying the Cornell Notetaking style.

Write the definition for each word or term at the right. To check your work, fold the paper back along the dotted line to see the correct answers.

______________________	principal
______________________	simple interest
______________________	balance
______________________	function
______________________	arithmetic sequence

Name ______________________ Class ______________ Date ______________

9E: Vocabulary Check (continued)

For use after Lesson 9-7

Write the vocabulary word or term for each definition. To check your work, fold the paper forward along the dotted line to see the correct answers.

the original amount deposited or borrowed	______________
interest calculated only on the principal	______________
the principal plus the interest earned	______________
a relationship that assigns exactly one output value to each input value	______________
a sequence where each term is the result of adding a fixed number to the previous term	______________

Name ______________________ Class ______________ Date ______________

Puzzle 9-7

Simple and Compound Interest

The solution to each of the exercises is hidden in the number-search at the bottom of the page. Solve each simple and compound interest exercise, and circle its answer in the number-search. Round each answer to the nearest cent.

1. What is the simple interest earned on $400 at a 10% interest rate over three years?
2. In one month, you earned $100 delivering newspapers. If you deposit the money in a savings account with a simple interest rate of 12%, how much interest will you earn in six years?
3. What is the simple interest accumulated on a $400 loan with 12% interest after 6 years?
4. A compound interest rate of 15% is offered on a savings account. You deposit $320 in the account. What is the total account balance after two years?
5. Find the simple interest on a $120 loan with 6% interest over three years.
6. You earn $1,000 during your summer vacation. You decide to invest your money in a savings account with a 3.1% interest rate. Using the compound interest rate formula, determine your savings account balance after four years.
7. Find the interest earned in two years by investing $3,500 in an account that pays 6.5% simple interest.
8. Robert borrowed $500 from the bank to purchase a new computer. With money earned from his after-school job, he will re-pay the bank after four years. If the bank charges 3.5% compound interest, what is the total amount must Robert repay?

5	3	6	.	2	0	1	.	2	0	6
7	6	.	4	2	3	1	.	1	2	1
3	.	4	2	3	.	2	0	.	4	9
.	0	4	1	7	.	9	3	6	.	3
7	0	3	1	2	0	.	0	0	6	2
6	2	0	.	.	2	8	8	.	0	0
4	5	5	.	0	0	9	4	.	1	1
6	8	.	0	0	2	3	.	1	4	6

Name ____________________ Class ____________ Date ____________

Practice 9-8

Transforming Formulas

Solve each formula for the indicated variable.

1. $d = rt$, for r

2. $P = 4s$, for s

3. $K = C + 273$, for C

4. $S = 180(n - 2)$, for n

5. $m = \frac{a + b + c}{3}$, for a

6. $P = 2b + 2h$, for b

7. $V = \frac{1}{3}Bh$, for B

8. $A = 2(\ell w + wh + \ell h)$, for ℓ, given $w = 5$, $h = 3$, and $A = 158$

9. $C = \frac{5}{9}(F - 32)$, for F, given $C = 25$

10. $F = ma$, for m, given $a = 9.8$ and $F = 117.6$

Solve.

11. In 1989, Dutch ice skater Dries van Wijhe skated 200 km at an average speed of 35.27 km/hr. How long was he skating?

12. A roofer calculates his bid price using the formula $P = 1.85s + 4.2f$, where s is the area of the roof in square feet and f is the length of the fascia in feet. Find the area of the roof with 190 feet of fascia and a price of $4,148.

Name ______________________ Class ______________ Date ______________

9-8 • Guided Problem Solving

GPS Student Page 475, Exercise 27:

Construction Bricklayers use the formula $N = 7\ell h$ to estimate the number of bricks needed to cover a wall. N is the number of bricks, ℓ is the length of the wall in feet, and h is the height. If 980 bricks are used to build a wall 20 ft long, how high is the wall?

Understand

1. Circle the information you will need to solve.
2. What are you being asked to do?

 ____

3. What units will your final answer be in?

 ____

Plan and Carry Out

4. What formula are you to use? ______________
5. How many bricks are used? ______________
6. How long is the wall? ______________
7. Substitute the values in the formula. ______________
8. Solve the equation. ______________
9. How tall is the wall? ______________

Check

10. Substitute your answer into the formula. Does your answer check?

 ____

Solve Another Problem

11. The formula used to find your target heart rate while exercising is $h = 220 - 0.6a$. The target heart rate in heartbeats per minute is h, and a is the age in years of the person exercising. What is the target heart rate for a 26-year-old person?

 ____

 ____

Name ______________________ Class ______________ Date ______________

Practice 9-8

Transforming Formulas

Solve each formula for the indicated variable.

1. $d = rt$, for r

____

2. $P = 4s$, for s

____

3. $K = C + 273$, for C

____

4. $V = \frac{1}{3}Bh$, for B

____

5. $C = \frac{5}{9}(F - 32)$, for F, given $C = 25$

____

6. $F = ma$, for m, given $a = 9.8$ and $F = 117.6$

____

Solve.

7. In 1989, Dutch ice skater Dries van Wijhe skated 200 km at an average speed of 35.27 km/hr. How long was he skating?

____

____

8. A roofer calculates his bid price using the formula $P = 1.85s + 4.2f$, where s is the area of the roof in square feet and f is the length of the fascia in feet. Find the area of the roof with 190 feet of fascia and a price of $4,148.

____

____

Name ______________________ Class ______________ Date ______________

Activity Lab 9-8

Transforming Formulas

Formulas, like other equations, can be rewritten to find the values of specific unknown variables. The formula for the volume of a cylinder is:

$$V = h \times \pi \times r^2$$

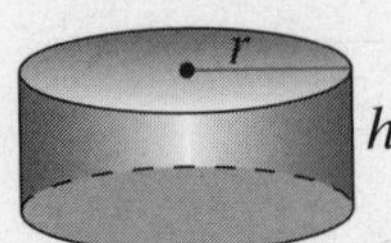

1. Rewrite the formula so that h is on one side of the equal sign and the other variables are on the other side.

____

2. Rewrite the formula again so that r^2 is on one side of the equal sign and the other variables are on the other side.

____

The table below shows the dimensions of three different cylinders.

	V	*h*	*r*
Cylinder A		10 cm	4 cm
Cylinder B	87.92 cm^3		2 cm
Cylinder C	339.12 cm^3	12 cm	

3. Which of the three formulas from Exercises 1 and 2 would you use to find the unknown volume of Cylinder A?

____

4. Which of the three formulas would you use to find the missing dimension of Cylinder B?

____

____

5. Which of the three formulas would you use to find the missing dimension of Cylinder C?

____

6. Use the formulas to find the missing values and write your answers in the table. Use 3.14 as an approximation for π.

Name ______________________ Class ______________ Date ______________

Reteaching 9-8

Transforming Formulas

A **formula** such as $I = prt$ states the relationship among unknown quantities represented by the variables I, p, r, and t. It means that *interest* equals the *principal* times the *rate* times the *time.*

You can use a formula by **substituting** values for the variables. Some formulas have numbers that do not vary, such as this formula for finding the perimeter of a square: $P = 4s$. The number 4 is a **constant.**

A Boeing 747 airplane traveled at 600 mph. At this speed how many hours did it take to travel 2,100 miles?

$d = r \cdot t$	Use the formula $d = rt$.
$2{,}100 = 600 \cdot t$	Substitute the known values.
$3.5 = t$	Divide to find the unknown value.

The Boeing 747 airplane traveled 2,100 miles in 3.5 hours.

---

1. Lisa rides her bike for 2 hours and travels 12 miles. Find her rate of speed.

a. Which formula should you use to find the rate? ______________

b. What is the rate of speed? ______________

Solve each formula for the values given.

2. $A = lw$ for A, given $l = 35$ m and $w = 22$ m

____

3. $P = 2l + 2w$ for l given $P = 30$ in. and $w = 7$ in.

____

4. $V = lwh$ for l given $V = 60\text{ ft}^3$, $w = 3$ ft, and $h = 5$ ft

____

5. $I = prt$ for $p = \$100$, $r = 0.05$, and $t = 2$ years

____

Name ______________________ Class ______________ Date ______________

Enrichment 9-8

Critical Thinking

The equation $d = r \times t$ relates rate (r), time (t), and distance (d).

1. If you are traveling at 55 mph, what formula would you use to find the distance you will travel over various lengths of time?

   ____

2. Sometimes you are given distances and need to know how long it would take to travel at various rates. Complete the table to find the time it would take to travel 500 miles at speeds of 40, 55, 60, 65, and 70 mph. Round your times to the nearest quarter hour, if necessary.

Rate (mph)					
Time (hours)					
Distance (miles)					

3. What operation did you use to find the time? Rewrite the equation so that t stands alone on one side of the equal sign.

   ____

4. Rewrite the equation so that r stands alone on one side of the equal sign.Explain your reasoning.

   ____

   ____

5. How is rewriting an equation like solving an equation?

   ____

6. Why would you want to rewrite an equation?

   ____

   ____

7. The equation to find the perimeter of a regular polygon can be written as $P = n \times s$ where P is the perimeter, n is the number of sides, and s is the length of each side. How could you rewrite the equation to find the length of a side?

   ____

Name ______________________ Class ______________ Date ______________

9F: Vocabulary Review Puzzle

For use with the Chapter Review

Study Skill Have a dictionary or a textbook's glossary available while you are studying. Look up any unknown words.

Find the words in the puzzle from the definitions. Circle them. Words can be forwards, backwards, up, down, or diagonally.

Y	R	A	T	N	E	M	E	L	P	M	O	C	I	P	I	A	U	D
B	X	T	F	Q	X	E	L	A	P	I	C	N	I	R	P	B	Y	L
F	S	N	Y	E	Q	D	P	C	O	N	J	E	C	T	U	R	E	X
C	I	X	Z	G	C	T	A	O	L	W	X	H	R	M	V	F	P	A
Q	M	Y	N	A	M	N	S	F	I	P	B	B	O	M	U	P	I	R
B	P	S	D	J	R	F	E	S	U	N	E	T	O	P	Y	H	D	I
U	L	L	M	G	O	U	N	R	H	N	A	C	C	O	U	Q	Q	T
V	E	A	E	R	C	N	G	P	E	E	O	R	U	J	F	P	S	H
T	H	W	L	H	O	C	I	C	E	F	C	G	O	C	W	U	E	M
N	V	W	Y	Q	M	T	L	O	H	Y	M	N	A	P	Z	D	Q	E
I	G	E	U	P	P	I	X	N	Z	L	I	U	A	X	T	D	U	T
O	T	L	D	X	O	O	D	G	G	V	P	L	C	L	E	W	E	I
P	P	C	R	J	U	N	I	R	U	I	M	L	C	R	A	H	N	C
D	V	R	O	N	N	K	M	U	J	S	O	Z	R	O	I	B	C	Z
I	U	I	H	O	D	R	A	E	X	S	J	Q	I	E	J	C	E	L
M	G	C	C	G	K	B	R	N	T	G	E	O	M	E	T	R	I	C
J	E	B	A	A	Y	T	Y	T	T	Y	S	M	Y	E	O	F	F	B
R	I	B	Z	C	Q	P	P	Q	U	X	I	Z	A	D	L	E	E	R
S	C	X	C	E	W	X	K	H	O	Q	R	J	J	E	P	E	A	X
A	O	O	Q	D	D	E	L	G	N	A	U	M	Q	W	B	T	E	Y

Definitions

- three dimensional figure with only one base
- point that divides a segment into two congruent segments
- a polygon with 10 sides
- set of numbers that follows a pattern
- prediction that suggests what you expect will happen
- interest calculated only on the principal
- the name of the side opposite the right angle
- set of all points in a plane that are the same distance from a given point
- a polygon with six sides
- this figure is made of two rays with a common endpoint
- sequence in which you add the same number to the previous term
- sequence in which you multiply the previous term by the same number
- the principal plus interest
- distance around a circle
- segment that has both endpoints on the circle
- figures that have the same size and shape
- two angles whose sum is 90 degrees
- relationship that assigns exactly one output value for each input value
- the amount of money that you deposit or borrow
- interest paid on the original principal plus any interest that has been left in the account

Name ____________________ Class ____________________ Date ____________________

Puzzle 9-8

Transforming Formulas

Circle the equation or equations in Column B that have been transformed from the equation in Column A. Fill the blanks at the bottom with the correct answers, in order, to learn which state has the highest population density.

A	B		
1. $P = 5s$	**N.** $s = \frac{P}{5}$	**R.** $s = \frac{5}{P}$	**P.** $P + 5 = s$
2. $a = \frac{b}{c}$	**H.** $b = \frac{c}{a}$	**D.** $b = \frac{a}{c}$	**E.** $b = a \cdot c$
3. $x = \frac{y + z}{3}$	**O.** $y = x - 3z$	**W.** $y = 3x - z$	**J.** $z = 3x - y$
4. $s = t - u$	**E.** $t = s + u$	**D.** $t = \frac{s}{u}$	**R.** $u = t - s$
5. $r = 2s + 7$	**I.** $s = \frac{r + 7}{2}$	**L.** $s = 2(r - 7)$	**S.** $s = \frac{R - 7}{2}$
6. $t = \frac{1}{3}rs$	**E.** $r = \frac{3t}{s}$	**L.** $r = \frac{s}{3t}$	**Y.** $s = \frac{3t}{r}$

___ ___ ___ ___ ___ ___ ___ ___ ___

Name ______________________ Class ______________ Date ______________

Chapter 9 Project: Happy Landings

Graphing Data

Beginning the Chapter Project

Imagine this—you have just opened your parachute and you are floating through the air. Exciting! How long it takes you to reach the ground can be predicted because the change in height versus time occurs in a predictable pattern. Many other things change in a predictable pattern, for instance, the height of a burning candle and the growth of money in a bank account.

In this chapter project, you will find how fast a container of water will empty if there is a hole in it. Your final project will be a graph of the data you collect.

Activities

Activity 1: Measuring

Select a plastic container for the project. Measure the height of the water level when the container is full. If you put a hole in the bottom, do you think the level will drop at a steady rate? Explain.

Activity 2: Collecting Data

Put a small hole in the bottom of the container. Measure the height of the water level every 30 seconds. How long does it take to empty? Use your data to make a table of the height of the water level at each time. For example:

Time	Height of Water
30 s	
1 min	
1 min 30 s	
2 min	
2 min 30 s	

Activity 3: Graphing

Make a graph of your table from Activity 2. Label the horizontal axis "Time" and the vertical axis "Water Level." Begin with time zero when the container is full, and end when the water level is zero. Connect the points and give your graph a title. Explain how the graph reflects the shape of your container.

Chapter 9 Project: Happy Landings (continued)

Finishing the Project

Your graph should be large, clear, and neat. Did the container empty at a steady rate? Be prepared to explain how the graph helps you answer this question.

Reflect and Revise

Ask a classmate to review your project with you. Is your table complete? Is your graph accurate? Is your explanation clear? If necessary, make changes to improve your project.

Extending the Project

Research the typical flow and release of sewerage and drainage pipes for your city. Is the rate of release constant or not? How do city engineers use this and other information to plan the sewerage and drainage for the city?

Research some manufacturers of sewage and drainage pipes. Which pipes are most prominently advertised? Find out if the manufacturers' products are used in your city's sewage and drainage system.

Go Online PHSchool.com

Visit PHSchool.com for information and links you might find helpful as you complete your project.

Name ______________________ Class ______________ Date ______________

Chapter Project Manager

Getting Started

Read about the project. As you work on it, you will need several sheets of paper. If available, a spreadsheet program also can be used. Keep all your work for the project in a folder, along with this Project Manager.

Checklist	Suggestions
❑ Activity 1: measuring	❑ Decide on the unit of measurement you will use.
❑ Activity 2: collecting	❑ Place the hole directly in the center of the bottom of your container.
❑ Activity 3: graphing	❑ The time is your input and the height is your output.
❑ Recommendations	❑ Run your experiment 2 or 3 times to ensure accuracy of your data.

Scoring Rubric

3 Your graph is clearly labeled and accurately reflects the water level across time. Your explanations are clear and concise. You include the data from your experiment.

2 Your graph is complete, and you explain your thinking and your observations clearly.

1 Your data, your graph, and your explanations are incomplete or do not provide a clear picture of your work.

0 You omit important parts of the project.

Your Evaluation of Project Evaluate your work, based on the Scoring Rubric.

Teacher's Evaluation of Project

Name ______________________ Class ______________ Date ______________

Chapter Project Teacher Notes

About the Project

The project allows students to apply their knowledge of percents to exploring investments.

Introducing the Project

Ask students:

- *Have you ever made an investment before?*
- *What do you think makes a good investment?*
- *How do investments work?*

Project Notebook

Encourage students to keep all project-related materials in a separate folder or notebook.

Activity 1: Interviewing

Assign some students to find introductory investment books in the library. Have them find a book with a glossary of commonly used investment terms. Make photocopies of the terms for the class. If books are unavailable, have students ask the adults being interviewed to define the investment terms they do not understand.

Activity 2: Collecting Data

If your newspaper does not have enough bank advertisements, students can find some representative CD rates online at the Bank-CD Rate Scanner Web site.

Activity 3: Displaying Data

Discuss what kinds of graphs would be most suitable for displaying the data.

Finishing the Project

Project Day

You may wish to plan a project day on which students share their completed projects. Encourage students to explain their process as well as their product.

Project Notebook

Ask students to review their project work and bring their notebooks up to date.

Visit PHSchool.com for information and links you might find helpful as you complete your project.

Name ______________________ Class ______________ Date ______________

✔ Checkpoint Quiz 1

Use with Lessons 9-1 through 9-3.

Write an expression for each sequence. Then find the next three terms.

1. 0.6, 1.8, 5.4, 16.2, …

2. 25, 18, 11, 4, …

3. Which sequence is geometric, Exercise 1 or 2? ______________

For Exercises 4–7, use the table at the right.

x	y
2	1
3	3
4	5
m	7
6	9
7	n

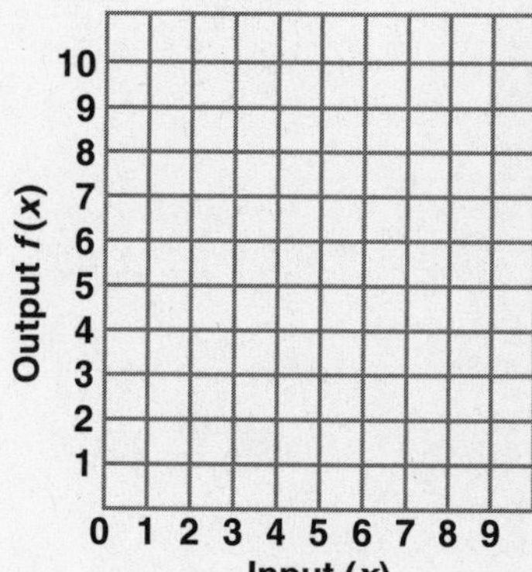

4. Find the values of m and n.

5. Graph the values in the table.

6. Use the graph to estimate the value of x for $y = 15$. ______________

7. Find the value of y for $x = 15$. ______________

- - - - ✂ -

Name ______________________ Class ______________ Date ______________

✔ Checkpoint Quiz 2

Use with Lessons 9-4 through 9-6.

1. Complete the table of values for $y = 1 + x$. Then make a graph.

x	y
1	
2	
3	
4	

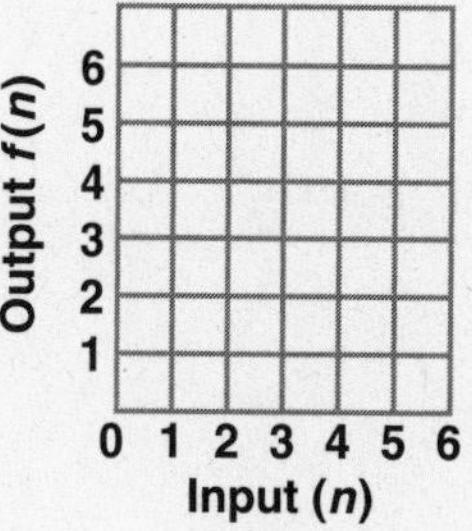

Write a rule for the function represented by each table.

2.

x	y
1	5
2	10
3	15
4	20

3.

x	y
1	−3
2	−2
3	−1
4	0

4.

x	y
1	3
2	5
3	7
4	9

Name ______________________ Class ______________ Date ______________

Chapter Test Form A

Chapter 9

Write a rule for each sequence. Find the next three terms.

1. 8, 14, 20, 26, . . .
2. 96, 84, 72, 60, . . .
3. 1, 4, 9, 16, . . .
4. 300, 150, 75, 37.5, . . .
5. 248, 246, 242, 236, . . .
6. 6, 12, 24, 48, . . .

Identify each sequence in Exercises 1–6 as either *arithmetic, geometric,* or *neither.*

7. Exercise 1: ______
8. Exercise 2: ______
9. Exercise 3: ______
10. Exercise 4: ______
11. Exercise 5: ______
12. Exercise 6: ______

Suppose you get an allowance starting at $0.05 a week. Each week thereafter, the amount you get doubles.

13. What kind of sequence is this?
14. During which week will your allowance be over $10?

Evaluate each function for $x = 0, 1,$ and 2.

15. $y = x^2 - 10$
16. $y = 3x + 2$
17. $y = x - 3$

Solve each formula for *n*.

18. $2n = 4xp - 6$
19. $t = 100(n + 3)$
20. $8a + 2n = 6b$

Name ______________________ Class ______________ Date ____________

Chapter Test (continued) Form A

Chapter 9

Write a function rule for each table.

21.

x	y
1	5
2	9
3	13
4	17

____

22.

x	y
0	6
2	2
4	−2
8	−10

____

23. Suppose you deposit $5,000 in a bank account that pays 4% interest compounded annually. How much will you have in your account at the end of 2 years? ______________________

24. The area of a trapezoid is found using the formula $A = \frac{1}{2}h(b_1 + b_2)$. Find the height of the trapezoid if the bases are 6 cm and 8 cm and the area is 56 cm^2. ______________________

The function table below shows the distance in miles that Nikki plans to bike each day during a 10-week training program. Use the table for Exercises 25–26.

Week	1	2	3	4	5	6	7	8	9	10
Distance (miles)	1	3	5	7	9	11	13	?	?	?

25. What are the last three values in the table? ______________________

26. Make a graph of the function using the data.

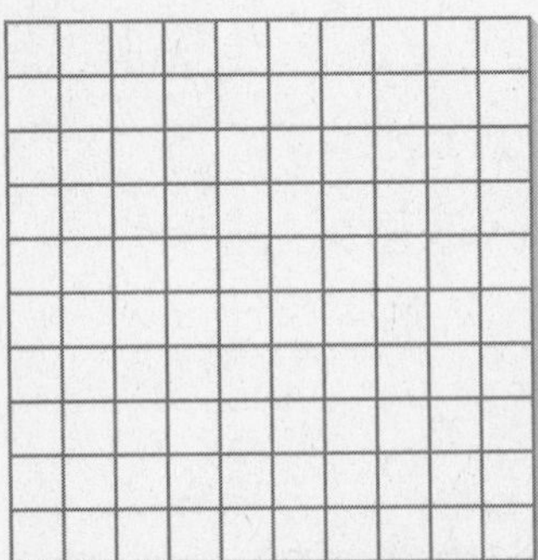

27. The graph below shows the time and total distance Jerry walked from his house to the Pizza Barn and back to his house. Which part of the graph represents the time he spent walking?

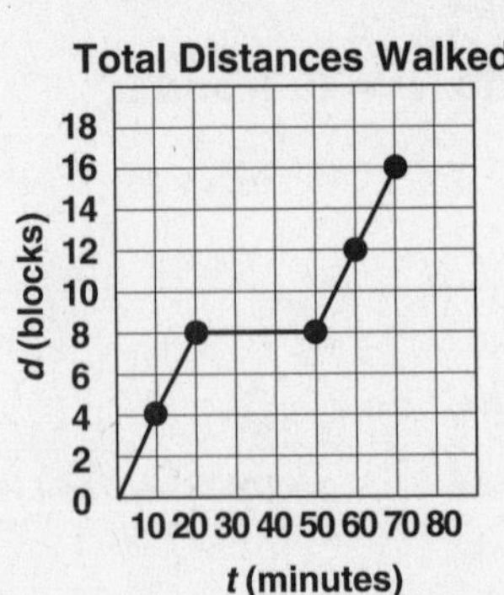

____

____

Name ______ Class ______ Date ______

Chapter Test — Form B

Chapter 9

Write a rule for each sequence. Find the next three terms.

1. 8, 14, 20, 26, . . .

2. 96, 84, 72, 60, . . .

3. 1, 4, 9, 16, . . .

4. 300, 150, 75, 37.5, . . .

Identify each sequence in Exercises 5–8 as either *arithmetic*, *geometric*, or *neither*.

5. Exercise 1: ______

6. Exercise 2: ______

7. Exercise 3: ______

8. Exercise 4: ______

Suppose you get an allowance starting at $0.05 a week. Each week thereafter, the amount you get doubles.

9. What kind of sequence is this? ______

10. During which week will your allowance be over $10?

Evaluate each function for $x = 0, 1,$ and 2.

11. $y = x^2 - 10$

12. $y = 3x + 2$

Solve each formula for *n*.

13. $2n = 4xp - 6$

14. $t = 100(n + 3)$

Chapter Test (continued) Form B

Chapter 9

Write a function rule for each table.

15.

x	y
1	5
2	9
3	13
4	17

____

16.

x	y
0	6
2	2
4	−2
8	−10

____

Solve.

17. Suppose you deposit $5,000 in a bank account that pays 4% interest compounded annually. How much will you have in your account at the end of 2 years? ______________________

The function table below shows the distance in miles that Nikki plans to bike each day during a 10-week training program. Use the table for Exercises 18–19.

Week	1	2	3	4	5	6	7	8	9	10
Distance (miles)	1	3	5	7	9	11	13	?	?	?

18. What are the last three values in the table? ______________________

19. Make a graph of the function using the data.

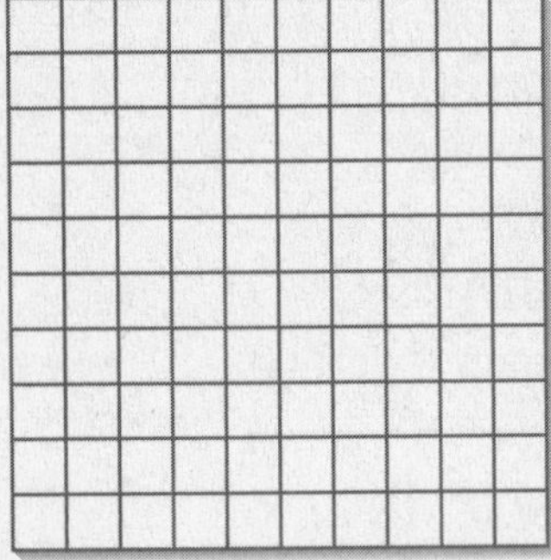

Name ______________________ Class ______________ Date ______________

Alternative Assessment Form C

Chapter 9

HOW OLD IS THAT TREE?

Do you know a candidate for the National Register of Big Trees? The Register is a list of the largest reported specimen of each tree species in the United States. The list below shows some of these champion trees.

Tree and Location	Height	Spread
Pecan Mer Rouge, Louisiana	160 ft	95 ft
American Beech Jamaica Plain, Massachusetts	144 ft	96 ft
Red Maple Macomb County, Michigan	136 ft	95 ft
Tulip Tree Macon County, North Carolina	135 ft	55 ft
California Plane Tree Santa Barbara, California	116 ft	158 ft

Show all of your work on a separate sheet of paper.

- A tree's height is the distance from the highest point on its crown to the spot where the soil meets the trunk.
- A tree's spread is the width of the area covered by its branches.

The diagram at the right illustrates height and spread.

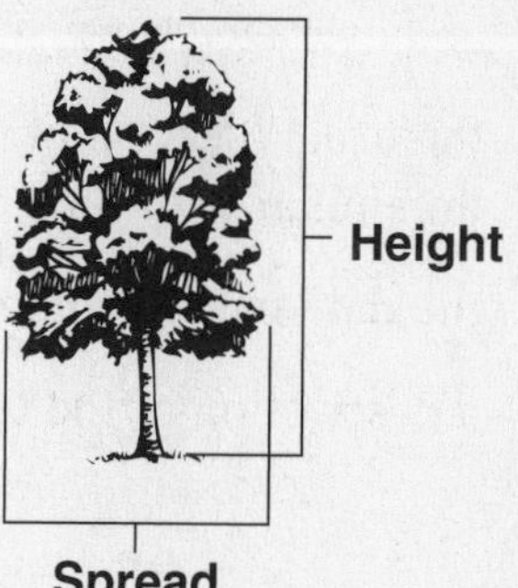

1. Based on the data above, do you think there is a pattern related to the height and spread of these champion trees? Explain.
2. Suppose you took one kind of tree, like a maple or an oak, and measured ten examples of that kind of tree. Do you think that you would find a pattern related to height and spread? Explain.
3. The National Register requires information about a tree trunk's circumference. It is always measured at a point 4.5 ft above the ground. You can use this information to measure the tree's age. A typical tree grows about 1 in. in circumference each year. For example, if a tree has a circumference of 2 ft, the tree is about 24 years old. In metric units, a tree's circumference increases about 2.5 cm each year.
   - **a.** Write a function table that shows the relationship between the age of a tree and its circumference, in inches.
   - **b.** Write a function table that shows the relationship between the age of a tree and its circumference, in centimeters.

Alternative Assessment (continued) Form C

Chapter 9

4. The circumference of a tree keeps growing throughout the tree's life. Once a tree reaches its "adult" height, its growth slows.

Decide which graph best represents the growth of a tree that has reached its adult height. Explain your choice.

A.

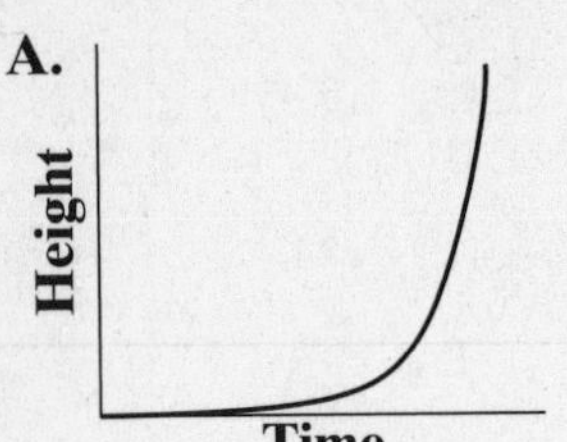

B.

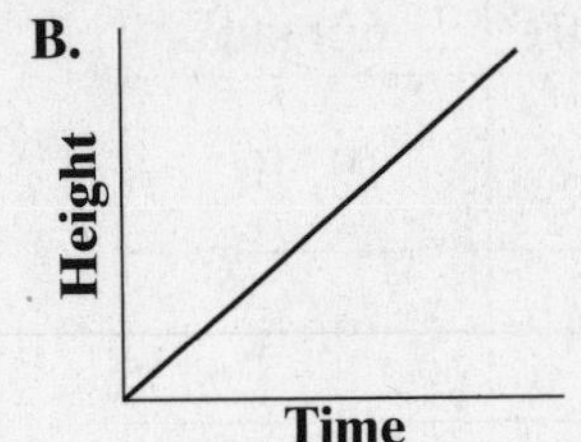

C.

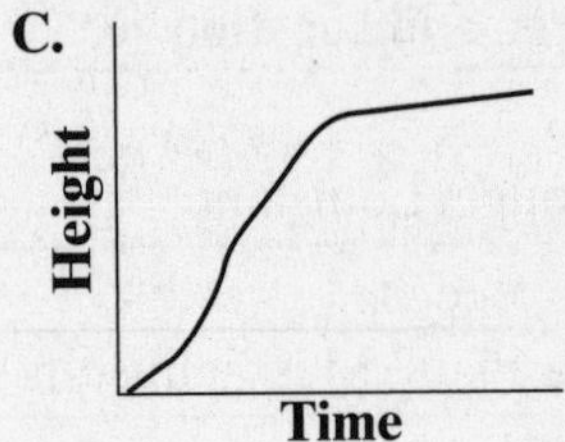

Excursion

Do you have a candidate for the National Register of Big Trees? Write a letter describing your nominee to the American Forestry Association. Your nominee should be a real tree in your community. Be sure to include the following information:

- the Latin genus and species name
- three required measurements: tree circumference, height, and average crown spread
- the exact location of the tree, detailed so that someone unfamiliar with the area can find it
- the date measured and by whom
- a description of the tree's physical condition

Name ______________________ Class ______________ Date ______________

Cumulative Review

Chapter 1–9

Multiple Choice. Choose the letter of the best answer.

1. A shirt, originally priced at $40, is marked down to $26. What is the percent of decrease?

   A. 35% B. 54%
   C. 65% D. not here

2. What is the volume of a cylinder with a base area of 24 m^2 and a height of 6 m?

   F. 36 m^3 G. 48 m^3
   H. 72 m^3 J. 144 m^3

3. Find the circumference of a circle with a radius of 4 ft. Use 3.14 for π.

   A. 6.28 ft B. 12.56 ft
   C. 25.12 ft D. 31.4 ft

4. Which lengths could be side lengths of a right triangle?

   F. 6, 6, 5 G. 8, 9, 10
   H. 7, 7, 7 J. 5, 12, 13

5. Find the mean, median, and mode for the data 10, 7, 10, 15, 21, 5, 32, 18, 26.

   A. 20, 21, 10 B. 16, 15, 10
   C. 15, 21, 5 D. 27, 21, 10

6. Which number has the same value as $|-13|$?

   F. $-|-13|$ G. $-|13|$
   H. 13 J. -13

7. Order –5, 6, 0, –2, and 1 from least to greatest.

   A. 0, 1, −2, −5, 6 B. 6, 1, 0, −2, −5
   C. −2, −5, 0, 1, 6 D. −5, −2, 0, 1, 6

8. Which choice is equivalent to the sum of –43 and 18?

   F. $18 + (-43)$ G. $-43 + (-18)$
   H. $-18 + 43$ J. $43 + (-18)$

9. Which number is the best estimate of $-210 \div 29$?

   A. −10 B. 9
   C. 8 D. −7

10. Which equation is equivalent to $\frac{x}{6} - 12 = -6$?

    F. $\frac{x}{6} = 18$ G. $6x = 6$
    H. $x = 36$ J. $x - 12 = 1$

11. Which rule could you use to find the next number in this sequence?
    −3, −1, 1, 3, 5, ...

    A. add −1 B. subtract 2
    C. add 2 D. subtract −2

12. The rule for one function is $y = 2x - 4$. The rule for a second function is $y = 4x - 2$. For which value of x are the output values opposites?

    F. $x = 1$ G. $x = -1$
    H. $x = 2$ J. $x = -2$

13. Evaluate $(-1)^{45}$.

    A. −145 B. −45
    C. −1 D. 1

Name ______________________ Class ______________ Date ______________

Cumulative Review (continued)

Chapter 1–9

14. A student graphed the distances traveled by a toy car after going down a ramp set at heights of 6 in., 12 in., and 18 in. Use the graph below to estimate the distance the toy car would travel if the height of the ramp were 2 ft.

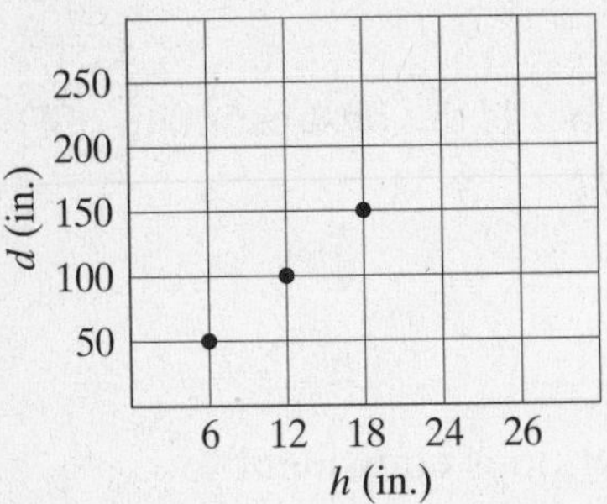

F. 24 in. **G.** 50 in.

H. 175 in. **J.** 200 in.

15. What is the rule for the function represented by the table below?

x	y
−1	−4
0	−1
1	2
2	5

A. $y = 3x + 1$

B. $y = -3x + 1$

C. $y = 3x - 1$

D. $y = -3x - 1$

16. You deposit \$500 in your savings account. The bank pays 4% interest each year. Use the formula $B = p(1 + r)^t$ to find the amount of money in your account after 2 years.

F. \$20.00 **G.** \$40.80

H. \$520.00 **J.** \$540.80

Extended Response

17. A student polled her classmates to determine the average amount of time spent daily watching television. She made a graph to show the results of her poll. Identify two facts you can draw from the graph.

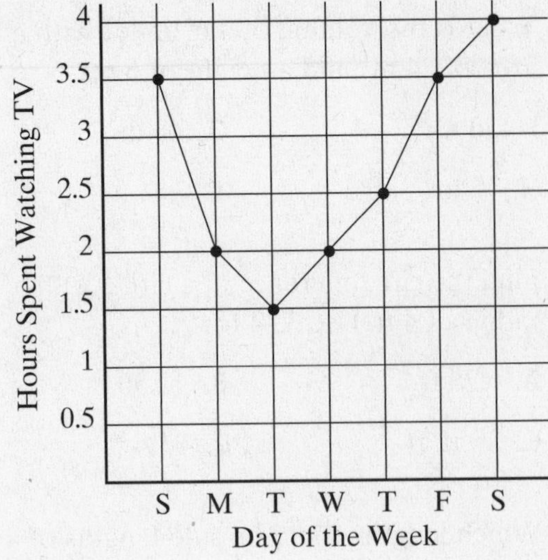

____

____

____

Short Response

18. Mark's family spends $\frac{3}{8}$ of a day traveling to a vacation home. Justin's family spends $\frac{5}{6}$ of a day traveling to a different vacation home. Which family spends more of a day traveling?

____

Name ______________________ Class ______________ Date ______________

Practice 10-1

Graphing Points in Four Quadrants

Name the point with the given coordinates.

1. $(-2, 2)$ ________ 2. $(8, 0)$ ________
3. $(4, -3)$ ________ 4. $(-7, 3)$ ________
5. $(0, -5)$ ________ 6. $(-8, -4)$ ________

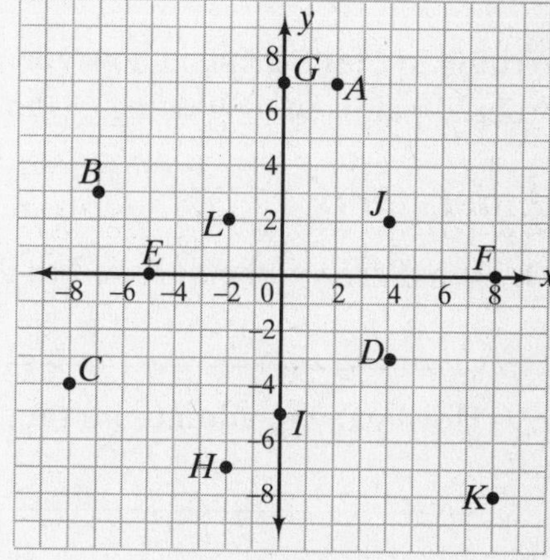

Write the coordinates of each point.

7. E ________ 8. A ________
9. H ________ 10. K ________
11. G ________ 12. J ________

Identify the quadrant in which each point lies.

13. $(-4, 3)$ ________
14. $(7, 21)$ ________
15. $(5, -8)$ ________
16. $(-2, -7)$ ________

17. Three vertices of a trapezoid are $(0, 6)$, $(-6, -1)$, and $(-6, -6)$. Find coordinates of a fourth vertex that would make this figure a proper trapezoid with one right angle.
    - On the grid at the right, graph the three vertices and draw the two sides.
    - Graph the fourth vertex of the trapezoid and draw the other two sides. What are the coordinates of the fourth vertex?

    ____

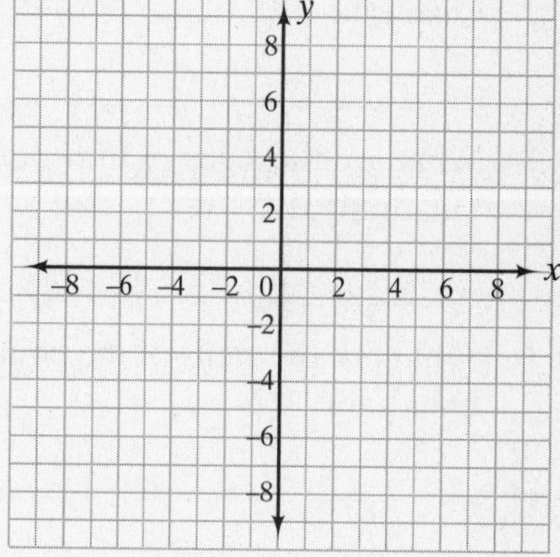

Graph each polygon on the grid at the right. Use (0, 0) as one vertex and label all vertices.

18. a square with sides 5 units long
19. a square with sides 4 units long
20. a rectangle with horizontal length 5 units and vertical length 3 units
21. a rectangle with horizontal length 3 units and vertical length 6 units

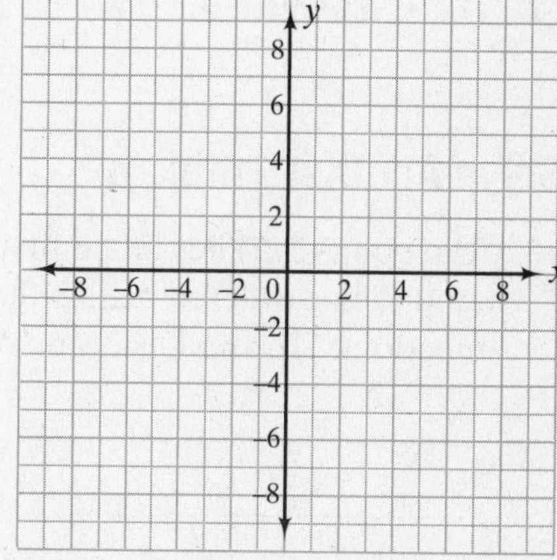

Name ______________________ Class ______________ Date ______________

10-1 • Guided Problem Solving

GPS Student Page 489, Exercise 35:

Writing in Math Explain how you can tell which quadrant an ordered pair is in by looking at the signs of its x- and y-coordinates.

Understand

1. What are you being asked to do?

____

2. How many quadrants are there and how are they labeled?

____

Plan and Carry Out

3. What are the signs of the coordinates of ordered pairs in Quadrant I?

____

4. What are the signs of the coordinates of ordered pairs in Quadrant II?

____

5. What are the signs of the coordinates of ordered pairs in Quadrant III?

____

6. What are the signs of the coordinates of ordered pairs in Quadrant IV?

____

Check

7. Did you explain the signs in each quadrant?

____

Solve Another Problem

8. The point (3, 5) lies in the first quadrant. Explain how to modify this ordered pair so that it would lie in Quadrant II, Quadrant III, and Quadrant IV.

____

____

Name ______________________ Class ______________ Date ______________

Practice 10-1

Graphing Points in Four Quadrants

Name the point with the given coordinates.

1. $(-2, 2)$ ________ 2. $(8, 0)$ ________

3. $(4, -3)$ ________ 4. $(-7, 3)$ ________

Write the coordinates of each point.

5. E ________ 6. A ________

7. H ________ 8. K ________

Identify the quadrant in which each point lies.

9. $(-4, 3)$ ________ 10. $(7, 21)$ ________ 11. $(-2, -7)$ ________

12. Three vertices of a trapezoid are $(0, 6)$, $(-6, -1)$, and $(-6, -6)$. Find coordinates of a fourth vertex that would make this figure a proper trapezoid with one right angle.

- On the grid at the right, graph the three vertices and draw the two sides.
- Graph the fourth vertex of the trapezoid and draw the other two sides. What are the coordinates of the fourth vertex?

____

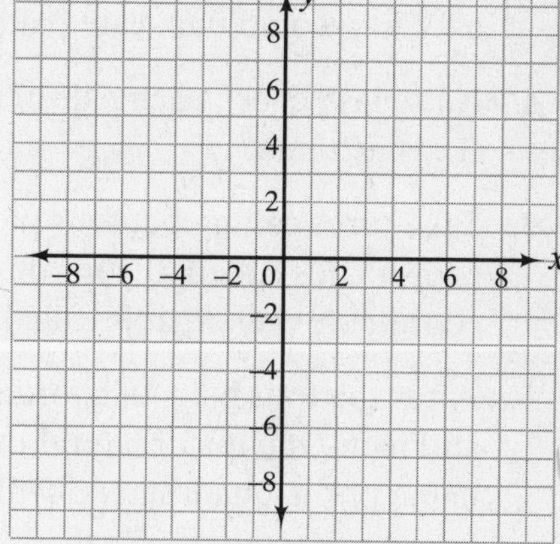

Graph each polygon on the grid at the right. Use (0, 0) as one vertex and label all vertices.

13. a square with side 5 units long

14. a rectangle with horizontal length 3 units and vertical length 6 units

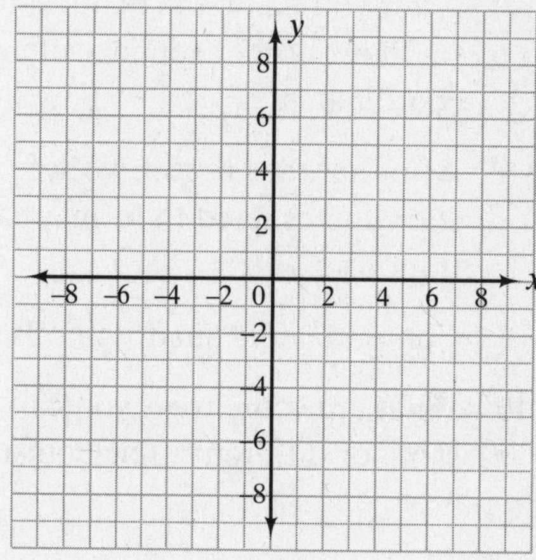

Name ______________________ Class ______________ Date ______________

Activity Lab 10-1

Graphing Points in Four Quadrants

Materials needed: small flag, index cards

Work as a class.

1. Place your classroom desks in a large rectangular grid. Your teacher will identify which rows will represent the x- and y-axis and will place a flag on the desk in the center to represent the origin.
2. Using the front of the room as the top of the grid, determine where on the coordinate plane you are sitting. Write the coordinates of your desk on an index card. Be sure to pay attention to the location of the origin. For example, if you are sitting two desks to the left and one desk in front of the origin, your coordinates will be $(-2, 1)$. Place all the cards in a pile.
3. a. Will any coordinate pairs appear more than once in the pile?

   b. What would duplicate pairs mean? Explain.
4. As a class, check each pair of coordinates and then place all the cards in a pile.
5. Take turns calling out four pairs of coordinates. Keep a list of the coordinates called. If your desk is located at one of the coordinate pairs that is called, stand up.
6. After the four pairs of coordinates have been called, look around and name the quadrilateral that has been formed. Write the name of the quadrilateral with the list of its coordinates on the board or on the overhead.
7. After you name the quadrilateral, the students who are standing sit. Play another round, calling out another set of four pairs of coordinates.
8. After another round, work in small groups to determine the coordinates need to form a parallelogram, a square, and a trapezoid.
9. Compare your quadrilaterals to those of other groups.
10. What are some ways you can classify your quadrilaterals as the same or different using coordinates?

Name ______________________ Class ______________ Date ____________

Reteaching 10-1

Graphing Points in Four Quadrants

The intersection of a horizontal number line and a vertical number line forms the **coordinate plane.** The coordinate plane below shows point A for the **ordered pair** $(3, -4)$.

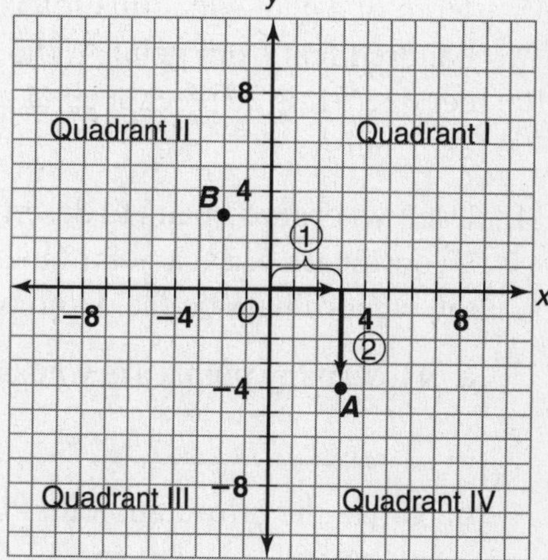

To graph point A with **coordinates** $(3, -4)$:

① Start at the origin, O. Move 3 units to the right.

② Move 4 units down for -4. Draw point A.

The axes form four **quadrants** in the coordinate plane.

- The point $(3, -4)$ is located in quadrant IV.
- Point B is located in quadrant II.

Name the point with the given coordinates.

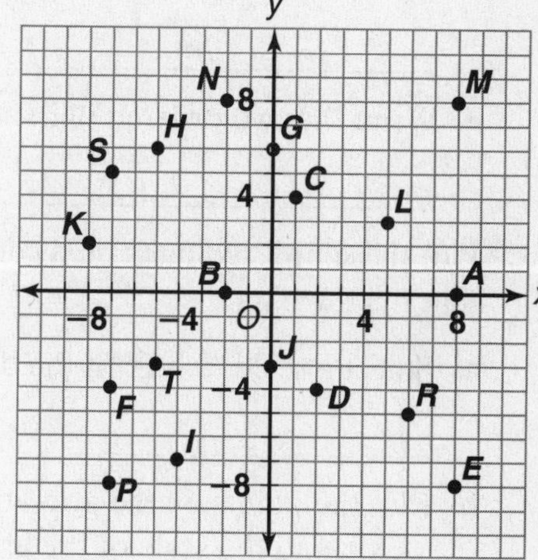

1. $(8, 0)$ ________ 2. $(8, -8)$ ________

3. $(1, 4)$ ________ 4. $(-7, -4)$ ________

5. $(6, -5)$ ________ 6. $(-5, -3)$ ________

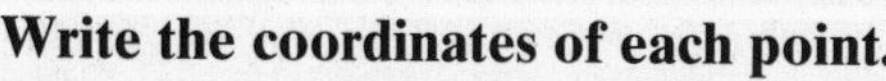

Write the coordinates of each point.

7. D ________ 8. G ________

9. I ________ 10. J ________

11. K ________ 12. L ________

Identify the quadrant in which each point lies.

13. F ________ 14. C ________ 15. D ________

16. N ________ 17. P ________ 18. S ________

Graph the polygon on the grid at the right. Use (0, 0) as one vertex and label all vertices.

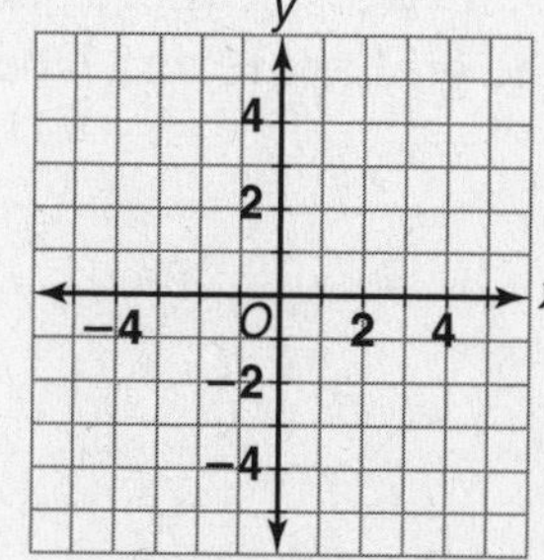

19. a square with side 6 units long

20. a rectangle with horizontal length 3 units and vertical length 6 units

Name ______________________ Class ______________ Date ____________

Enrichment 10-1

Graphing Points in Four Quadrants

Using a Diagram

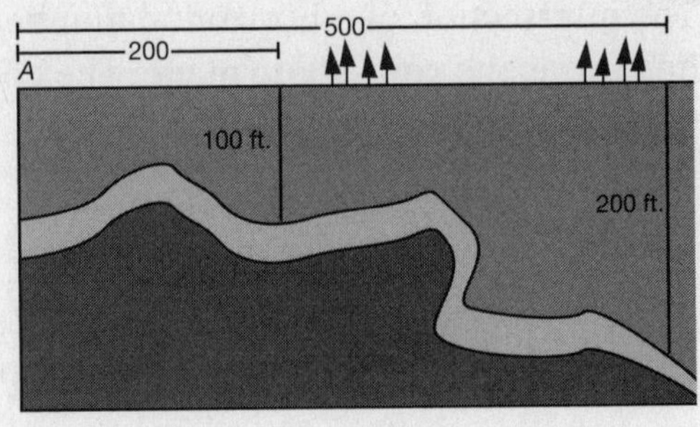

The depth of a geologic formation is not always the same. Two hundred feet from point A, the formation shown is 100 feet deep. It is 200 feet deep at a distance of 500 feet from A.

1. Use two ordered pairs to describe this data. Let the x-coordinate of each point be the distance from A and the y-coordinate be the depth of the formation.

a. How many points are you asked to describe?

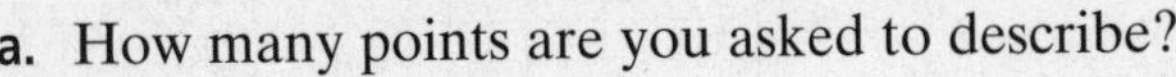

b. Circle the information that tells what each coordinate will represent.

c. Will a positive or a negative number represent the

x-coordinate? ______________ y-coordinate? ______________

d. Write the two ordered pairs to represent the data.

____

2. Plot these ordered pairs on a coordinate plane. Choose a scale that fits the data.

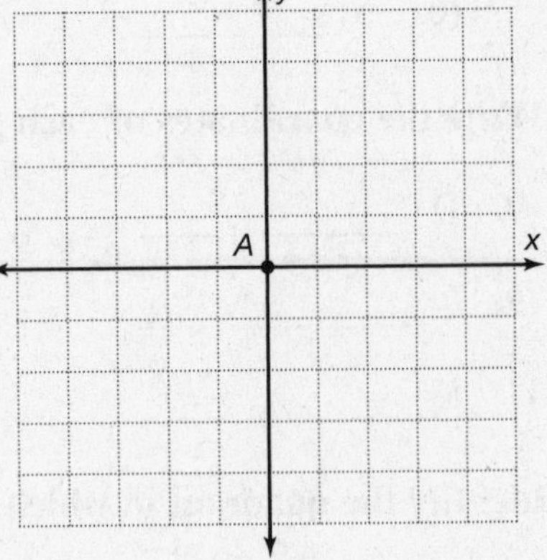

a. Select a scale to best fit the data.

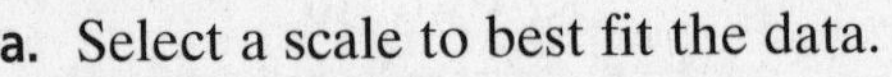

b. Plot the points on the grid at the right. Label the x-axis, the y-axis, and the scale of the graph.

c. Could you use a different scale to graph the data? Explain.

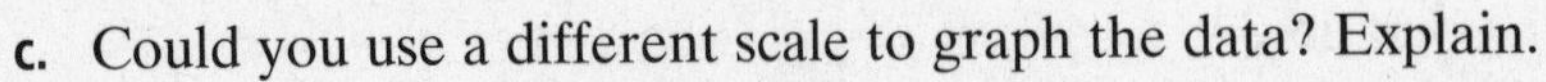

____

3. A boat is anchored 300 ft east of shore. A diver dove 50 ft down into the lake. Write an ordered pair that describes the diver's position relative to the shore and the lake's surface. Plot the point on the grid above and label it point X.

____

Name ________________ Class ________________ Date ________________

10A: Graphic Organizer

For use before Lesson 10-1

Study Skill As you learn new skills, practice them regularly. Each time you work a problem, it should seem easier than the time before. Keep a list of problems that you want to spend extra time practicing.

Write your answers.

1. What is the chapter title?

____

2. How many lessons are there in this chapter?

____

3. What is the topic of the Test-Taking Strategies page?

____

____

4. Complete the graphic organizer below as you work through the chapter.
   - In the center, write the title of the chapter.
   - When you begin a lesson, write the lesson name in a rectangle.
   - When you complete a lesson, write a skill or key concept in a circle linked to that lesson block.
   - When you complete the chapter, use this graphic organizer to help you review.

Name ______________________ Class ______________ Date ______________

Puzzle 10-1

Graphing Points in Four Quadrants

Use the coordinates given below each blank to locate the correct letter on the graph. Write the letter on the blank to answer the riddles.

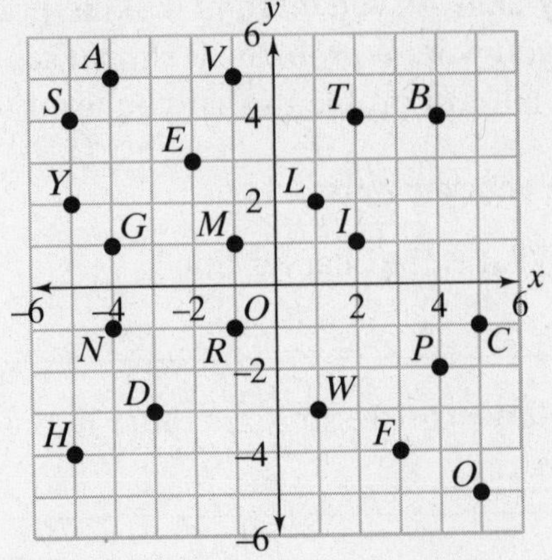

1. The capital of Nebraska is named after which U.S. President?

   ___ ___ ___ ___ ___ ___ ___
   $(-4, 5)$ $(4, 4)$ $(-1, -1)$ $(-4, 5)$ $(-5, -4)$ $(-4, 5)$ $(-1, 1)$

   ___ ___ ___ ___ ___ ___ ___
   $(1, 2)$ $(2, 1)$ $(-4, -1)$ $(5, -1)$ $(5, -5)$ $(1, 2)$ $(-4, -1)$

2. What is the capital of Florida?

   ___ ___ ___ ___ ___ ___ ___ ___ ___ ___ ___
   $(2, 4)$ $(-4, 5)$ $(1, 2)$ $(1, 2)$ $(-4, 5)$ $(-5, -4)$ $(-4, 5)$ $(-5, 4)$ $(-5, 4)$ $(-2, 3)$ $(-2, 3)$

Write your own riddle. Fill in the graph with the letters you need to answer your riddle. Throw in a few extra letters just for fun. Then write the **ordered pairs** below the answer line so the corresponding letters will give the answer to your riddle. Exchange with a friend and solve each other's riddles.

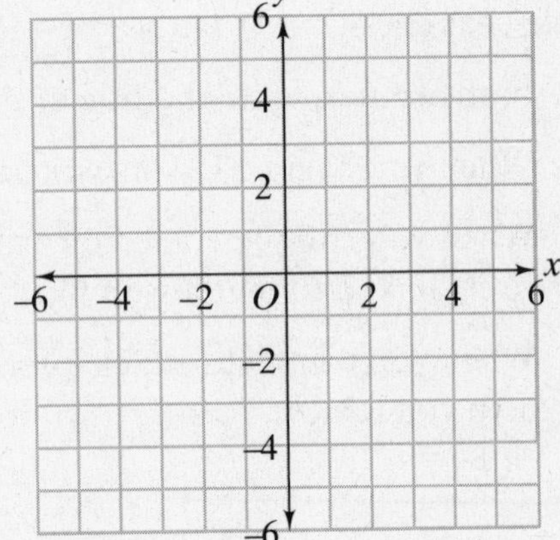

Riddle: ______________________________

____

____

Answer: ______________________________

____

____

Name ______________________ Class ______________ Date ______________

Practice 10-2

Graphing Linear Equations

Determine whether each ordered pair is a solution of $y = x - 4$.

1. (0, −4) ________ **2.** (5, −1) ________ **3.** (−3, −7) ________ **4.** (−7, −3) ________

Find three solutions for each equation.

5. $y = x + 5$ ______________________________

6. $y = -x + 7$ ______________________________

7. $y = 2x - 1$ ______________________________

Graph each linear equation.

8. $y = 3x - 1$

9. $y = -2x + 1$

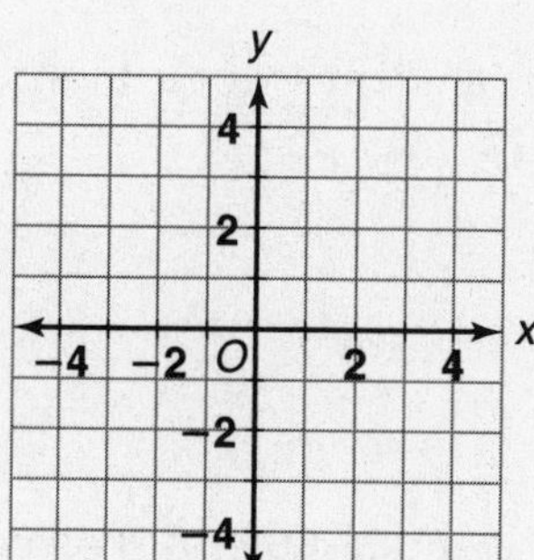

10. $y = 2x - 4$

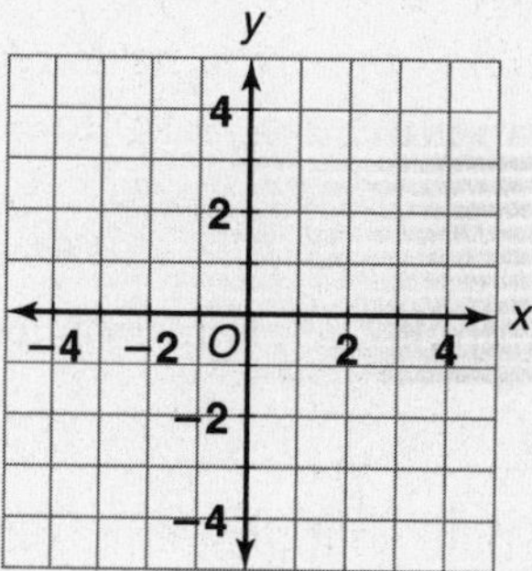

11. The graph of $y = -x$ passes through which quadrants?

____

12. Use the graph below to determine the coordinates of the point that is a solution of the equations of lines p and q.

____

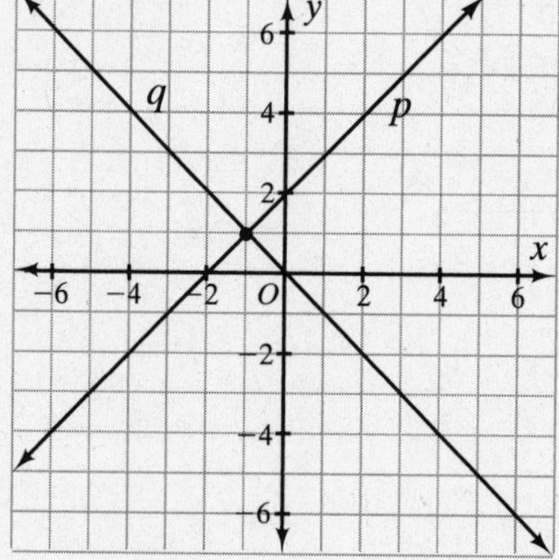

Name ______________________ Class ______________ Date ______________

10-2 • Guided Problem Solving

GPS Student Page 494, Exercise 39:

Error Analysis A student says that $(-1, -5)$ is a solution of $y = -3x - 2$. What error do you think the student made?

Understand

1. Is $(-1, -5)$ a correct solution to the equation? How do you know this from just reading the question?

____

____

Plan and Carry Out

2. To find the error, try to recreate the student's work. First, substitute $x = -1$ into $-3x - 2$.

____

3. Simplify the expression to find the value of y.

____

4. Would your answer be different if you simplified $-3(-1)$ to -3 and then subtracted 2? What would you get?

____

5. What mistake do you think the student made?

____

Check

6. What if the student substituted -5 for y and then solved the equation? Solve the problem this way and identify an error the student could make to get $x = -1$.

____

Solve Another Problem

7. A student gives $(2, -9)$ as a solution to the equation $y = 2x - 5$. What error do you think the student made?

____

____

Name ______________________ Class ______________ Date ______________

Practice 10-2

Graphing Linear Equations

Determine whether each ordered pair is a solution of $y = x - 4$.

1. (0, −4) ________
2. (5, −1) ________
3. (−3, −7) ________

Find three solutions for each equation.

4. $y = x + 5$

____

5. $y = 2x - 1$

____

Graph each linear equation.

6. $y = 3x - 1$

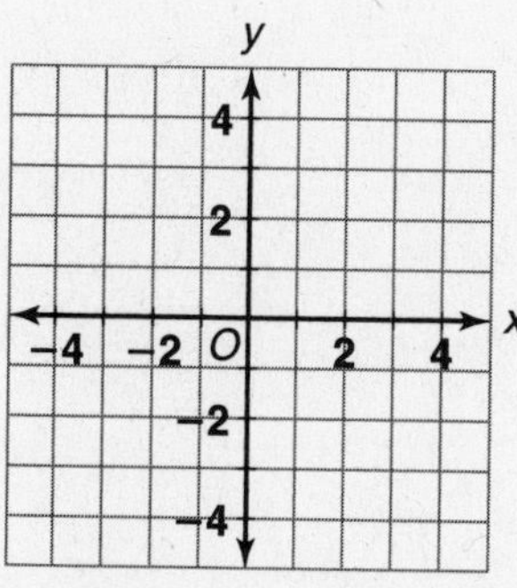

7. $y = -2x + 1$

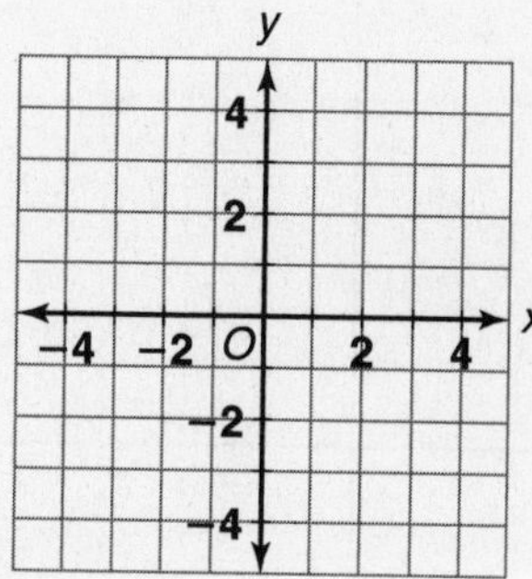

8. The graph of $y = -x$ passes through which quadrants?

____

9. Use the graph below to determine the coordinates of the point that is a solution of the equations of lines p and q.

____

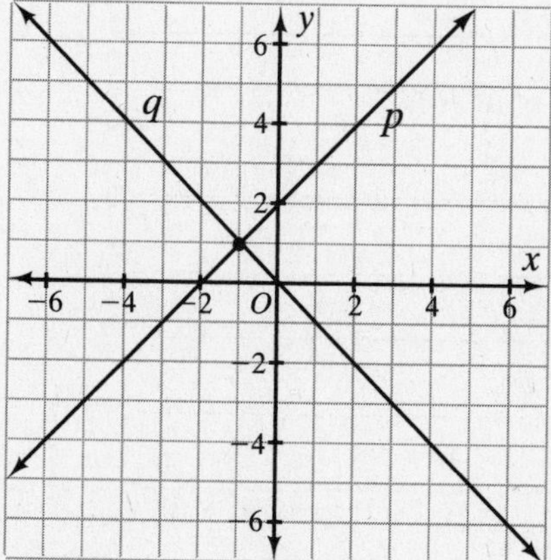

Name ________________________ Class ________________ Date ________________

Activity Lab 10-2

Graphing Linear Equations

Use the equation $y = x - 2$ to complete the table.

x	$x - 2$	y	(x, y)
0			
1			
2			
3			

1. Graph the equation.

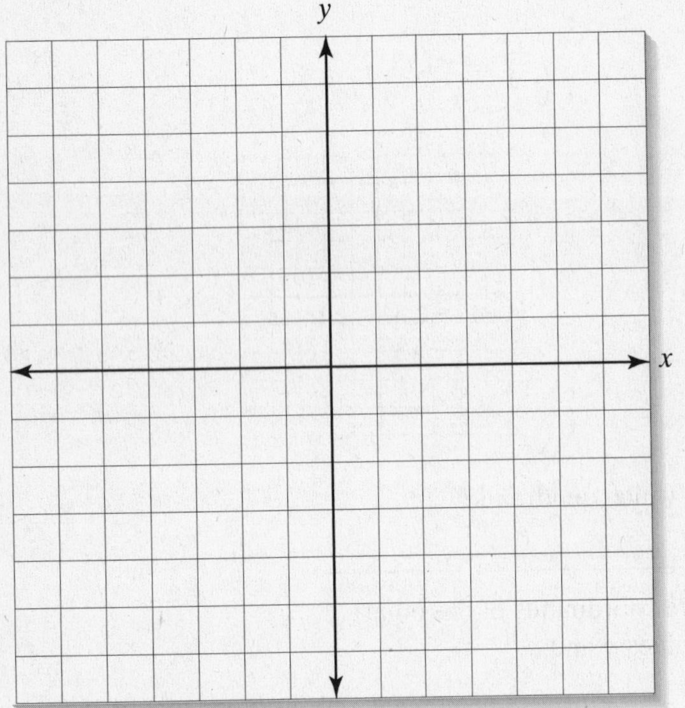

2. Is $(-2, -3)$ a solution of the equation? ________________

3. How does a graph of the equation show that $(6, 5)$ is not a solution?

____

____

4. If $x = 6$, then what is y? ________________

5. Does the graph show that $(-4, -6)$ is a solution? ________________

6. Are negative values possible solutions? ________________

7. How does the graph show solutions of the linear equation?

____

Name ______________________ Class ______________ Date ______________

Reteaching 10-2

Graphing Linear Equations

The **solutions** of $y = x + 3$ are the (x, y) pairs that make the equation true.

The solutions can be listed in a table.

x	$x + 3$	y	(x, y)
0	$0 + 3$	3	$(0, 3)$
1	$1 + 3$	4	$(1, 4)$
-2	$-2 + 3$	1	$(-2, 1)$

If all the solutions lie on a line, the equation is a **linear equation** and the line is its **graph.**

$y = x + 3$ is a linear equation.

The solutions can be graphed in the coordinate plane, as shown.

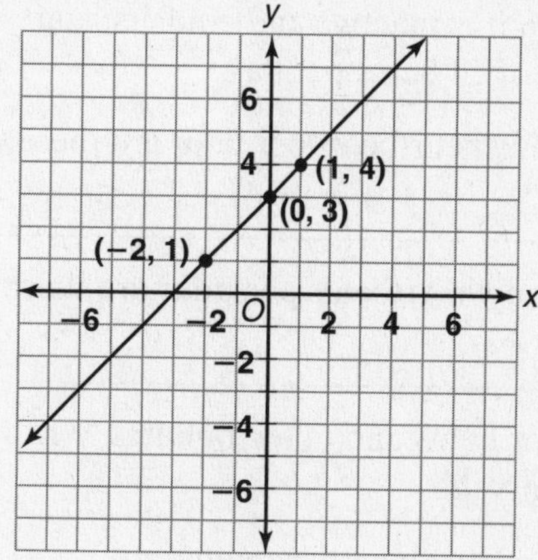

Complete each table.

1. $y = x - 4$

x	$x - 4$	y	(x, y)
2			
4			
6			

2. $y = 3x$

x	$3x$	y	(x, y)
-1			
0			
3			

3. $y = -x + 1$

x	$-x + 1$	y	(x, y)
0			
2			
-3			

Graph each linear equation.

4. $y = x - 5$

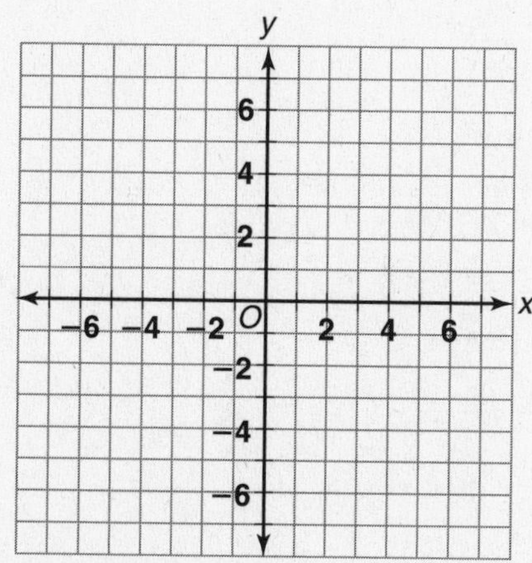

5. $y = 3x - 4$

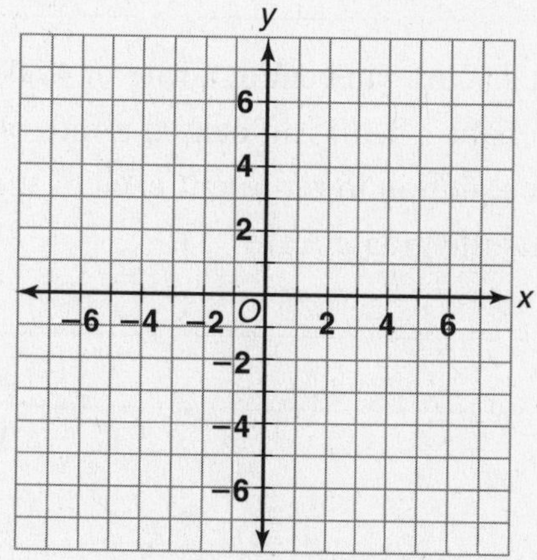

Name ______________________ Class ______________ Date ______________

Enrichment 10-2

Graphing Linear Equations

Critical Thinking

When an insect is active, its heart can beat at a rate of 140 beats per minute. When it is inactive and cold, its heart rate can slow to an average rate of 24 beats per day.

1. How many heartbeats per hour are there when an insect is active?

____

2. How many heartbeats per hour are there when an insect is inactive?

____

3. Use b for beats and m for minutes. Write the equation that represents the

   a. active heartbeat per minute. ______________

   b. inactive heartbeat per minute. ______________

4. Graph the equations on the same coordinate plane.

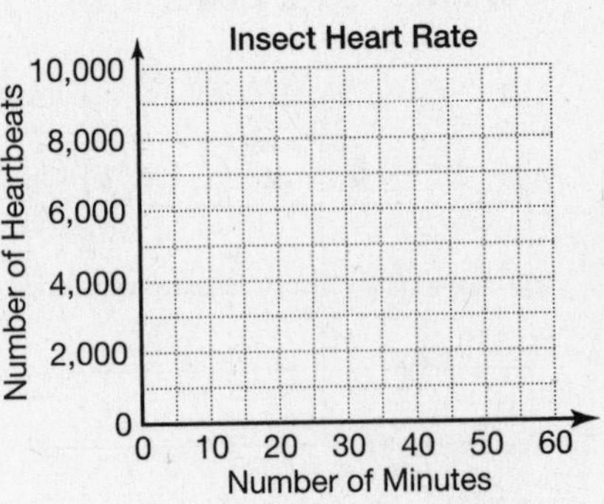

   a. Describe the similarities and differences of each graph.

   ____

   b. How can you tell, by looking, which graph represents the lesser rate?

   ____

   c. Do you have to graph the equations to tell which rate is the lesser one? Explain.

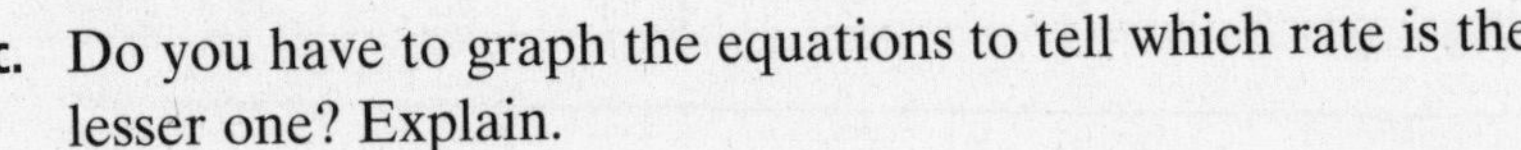

   ____

   d. For an active insect, how many heartbeats would you expect in 50 min? in 2 h?

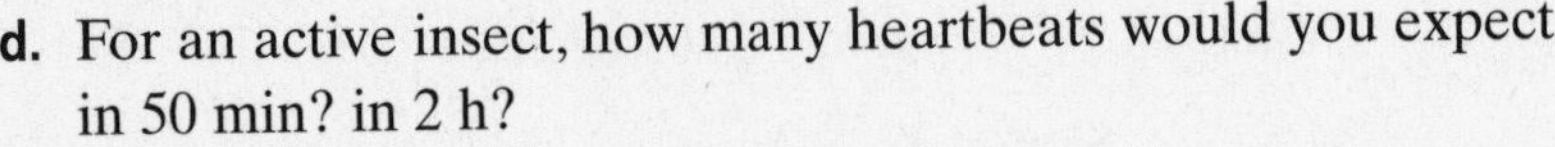

   ____

5. An adult's heart can beat at a rate of 4,800 times per hour. A newborn baby's heart can beat at a rate of 140 times per minute. Write an equation to represent each of these as $\frac{\text{beats}}{\text{hour}}$. Which represents the greater rate?

____

____

Name ______________________ Class ______________ Date ______________

Puzzle 10-2

Graphing Linear Equations

Letters are associated with points on this graph. They decode the secret word.

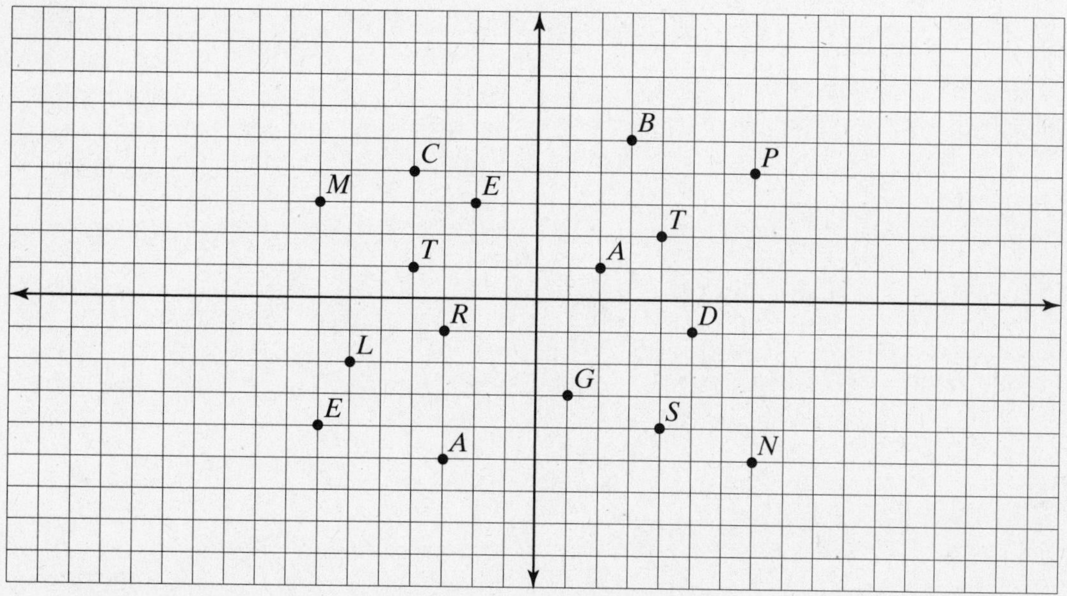

To decode the secret word, solve each system of equations graphically. Draw the lines on the graph shown above. If the solution corresponds to a point associated with a letter, then write the letter in the appropriate blank below.

1. $x + y = 3$

$x - y = 1$

2. $x = 3y$

$3y - 6 = 2x$

3. $x = \frac{1}{3}y + 2$

$-2x - y = 1$

4. $3x - 3y = -15$

$-3x - 3y = -3$

5. $x + y = 8$

$-x + 2y = 7$

6. $x - 3y = 0$

$5x - y = -14$

7. $-x - y = 8$

$2x - y = -1$

The secret word that you will write below comes from an Arabic word that means the reuniting of broken parts. It was first used by an Arabic mathematician around A.D. 825.

____ ____ ____ ____ ____ ____ ____.
1 2 3 4 5 6 7

Name ______________________ Class ______________ Date ______________

Practice 10-3

Finding the Slope of a Line

Find the slope of each line.

1. ______________________

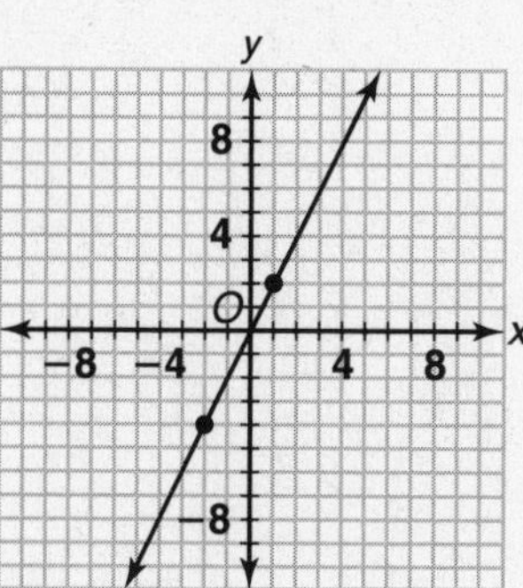

2. ______________________

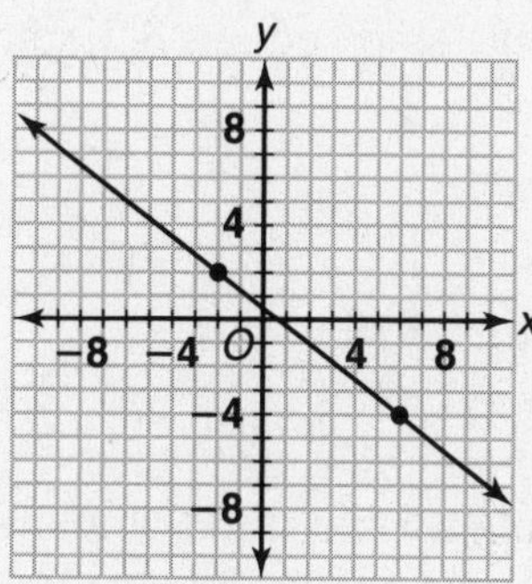

Use the coordinate plane to graph the given points. Find the slope of the line through the points.

3. $(-4, 6), (8, 4)$ ______________________

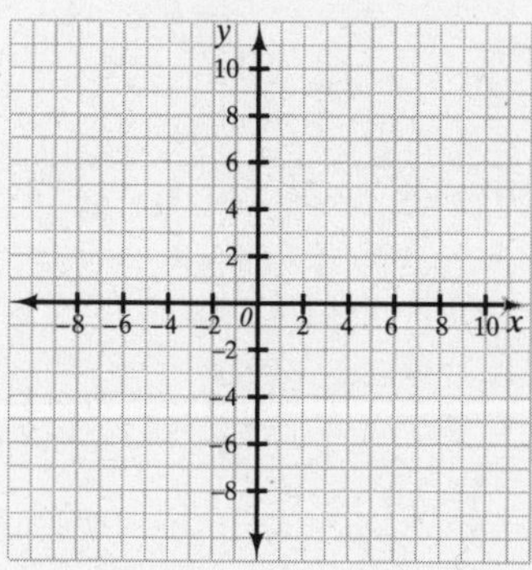

4. $(-1, 3), (4, 6)$ ______________________

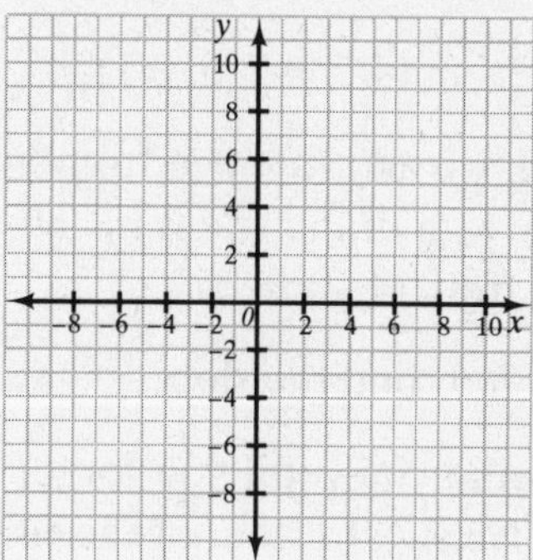

5. Up which slope would it be easiest to push a heavy cart: $\frac{1}{2}, \frac{1}{6}, 3$, or 5? ______________

6. Which slope would probably give you the greatest speed down a hill when you are skiing: $\frac{1}{8}, \frac{1}{4}$, 1, or 2? ______________

7. Which slope would be the most dangerous for a roofer trying to repair a roof: $\frac{1}{16}, \frac{1}{10}, \frac{1}{2}$, or $\frac{3}{2}$? ______________

Draw a line with the given slope through the given point.

8. $P(5, 1)$, slope $= -\frac{1}{3}$

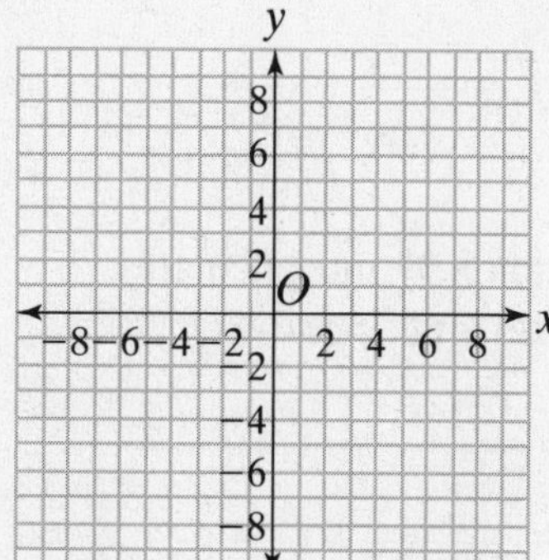

9. $K(-2, 4)$, slope $= 3$

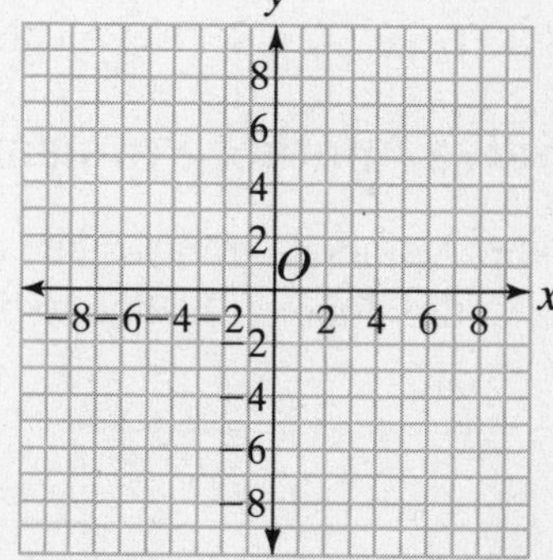

Name ______________________ Class ______________ Date ______________

10-3 • Guided Problem Solving

GPS Student Page 501, Exercise 20:

Error Analysis Your classmate graphs a line through (4, 2) and (5, −1) and finds that the slope equals 3. Explain why your classmate is incorrect.

Understand

1. What are you being asked to do?

____

2. What is the formula for the slope of a line?

____

Plan and Carry Out

3. Graph the two points on a coordinate plane and draw the line that passes through them.

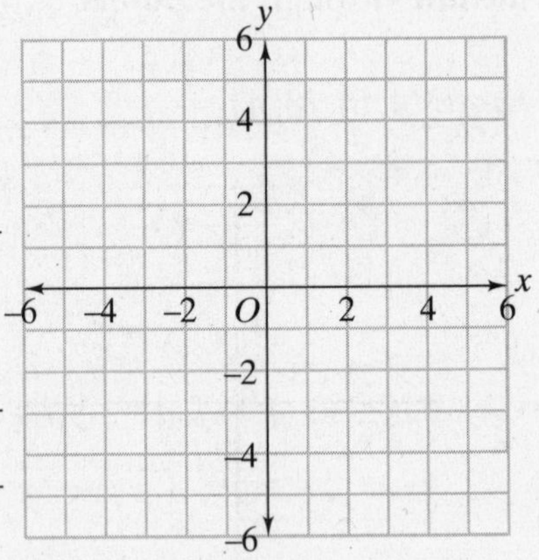

4. What is the run from (4, 2) to (5, −1)? ______________

5. The line slants down as you move from (4, 2) to (5, −1), so the sign of the rise is negative. What is the rise from (4, 2) to (5, −1)? ______________

6. Calculate rise/run to find the slope. ______________

7. What answer would you get if you forgot to put the negative sign in front of the rise? ______________

8. Why is your classmate incorrect?

____

Check

9. What are the rise and run if you calculate the rise and run by moving right to left, from (5, −1) to (4, 2)?

____

10. Calculate the slope using the rise and run from Step 9. Do you get the same answer? ______________

Solve Another Problem

11. A student graphs a line through points (3, −1) and (5, 3) and calculates the slope of the line to be −2. Explain why the student is incorrect.

____

____

Name ______________________ Class ______________ Date ______________

Practice 10-3

Finding the Slope of a Line

Find the slope of each line.

1. ______________________

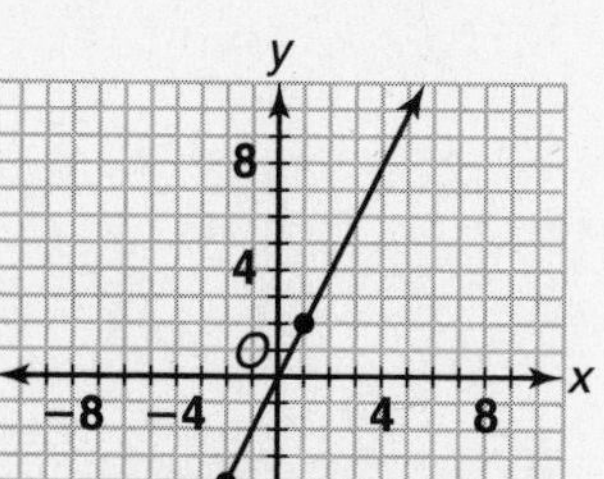

2. ______________________

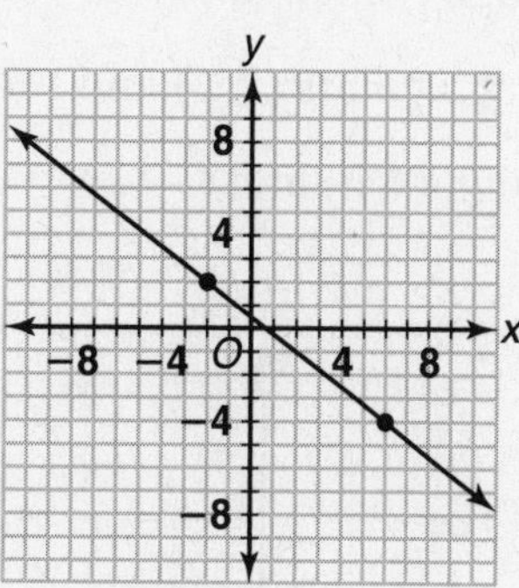

Use the coordinate plane to graph the given points. Find the slope of the line through the points.

3. 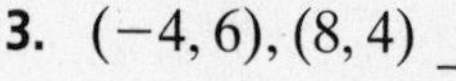 $(-4, 6), (8, 4)$ ______________________

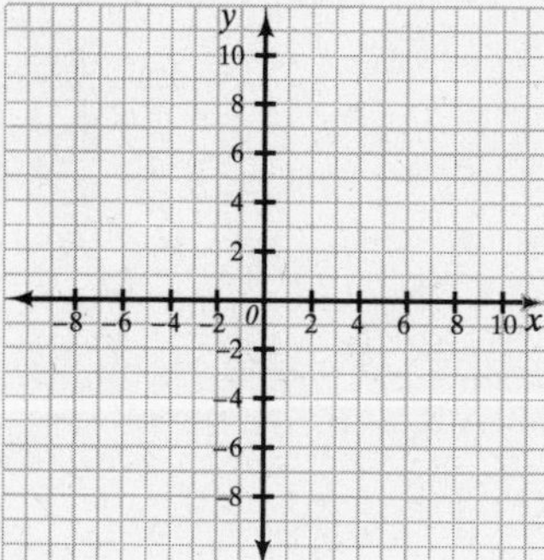

4. $(-1, 3), (4, 6)$ ______________________

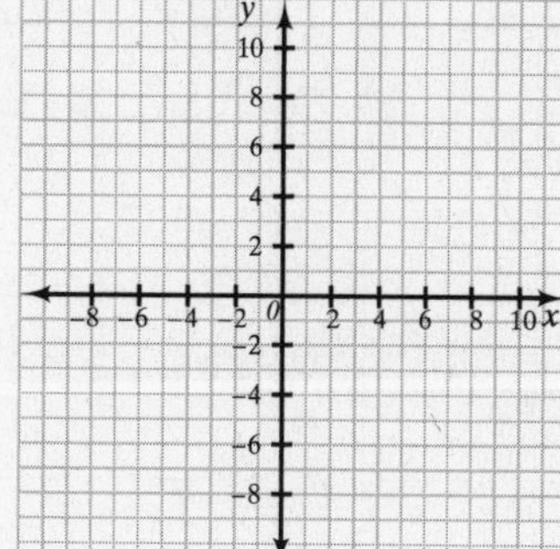

5. Which slope would be the most dangerous for a roofer trying to repair a roof: $\frac{1}{16}$, $\frac{1}{10}$, $\frac{1}{2}$, or $\frac{3}{2}$? ______________

Draw a line with the given slope through the given point.

6. $P(5, 1)$, slope $= -\frac{1}{3}$

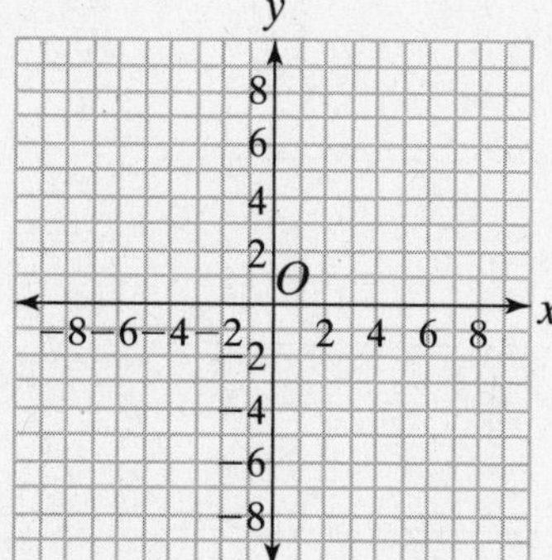

7. $K(-2, 4)$, slope $= 3$

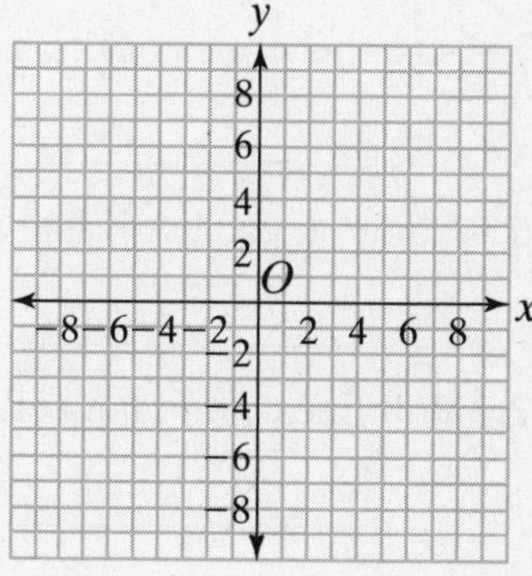

Name ______________________ Class ______________ Date ______________

Activity Lab 10-3

Finding the Slope of a Line

Materials needed: pencil and ruler

1. Graph line a through points $(0, 0)$ and $(4, 3)$.
2. Graph line b through points $(2, 1)$ and $(-5, -4)$.
3. Graph line c through $(4, 6)$ and $(-4, 0)$.

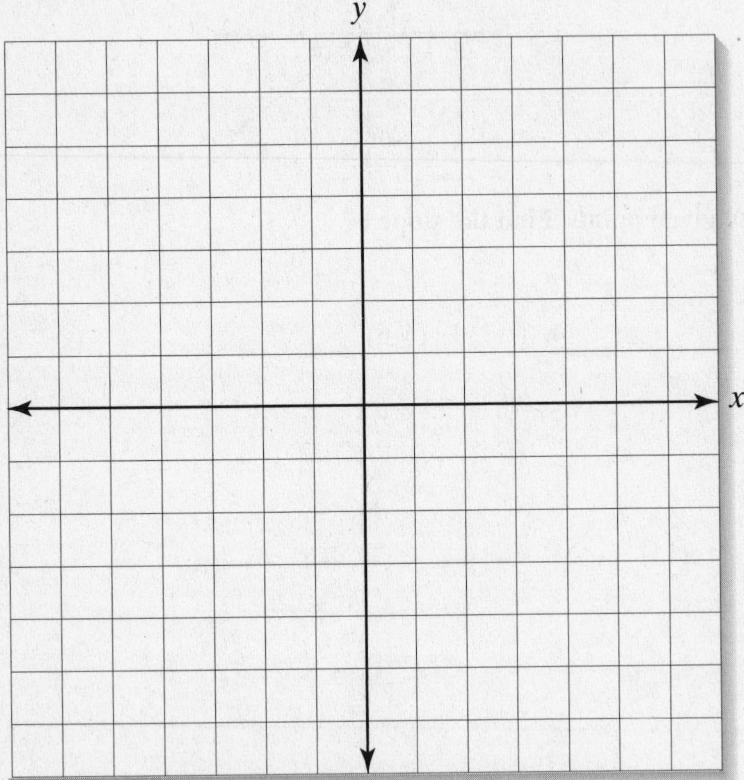

4. Find the slopes of lines a, b, and c.

____

5. Are the slopes of the lines positive or negative?

____

6. Can you predict if line a and line b will meet?

____

7. Will lines a and c meet?

____

Name ______________________ Class ______________ Date ______________

Reteaching 10-3

Finding the Slope of a Line

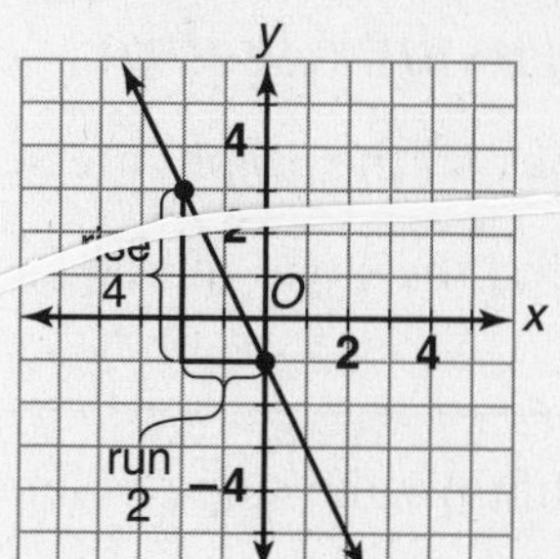

The steepness of a line is measured by its **slope.** To find the slope of a line, follow these steps.

① Pick any two points on the line. Find the *rise,* or vertical change. Here, the rise is −4.

② Find the *run,* or horizontal change. Here, the run is 2.

③ Find the ratio of rise to run.

$$\text{slope} = \frac{\text{rise}}{\text{run}} = \frac{-4}{2} = -2$$

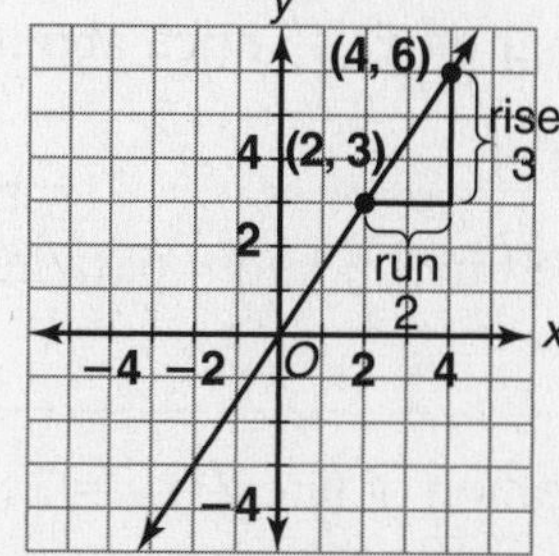

Sometimes the two points are given, such as (2, 3) and (4, 6). Graph both points. Draw their line. Then determine the slope.

$$\text{slope} = \frac{\text{rise}}{\text{run}} = \frac{3}{2}$$

The slope of the line through (2, 3) and (4, 6) is $\frac{3}{2}$.

Find the slope of each line.

1. 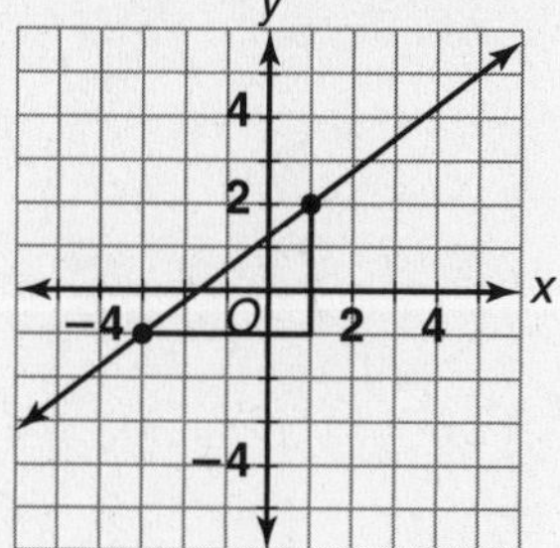

2. 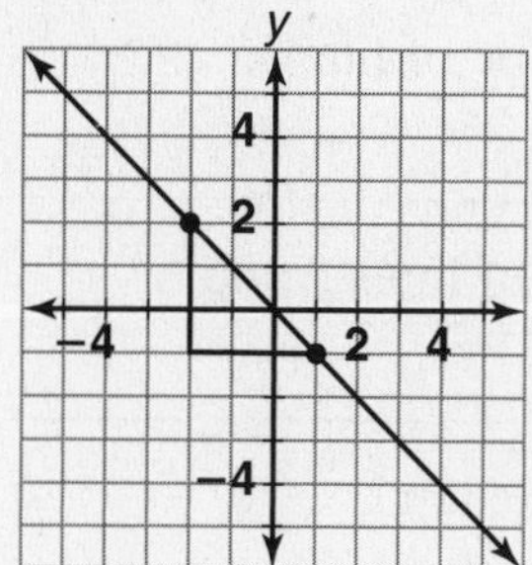

3. 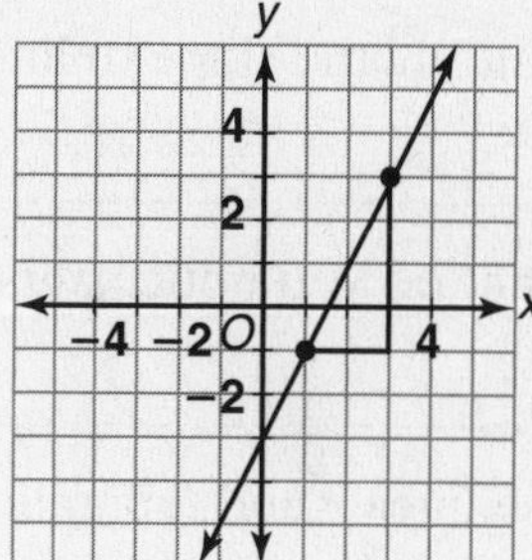

slope $= \frac{\text{rise}}{\text{run}} =$ ______ slope $= \frac{\text{rise}}{\text{run}} =$ ______ slope $= \frac{\text{rise}}{\text{run}} =$ ______

Draw a line with the given slope through the given point.

4. $B(3, 5)$, slope $= 3$

y
4
2
x
−4 −2 O 2 4
−2

5. $Z(1, -1)$, slope $= -1$

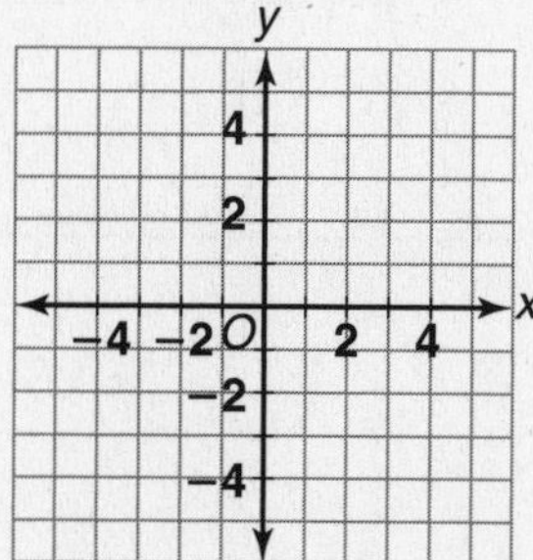

6. $S(1, -2)$, slope $= 2$

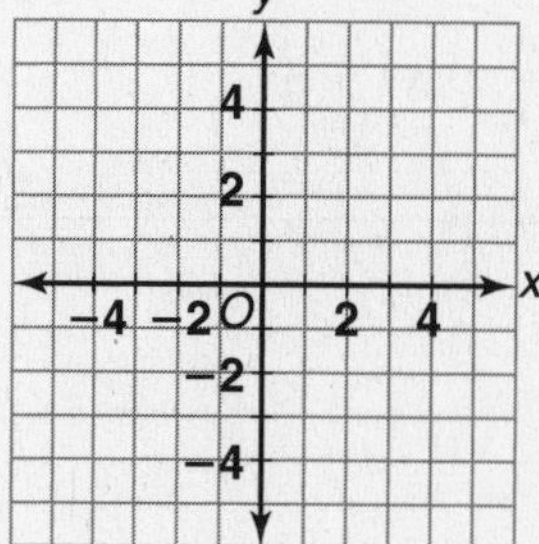

Name ______________________ Class ______________ Date ____________

Enrichment 10-3

Finding the Slope of a Line

Patterns in Algebra

The lines on the graph intersect at one point.

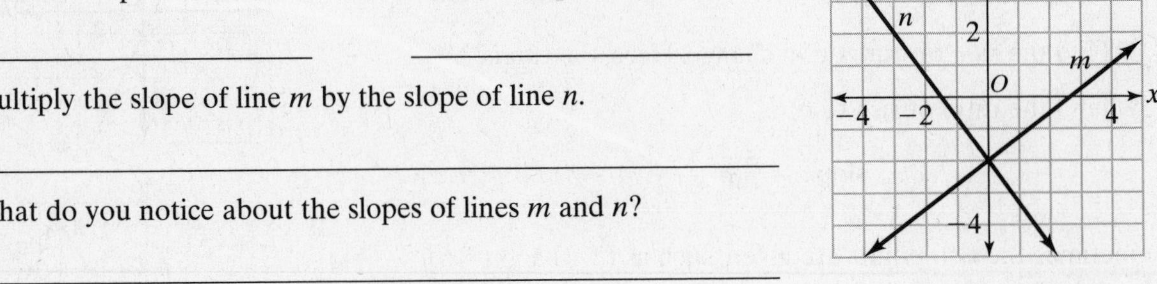

1. Find the slope of line m. **2.** Find the slope of line n.

______________________ ______________________

3. Multiply the slope of line *m* by the slope of line *n*.

____

4. What do you notice about the slopes of lines *m* and *n*?

____

5. Are lines *m* and *n* parallel or perpendicular?

____

The equation of line *g* is $y = 2x + 1$. The equation for line *h* is $y = \frac{-1}{2}x + 1$.

6. Find the slope of line *g*. **7.** Find the slope of line *h*.

______________________ ______________________

8. Multiply the slope of line *g* by the slope of line *h*.

____

9. What do you notice about the slopes of lines *g* and *h*?

____

10. Are lines *g* and *h* parallel or perpendicular?

____

11. Write a "rule" for determining how you know when two lines are perpendicular.

____

____

Write an equation for a line perpendicular to the line with the given equation.

12. $y = -3x + 1$ **13.** $y = \frac{3}{5}x - 10$ **14.** $y = \frac{-1}{7}x + 4$

______________________ ______________________ ______________________

Name ______________________ Class ______________ Date ______________

10B: Reading Comprehension

For use after Lesson 10-3

Study Skill Go to class prepared. Always bring your textbook, notebook or paper, and a pencil, unless your teacher tells you otherwise.

Below is a coordinate map of the midwestern and eastern United States. The horizontal scale uses letters and the vertical scale uses numbers to identify various locations. Use the map to answer the questions below. Letters are typically written first, followed by numbers.

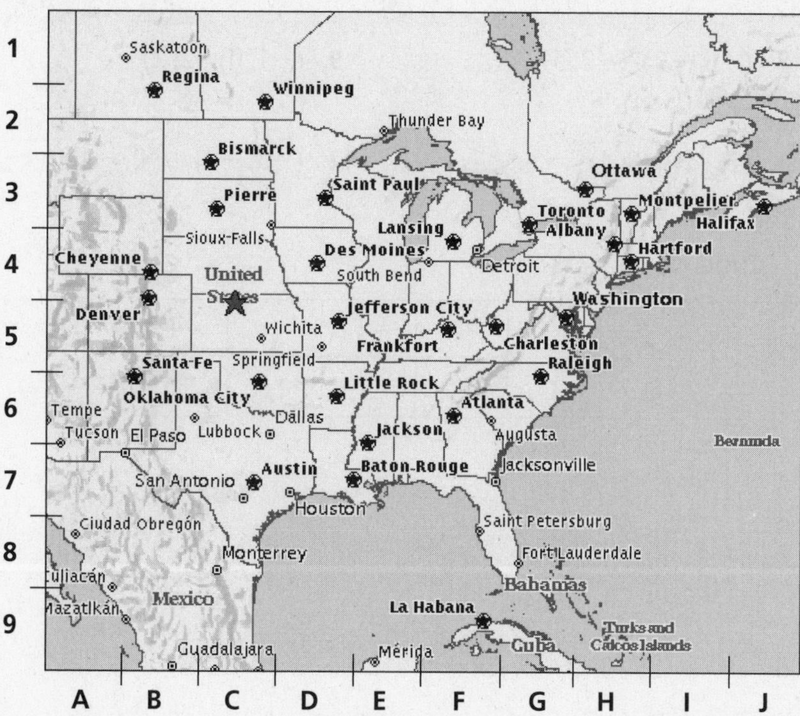

1. What are the coordinates for Tucson?

____

2. What are the coordinates for Montpelier?

____

3. Which state capital is located at D4?

____

4. Which cities are located at C7?

____

5. How would you identify the location of Bismarck?

____

6. What is the difference in the vertical coordinates for Atlanta and Saint Paul?

____

7. **High-Use Academic Words** In Exercise 5, what does it mean to identify?

a. to come together to form a single unit

b. to show that you recognize something

Name ____________________ Class ____________ Date ____________

Puzzle 10-3

Finding the Slope of a Line

For each exercise, find the slope of the line through the given pair of points. Use your answers and the code key to fill in the blanks and solve the puzzle.

1. (0, 0), (−5, 10)
2. (−1, 0), (−5, 2)
3. (0, 5), (−3, 11)
4. (3, 1), (0, 1)
5. (4, 2), (7, 6)
6. (9, −2), (5, −1)
7. (6, 2), (5, 7)
8. (−6, −2), (−2, 5)
9. (−1, 0), (2, 2)
10. (0, 3), (10, 3)
11. (2, −3), (8, 4)
12. (−3, −3), (−2, −4)

Code Key

2	0	−5	0	$-\frac{1}{2}$	$\frac{4}{3}$	$\frac{7}{4}$	$\frac{7}{6}$	−2	$-\frac{1}{4}$	$\frac{2}{3}$	−1
S	B	E	R	R	U	I	T	E	Y	H	N

To find the slope of a line, divide the...

___ ___ ___ ___   ___ ___   ___ ___ ___   ___ ___ ___

4 8 1 3   10 6   11 9 7   2 5 12

Name ______________________ Class ______________ Date ______________

Practice 10-4

Graphing Nonlinear Relationships

Match each graph with one of the equations below.

1. 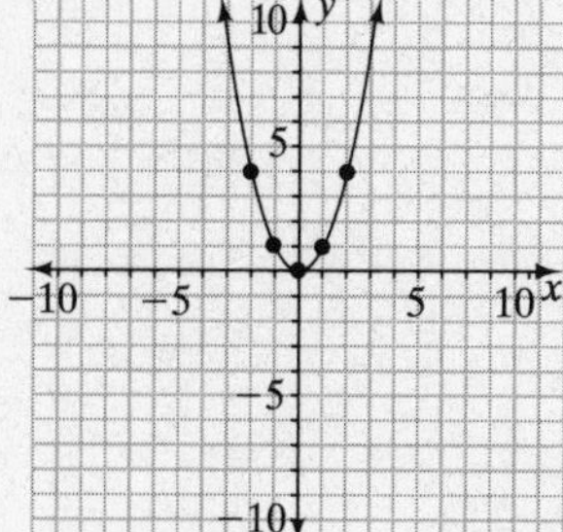

____

2. 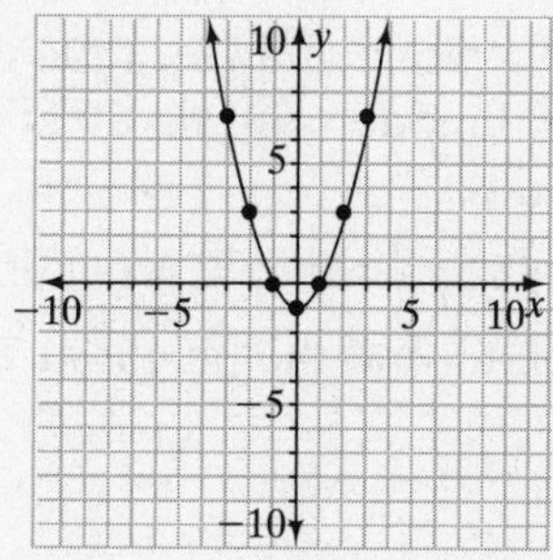

____

3. 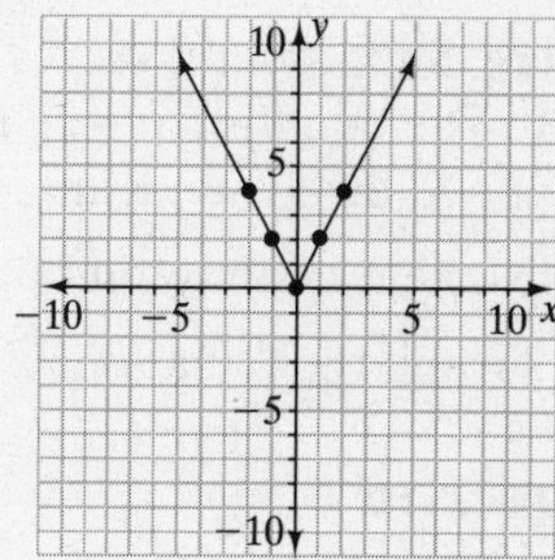

____

4. 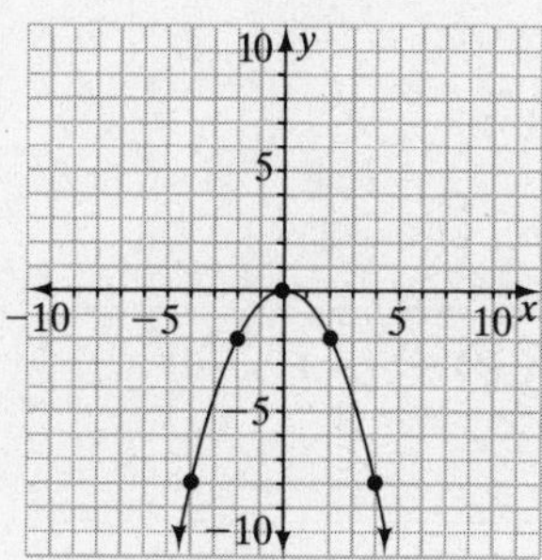

____

5. 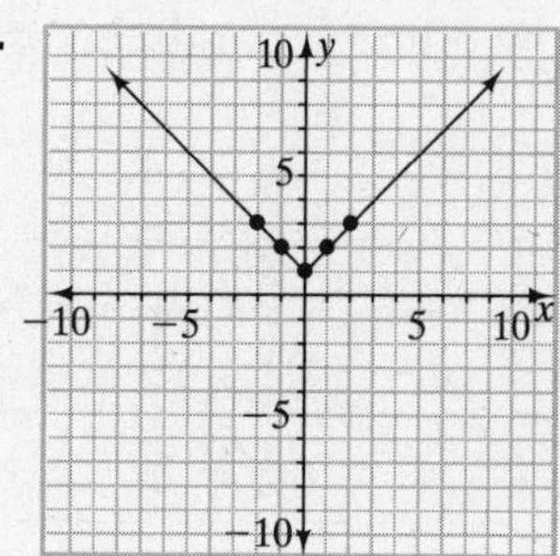

____

6. 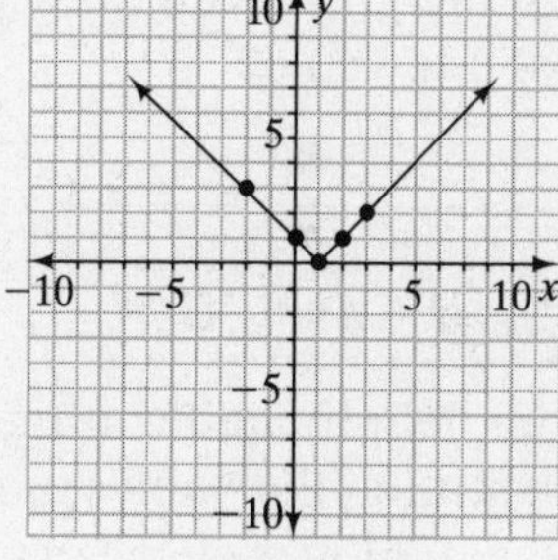

____

A. $y = |x - 1|$ **B.** $y = x^2$ **C.** $y = -\frac{1}{2}x^2$

D. $y = |x| + 1$ **E.** $y = |2x|$ **F.** $y = x^2 - 1$

7. **a.** Complete the table below for the equation $y = x^2 + 2$.

x	−3	−2	−1	0	1	2	3
y							

b. Graph the ordered pairs and connect the points as smoothly as possible.

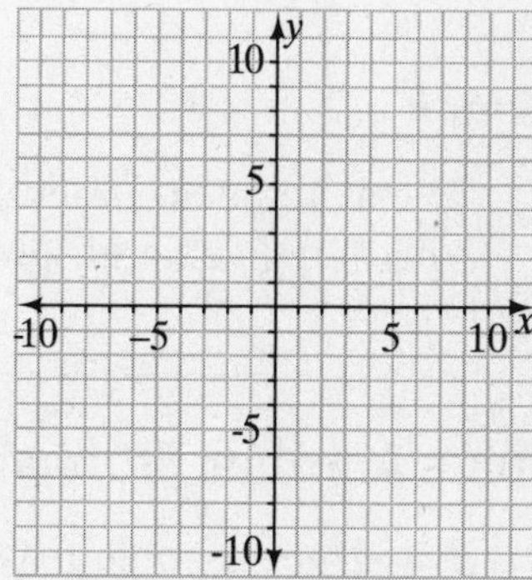

c. Describe how this graph is different from the graph of $y = x^2$.

____

____

Name ______________________ Class ______________ Date ______________

10-4 • Guided Problem Solving

GPS Student Page 507, Exercise 30:

Skydiving Suppose a skydiver leaps from a plane at an altitude of 12,000 ft. The equation $h = -16t^2 + 12{,}000$ models the skydiver's height above the ground, in feet, at t seconds.

a. Make a table to find the height at 0, 5, 10, and 20 seconds.

b. Graph the equation. Use the graph to find the height at 12 s.

Understand

1. What does the variable t in the equation represent? h?

____

2. Will the graph you draw for part (b) be a line, a parabola, or an absolute value?

____

Plan and Carry Out

3. Complete the table at right by subsituting the values of t into the equation and solving for h.

t	0	5	10	20
h				

4. Graph each (t, h) ordered pair from the table on the coordinate plane at the right. The t values are on the horizontal axis, and the h values are on the vertical axis. Connect the points with a smooth curve.

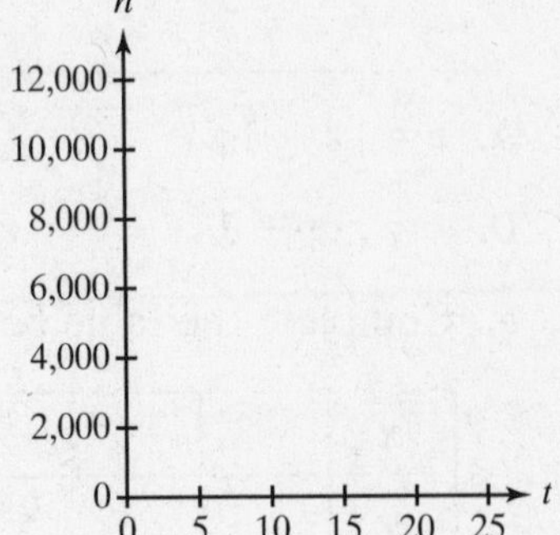

5. Find the point on the curve that corresponds to $t = 12$. What value of h does the graph pass through at that point?

____

6. How many feet above the ground is the skydiver after 12 s?

____

Check

7. To check the accuracy of your graph, substitute $t = 12$ into the equation given and solve. Is your answer for Step 6 reasonable?

____

Solve Another Problem

8. You drop an apple from a hot-air balloon that is 200 ft above the ground. The equation $h = 200 - 16t^2$ gives the height, in feet, of the apple after falling for t seconds. Use a graph to find the height of the apple after 2 seconds.

____

Name ______________________ Class ______________ Date ______________

Practice 10-4

Graphing Nonlinear Relationships

Match each graph with one of the equations below.

1.

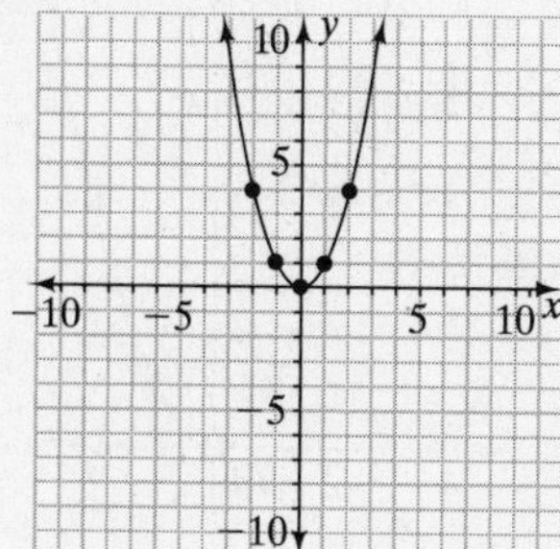

____

2.

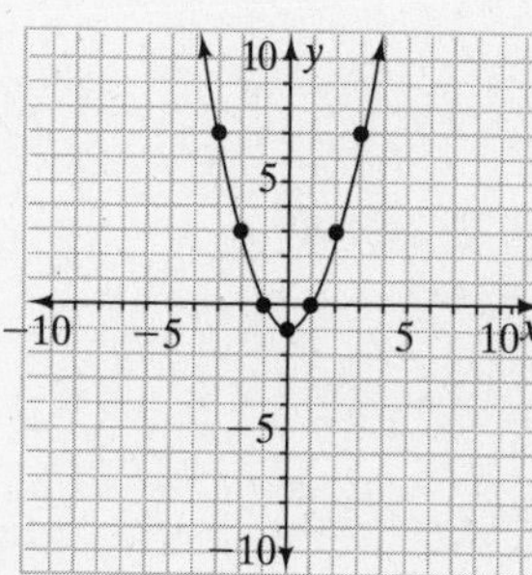

____

3.

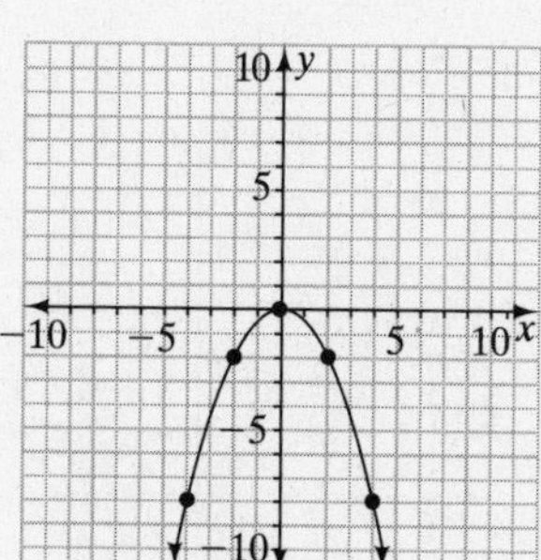

____

4.

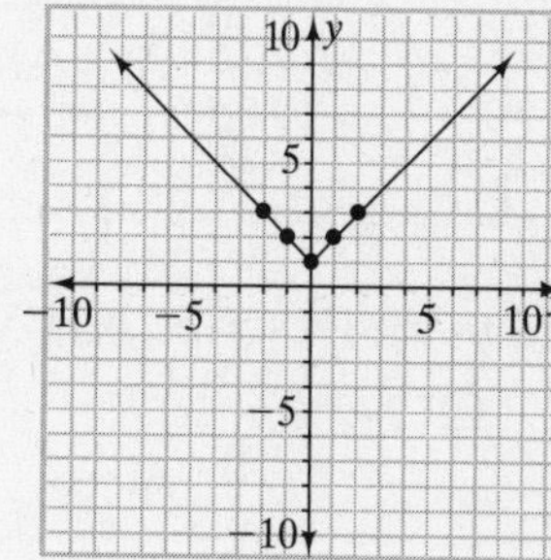

____

A. $y = x^2$

B. $y = -\frac{1}{2}x^2$

C. $y = |x| + 1$

D. $y = x^2 - 1$

5. a. Complete the table below for the equation $y = x^2 + 2$.

x	−3	−2	−1	0	1	2	3
y							

b. Graph the ordered pairs and connect the points as smoothly as possible.

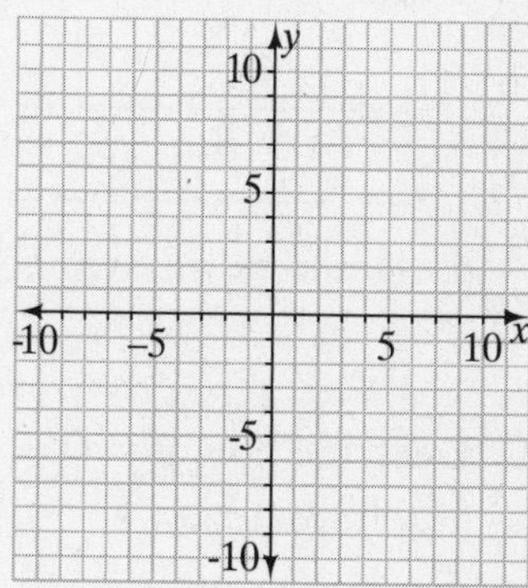

c. Describe how this graph is different from the graph of $y = x^2$.

____

____

Name ____________________ Class ____________ Date ____________

Activity Lab 10-4

Graphing Nonlinear Relationships

The graph at the right shows $y = x^2$. Compare this graph to the ones you complete below.

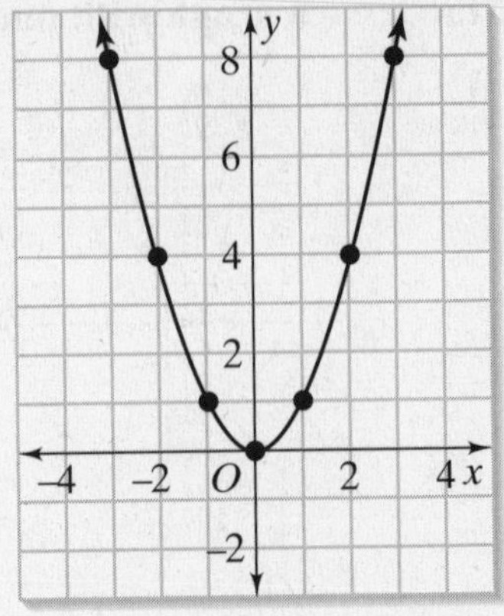

1. a. Complete the table for the equation $y = (x + 1)^2$.

x	−4	−3	−2	−1	0	1	2
y							

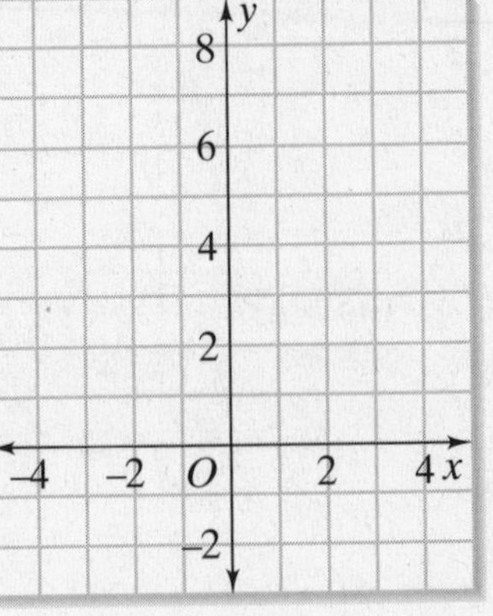

b. Graph the ordered pairs. Describe how your graph compares to the graph shown for $y = x^2$.

____

____

2. a. Complete the table for the equation $y = (x - 1)^2$.

x	−2	−1	0	1	2	3	4
y							

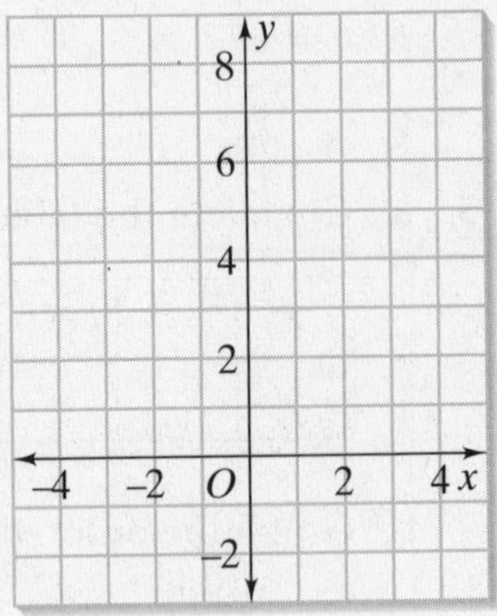

b. Graph the ordered pairs.

c. How does this graph compare with the graphs in Exercise 1 above?

____

____

d. Describe the symmetry of this graph.

____

3. Describe how $y = (x - 4)^2$ and $y = (x + 3)^2$ will appear after graphing them.

____

____

____

Name ______________________ Class ______________ Date ______________

Reteaching 10-4

Graphing Nonlinear Relationships

The graph of $y = x^2 - 1$ is a U-shaped curve called a **parabola.** To graph a parabola:

① Make a table of values.

x	$x^2 - 1$	y	(x, y)
−2	$(-2)^2 - 1$	3	(−2, 3)
−1	$(-1)^2 - 1$	0	(−1, 0)
0	$0^2 - 1$	−1	(0, −1)
1	$1^2 - 1$	0	(1, 0)
2	$2^2 - 1$	3	(2, 3)

② Graph the points.

③ Draw the U shape.

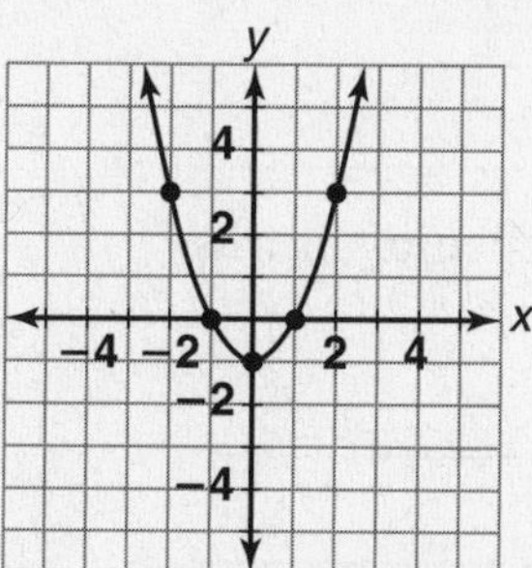

The graph of $y = 2|x|$ is called an **absolute value equation.** Its graph is V-shaped. To graph the equation:

① Make a table of values.

x	$2\|x\|$	y	(x, y)
−2	$2 \cdot 2$	4	(−2, 4)
−1	$2 \cdot 1$	2	(−1, 2)
0	$2 \cdot 0$	0	(0, 0)
1	$2 \cdot 1$	2	(1, 2)
2	$2 \cdot 2$	4	(2, 4)

② Graph the points.

③ Draw the V shape.

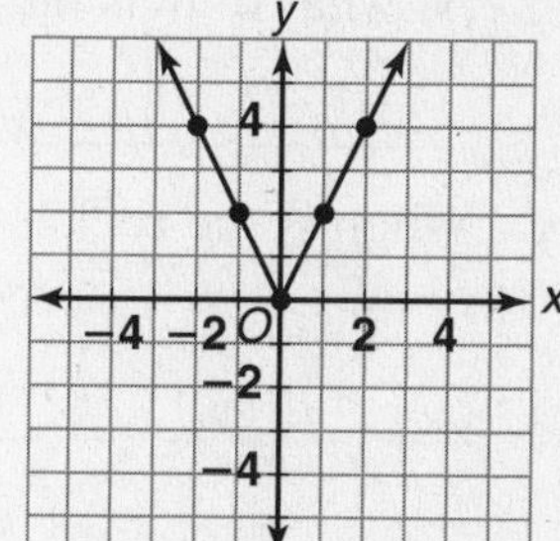

Make a table of values for each equation. Then graph each equation.

1. $y = x^2 - 2$

x	y
−2	
−1	
0	
1	
2	

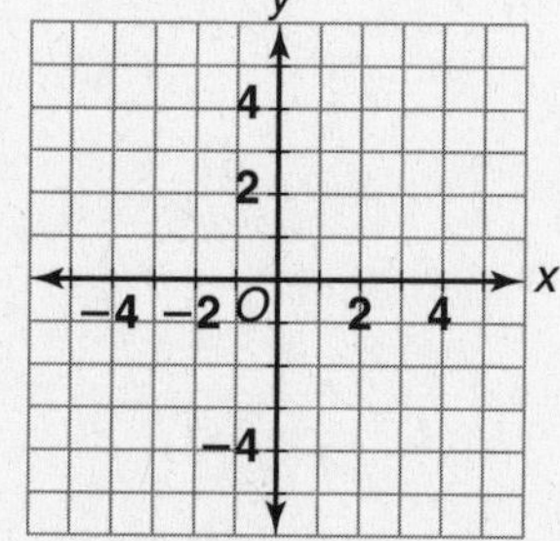

2. $y = 2x^2 - 3$

x	y
−2	
−1	
0	
1	
2	

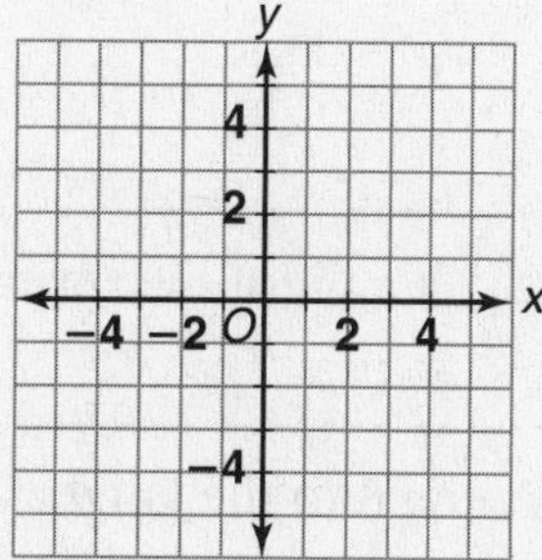

3. $y = \frac{1}{2}|x| + 1$

x	y
−2	
−1	
0	
1	
2	

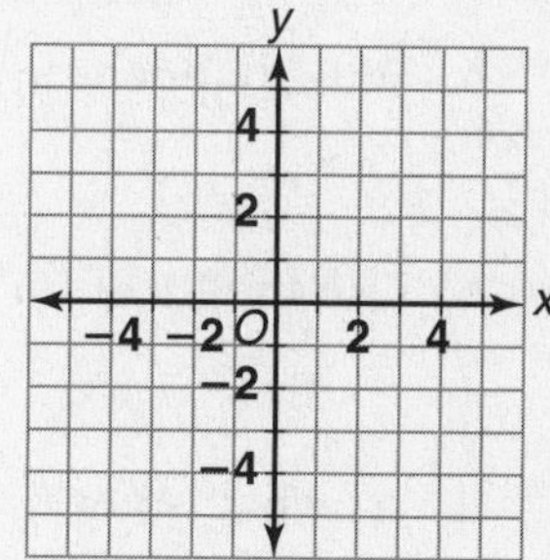

Name ______________________ Class ______________ Date ______________

Enrichment 10-4

Graphing Nonlinear Relationships

Algebra Application

A toy rocket was launched into the air. The function $h = 50t - 5t^2$ describes this situation, where h is the height in meters and t is the time in seconds.

The graph of the rocket's motion is shown at the right.

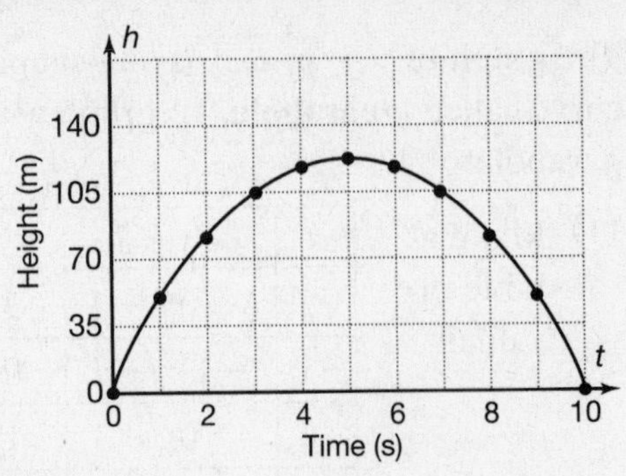

1. **a.** Can there be more than one time for each height? Why?

____

____

b. At what time is the height 0 meters?

____

c. When is the rocket 105 m in the air? What is happening at this time?

____

____

d. What is the height at 10 s? What is happening to the rocket?

____

e. Why doesn't the graph extend below the x-axis?

____

____

2. An object is launched into the air. The function $h = 80t - 16t^2$ describes this situation, where h is the height in feet and t is the time in seconds.

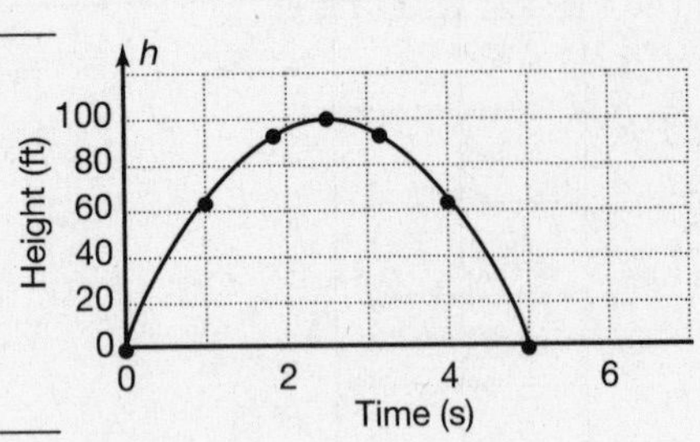

a. When is the object 64 feet in the air? Explain.

____

____

b. What happens at $2\frac{1}{2}$ s?

____

c. Use the function to determine the height of the object at $\frac{5}{8}$ s.

____

d. At what other time is the height equal to the height you found in part c?

____

Name ____________________ Class ____________ Date ____________

Puzzle 10-4

Graphing Nonlinear Relationships

To decode the secret word, complete the table for the equation $y = x^2$ using integer values of x from -3 to 3. Draw a curve through the points. To solve the puzzle, write the letters of the points on the curve, in order, on the blanks below.

x	-3	-2	-1	0	1	2	3
y							

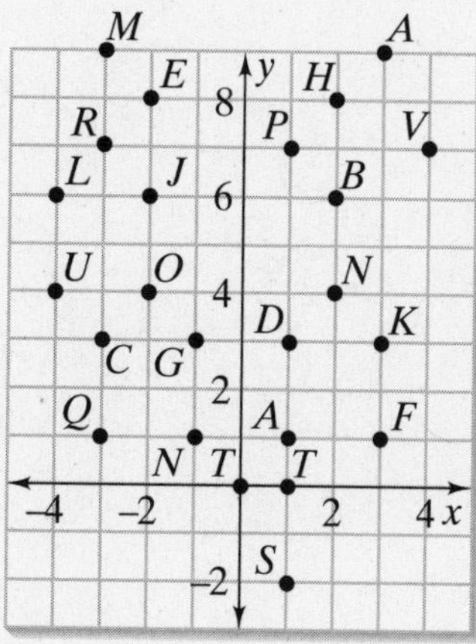

The highest point in this state is Granite Peak at 12,799 feet.

___ ___ ___ ___ ___ ___ ___

Name ______________________ Class ______________ Date ______________

Practice 10-5

Translations

Use the graph at the right for Exercises 1–3.

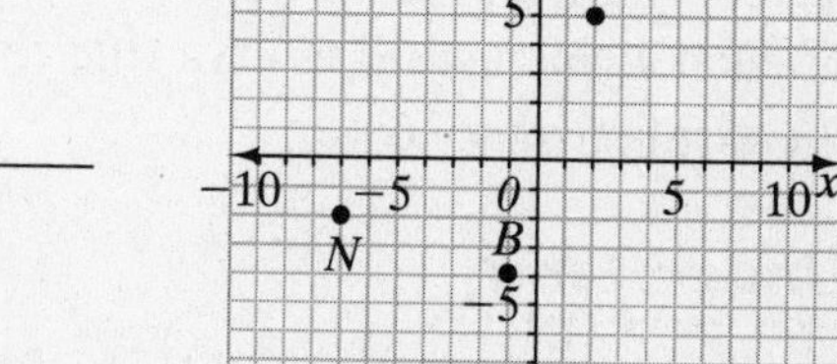

1. Give the coordinates of point A after it has been translated down 3 units. ______________

2. Give the coordinates of point B after it has been translated left 3 units. ______________

3. What are the coordinates of point N after it is translated right 8 units and up 5 units? ______________

Graph each translation of *ABCD*. Use arrow notation to show the translation.

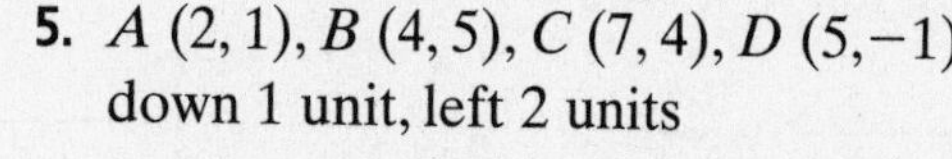

4. $A\ (2, 1), B\ (4, 5), C\ (7, 4), D\ (5, -1)$; right 2 units

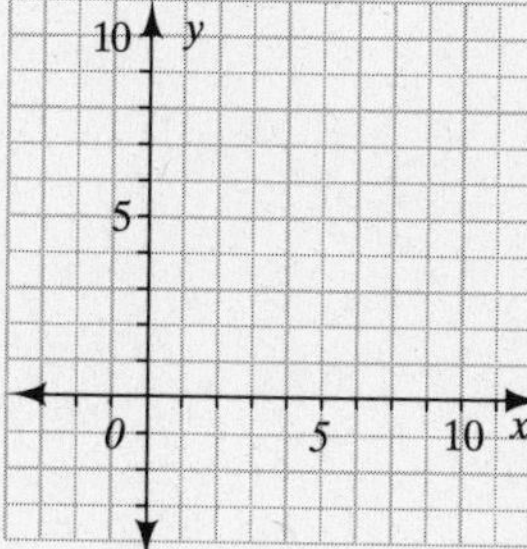

____

5. $A\ (2, 1), B\ (4, 5), C\ (7, 4), D\ (5, -1)$; down 1 unit, left 2 units

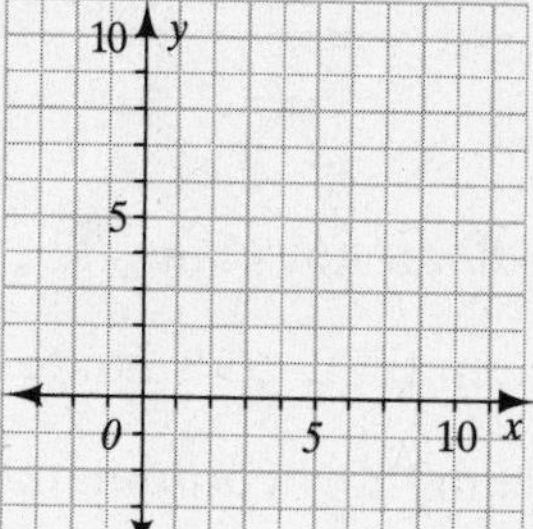

____

Write the rule for the translation shown in each graph.

6.

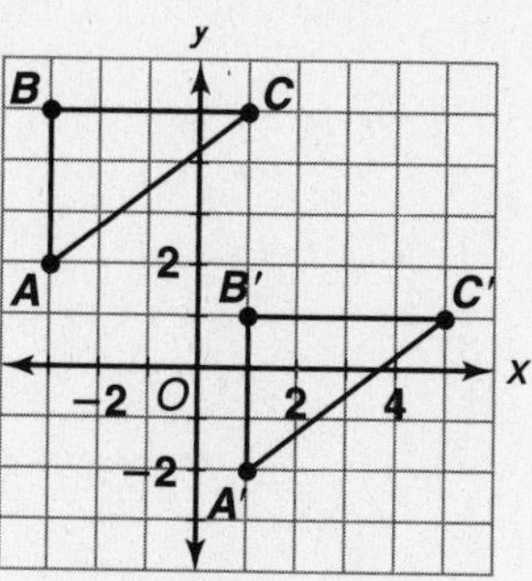

____

7.

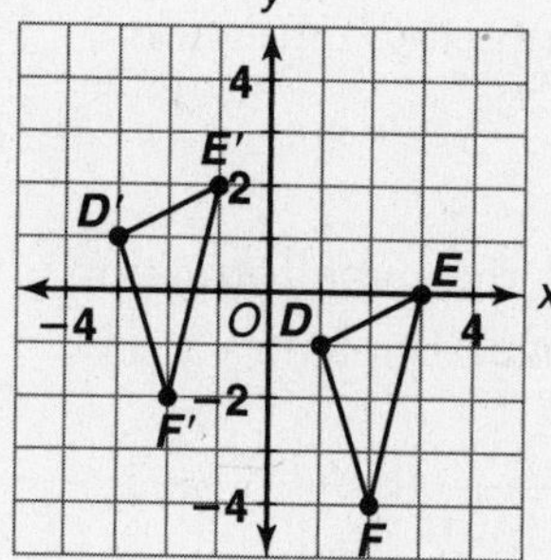

____

Name ______ Class ______ Date ______

10-5 • Guided Problem Solving

GPS Student Page 513, Exercise 22:

Aviation Three airplanes are flying in a triangular formation. After 1 min, airplane P moves to P'. Give the new coordinates of each airplane and write a rule to describe the direction that the airplanes move.

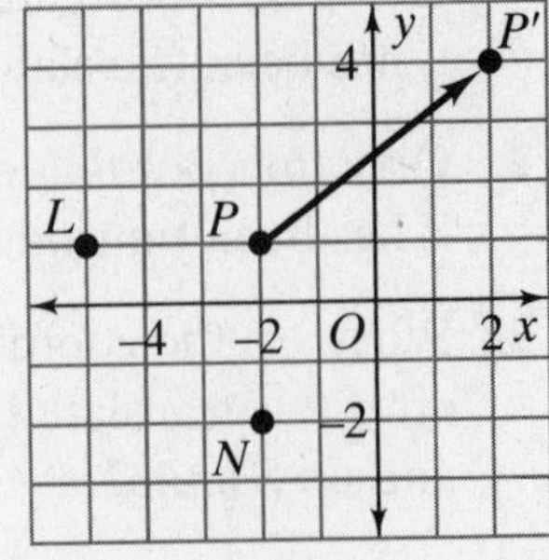

Understand

1. What are you being asked to do?

______

2. How does finding the new coordinates of airplane P help you to determine the new coordinates of airplanes L and N?

______

______

Plan and Carry Out

3. What is the new coordinate for plane P? ______

4. What is the difference in the x-coordinates of P and P'? ______

5. What is the difference in the y-coordinates of P and P'? ______

6. Use the differences found in Steps 4 and 5 to find the new coordinates for airplane L. ______

7. Use the differences found in Steps 4 and 5 to find the new coordinates for airplane N. ______

8. Write a rule to describe the translation. ______

Check

9. Are the airplanes in the same formation after the move as they were before the move? Explain.

______

______

Solve Another Problem

10. Three airplanes are flying in a triangular formation. If airplane P moves to P', find the new coordinates of the other two planes and write a rule to describe the move.

______

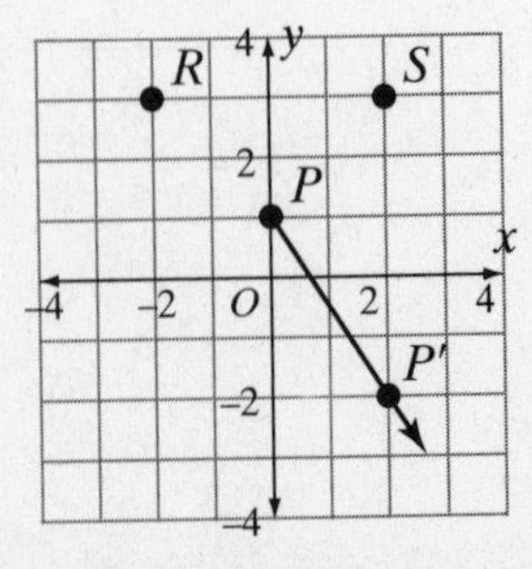

Name ______________________ Class ______________ Date ______________

Practice 10-5

Translations

Use the graph at the right for Exercises 1–3.

1. Give the coordinates of point A after it has been translated down 3 units.

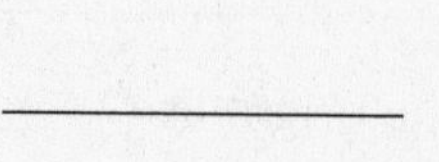

2. Give the coordinates of point B after it has been translated left 3 units.

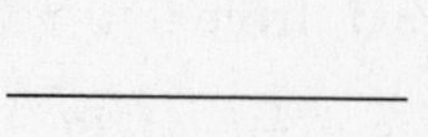

3. What are the coordinates of point N after it is translated right 8 units and up 5 units?

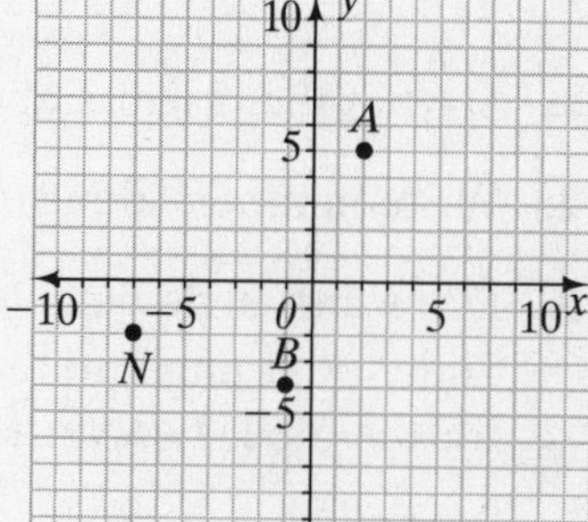

Graph each translation of *ABCD*.
Use arrow notation to show the translation.

4. $A\ (2, 1), B\ (4, 5), C\ (7, 4), D\ (5, -1)$; right 2 units

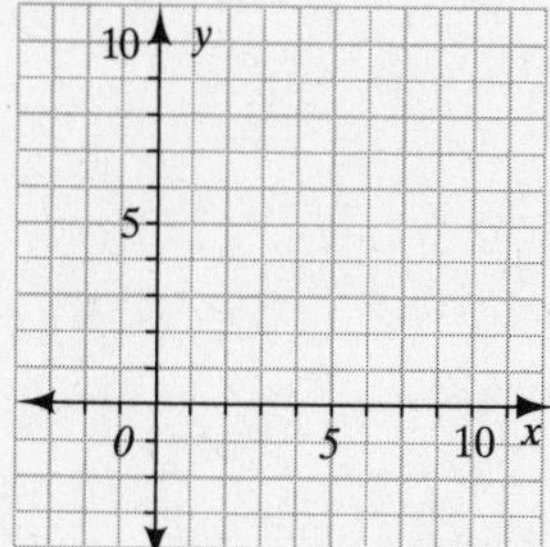

5. $A\ (2, 1), B\ (4, 5), C\ (7, 4), D\ (5, -1)$; down 1 unit, left 2 units

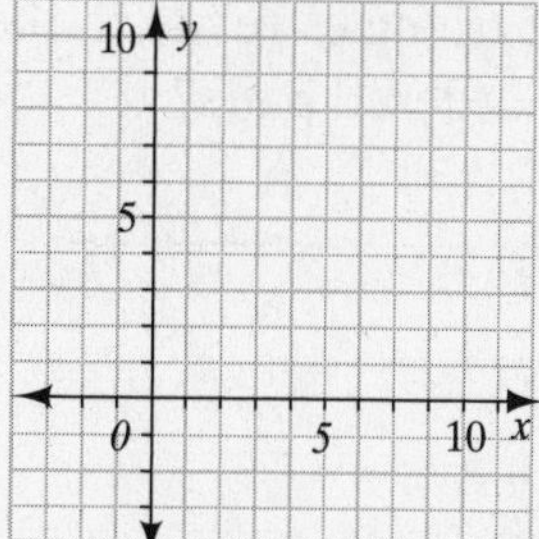

Write the rule for the translation shown in each graph.

6.

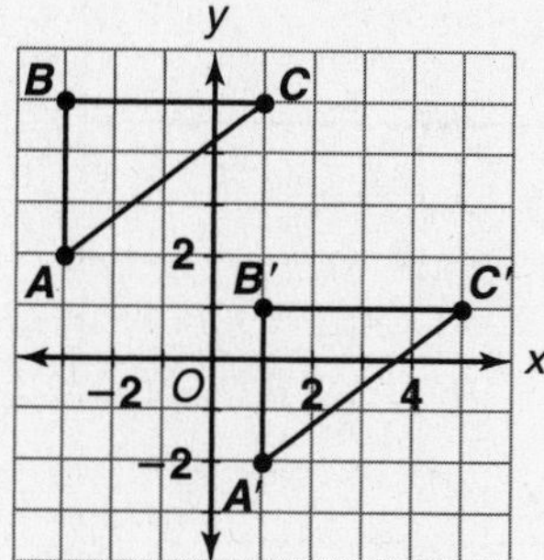

7.

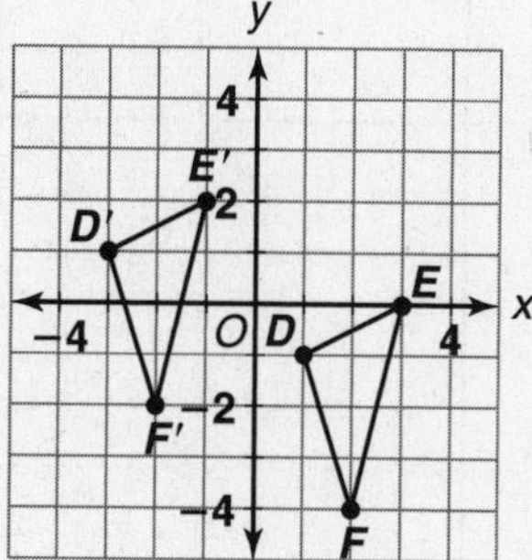

Name ________________________ Class ________________ Date ____________

Activity Lab 10-5

Translations

Materials needed: pencil and ruler

1. Start at the origin. Label the origin as O.
2. Write numbers along each axis from 0 to 7 and 0 to -7.
3. Draw a triangle with vertices $A(-5, 4)$, $B(-3, 6)$, and $C(-1, 4)$. Slide the triangle so that A' is at $(1, 4)$. Write the ordered pairs for the other two vertices.

   ____

4. Draw a triangle with vertices $D(1, 3)$, $E(3, 1)$, and $F(5, 3)$. Draw the flip of the triangle with point $E'(3, -1)$. Write the ordered pairs for the other two vertices.

   ____

5. How do your pairs of triangles relate to the each other? What do you notice about the ordered pairs?

   ____

   ____

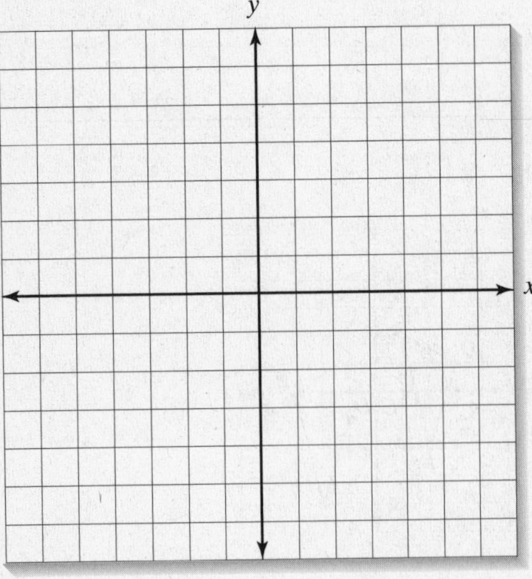

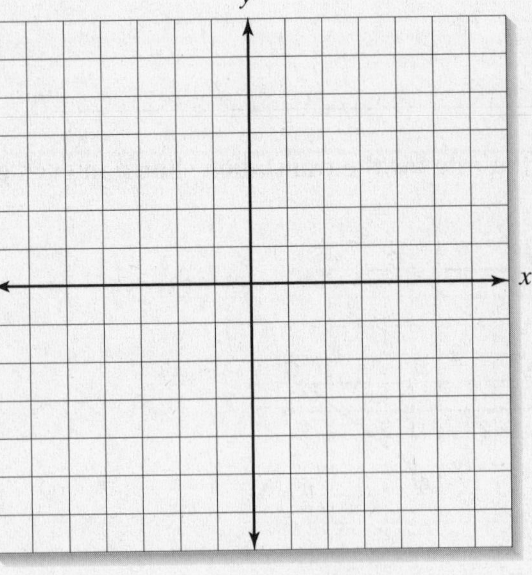

Name ______________________ Class ____________ Date ____________

Reteaching 10-5

Translations

Movements of figures on a plane are called **transformations.** A translation, or slide, moves all points the same distance and direction.

The translation $(x, y) \rightarrow (x + 4, y - 1)$ moves *each* point to the right 4 units and down 1 unit.

$A(-3, 1)$ moves to $(-3 + 4, 1 - 1)$, where point $A'(1, 0)$ is its **image.**

The square $ABCD$ moves to its image square $A'B'C'D'$.

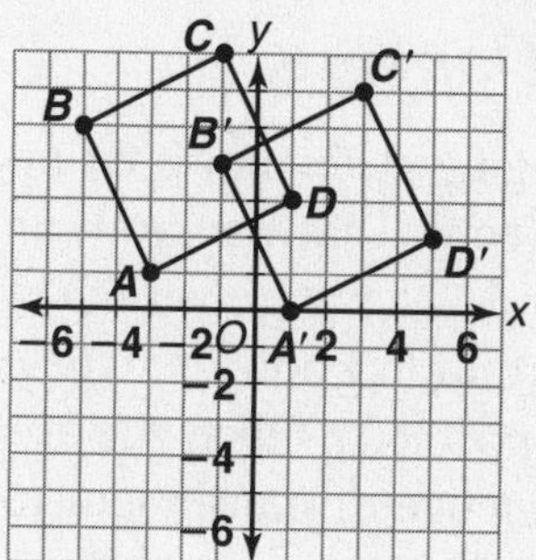

Complete the following for the figure above.

1. $B(-5, 5) \rightarrow B'$ (_____, _____)
2. $C(-1, 7) \rightarrow C'$ (_____, _____)
3. D(_____, _____) $\rightarrow D'$(_____, _____)

Graph each translation of figure *PRST*.

4. right 2 units

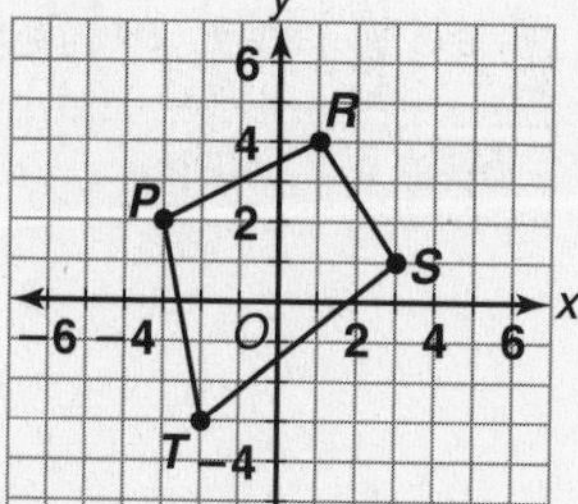

5. left 2 units, down 2 units

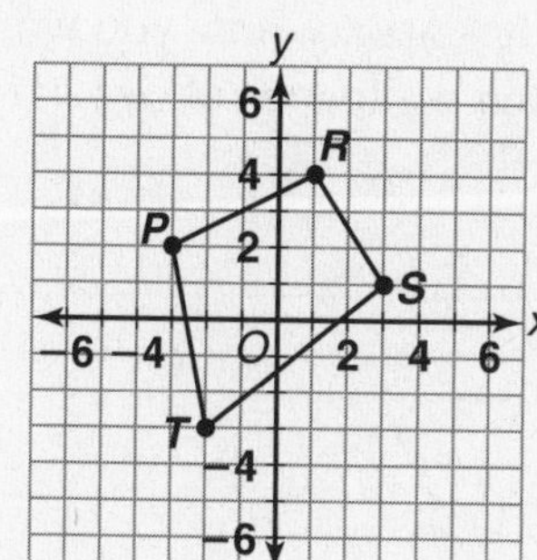

6. right 1 unit, up 3 units

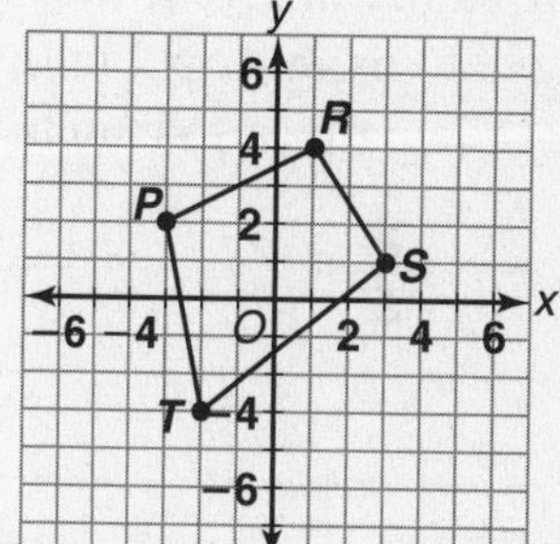

Complete the rule for each translation.

7. right 3 units, up 1 unit

   $(x, y) \rightarrow$ ____________

8. left 4 units, up 5 units

   $(x, y) \rightarrow$ ____________

9. left 1 unit, down 9 units

   $(x, y) \rightarrow$ ____________

Write a rule for the translation.

10. left 1 unit, down 3 units

    ____

11. right 1 unit, up 2 units

    ____

12. left 3 units, up 2 units

    ____

Name ______________________ Class ______________ Date ______________

Enrichment 10-5

Translations

Visual Thinking

When hanging wallpaper it is important that the pattern of the paper aligns perfectly. That way, you cannot see where one sheet begins and another ends. There are various types of patterns found in wallpaper. It is important to know the type of *match* that the paper has in order to hang it correctly. Once you are aware of the match, you can use your knowledge of translations to align the patterns of the wallpaper.

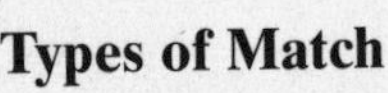

Types of Match

Drop match—The pattern runs diagonally across the wall so that every other strip is the same along the ceiling line. An example is the wallpaper with flowers shown to the right.

Strip 1 Strip 2

Straight-across match—The elements of the pattern in each strip are an equal distance from the ceiling line. Notice how the wallpaper pattern is perfectly aligned across the top in the sample to the right.

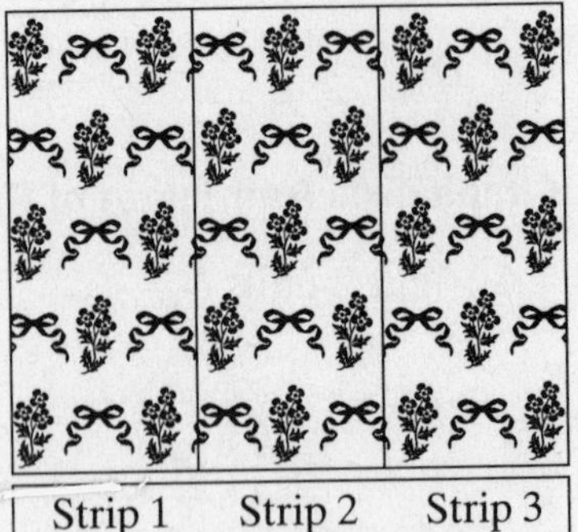

Strip 1 Strip 2 Strip 3

1. Explain, using your knowledge of translations, how you would have to hang strip 3 in the drop match wallpaper above in order for the pattern to match.

____

____

____

____

2. When hanging strip 3 of the straight-across match wallpaper, you had to cut the strip in half vertically since the wall ended in a corner. Explain how you would match up the pattern around the corner when you hang strip 4.

____

____

____

____

____

Name ______________________ Class ______________ Date ______________

10C: Reading/Writing Math Symbols

For use after Lesson 10-5

Study Skill Read aloud or recite when you are studying at home; reciting a rule or formula can help you to remember it and recall it for later use.

Write each mathematical statement in words.

1. $m\angle A = 47^\circ$

____

2. $M(-2, 0)$

____

3. $y = 8x + 4$

____

4. $P(3, 4) \rightarrow P'(5, 2)$

____

5. $(x, y) \rightarrow (x - 2, y + 1)$

____

____

6. (x, y) for $x > 0$ and $y > 0$

____

____

7. $C(1, 2)$, slope $= \frac{1}{2}$

____

____

Use appropriate symbols to identify the parts of circle *C*.

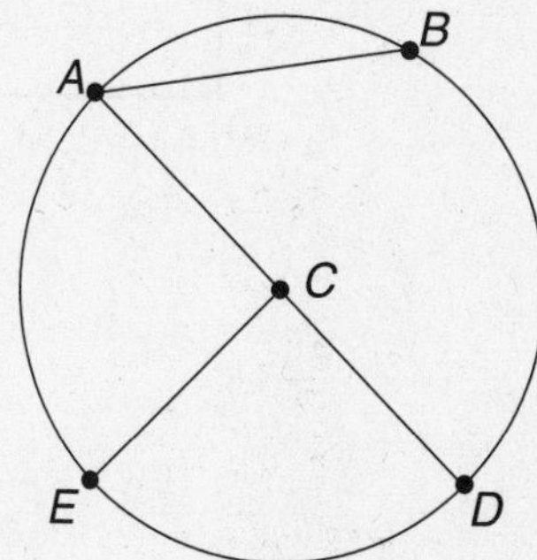

8. two chords

____

9. three radii

____

10. one diameter

____

11. three central angles

____

12. two semicircles

____

Name ____________________ Class ____________ Date ____________

Puzzle 10-5

Translations

Refer to the graph to answer the questions.

1. Write the coordinates of each point. The first one is done for you.

   E (4, 11)

   R (___, ___)

   P (___, ___)

2. For each ordered pair above, subtract 2 from the *x*-coordinate and subtract 5 from the *y*-coordinate. Record the coordinates below and write the letter associated with each new point. Then draw the new triangle. The coordinates of the first new point are given as a clue.

   ___ (2, 6)

   ___ (___, ___)

   ___ (___, ___)

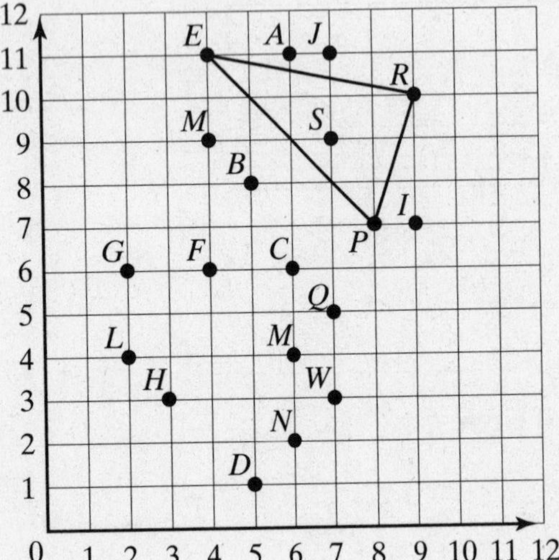

Name ______________________ Class ______________ Date ______________

Practice 10-6

Line Symmetry and Reflections

Use the graph at the right for Exercises 1–3.

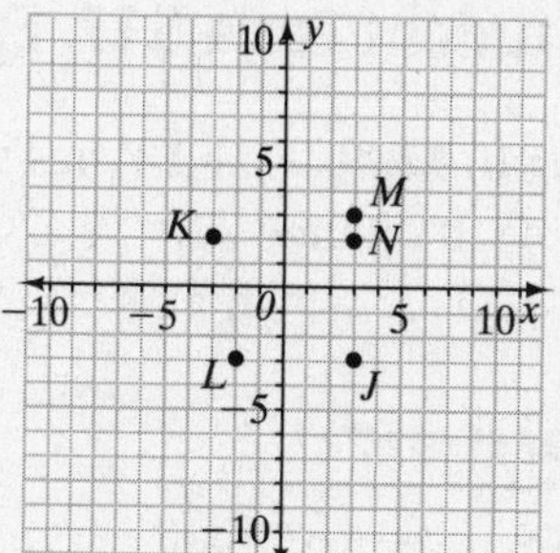

1. For which two points is the x-axis a line of reflection?

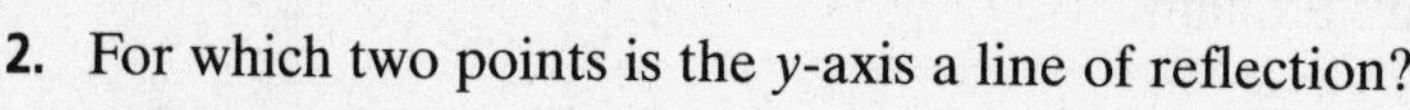

2. For which two points is the y-axis a line of reflection?

____

3. Points L and J are not reflections across the y-axis. Why not?

____

____

$\triangle A'B'C'$ is a reflection of $\triangle ABC$ over the x-axis. Draw $\triangle A'B'C'$ and complete each statement.

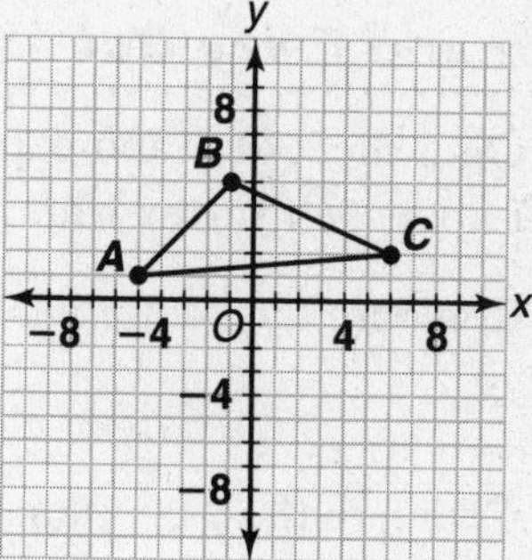

4. $A(-5, 1) \rightarrow A'(x, y)$ ______________________________

5. $B(-1, 5) \rightarrow B'(x, y)$ ______________________________

6. $C(6, 2) \rightarrow C'(x, y)$ ______________________________

Draw the lines of symmetry for each figure. If there are no lines of symmetry, write *none*.

7. 

8. 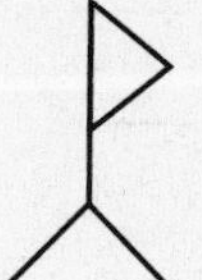

9. 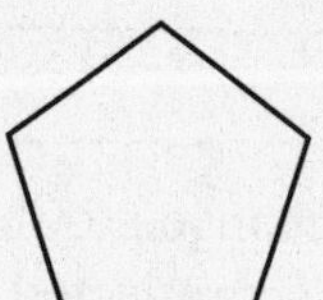

10. 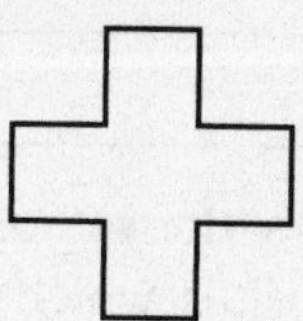

Graph each point and its reflection across the indicated axis. Write the coordinates of the reflected point.

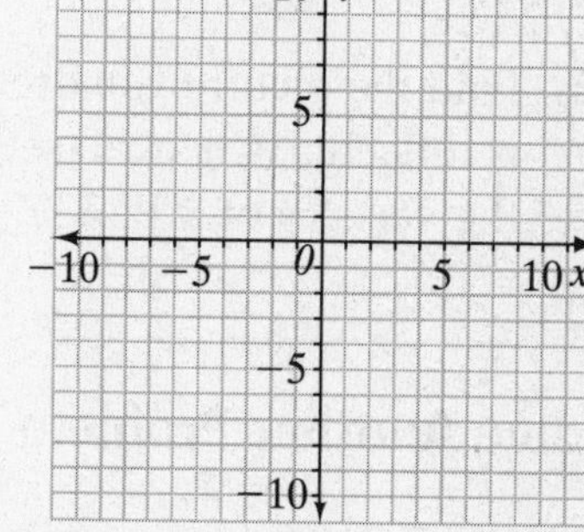

11. $V(-3, 4)$ across the y-axis ______________________________

12. $W(-4, -2)$ across the x-axis ______________________________

13. $X(2, 2)$ across the x-axis ______________________________

14. $Y(0, 3)$ across the x-axis ______________________________

15. $Z(4, -6)$ across the y-axis ______________________________

10-6 • Guided Problem Solving

GPS Student Page 517, Exercise 25:

Writing in Math $\triangle WXY$ has vertices $W(-4, -2)$, $X(4, 2)$, and $Y(1, -4)$. Its image $\triangle W'X'Y'$ has vertices $W'(-4, 2)$, $X'(4, -2)$, and $Y'(1, 4)$. Over which axis is $\triangle WXY$ reflected? Explain.

Understand

1. What are you being asked to do?

____

2. What is a good way to visualize the problem?

____

Plan and Carry Out

3. On a sheet of graph paper, graph triangles $\triangle WXY$ and $\triangle W'X'Y'$. Label each vertex with its coordinates.

4. Compare the x-coordinates of both triangles. What do you notice?

____

5. Compare the y-coordinates of both triangles. What do you notice?

____

____

6. If only the y-coordinates are changed to their opposites, which axis is an object reflected over? ______________

7. Over which axis was $\triangle WXY$ reflected? ______________

Check

8. Fold the picture you drew in Step 3 over the axis across which it is reflected. Check to see if the vertices of $\triangle$WXY correspond to the vertices of $\triangle W'X'Y'$. Does your answer check?

____

Solve Another Problem

9. $\triangle ABC$ has vertices $A(1, 3)$, B$(-2, 2)$, and $C(-1, -4)$. Its image $\triangle A'B'C'$ has vertices $A'(-1, 3)$, $B'(2, 2)$, and $C'(1, -4)$. Over which axis was ABC reflected? Explain.

____

Name ____________________ Class ____________ Date ____________

Practice 10-6

Line Symmetry and Reflections

Use the graph at the right for Exercises 1 and 2.

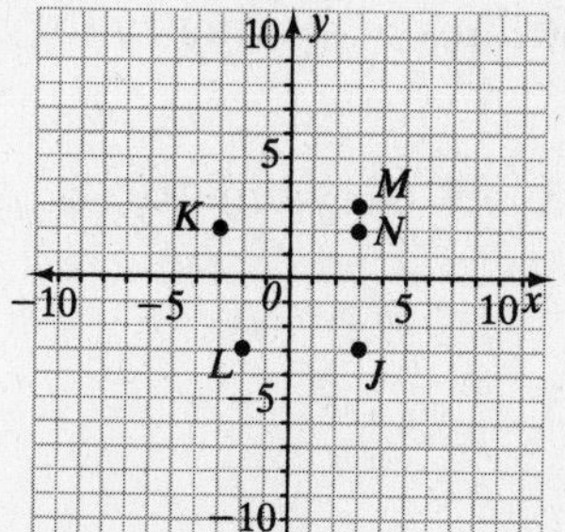

1. For which two points is the x-axis a line of reflection?

____

2. For which two points is the y-axis a line of reflection?

____

$\triangle A'B'C'$ is a reflection of $\triangle ABC$ over the x-axis. Draw $\triangle A'B'C'$ and complete each statement.

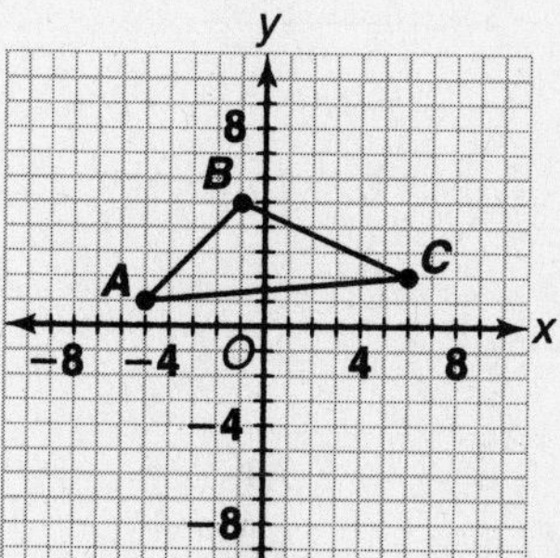

3. $A(-5, 1) \rightarrow A'(x, y)$ ____________________

4. $B(-1, 5) \rightarrow B'(x, y)$ ____________________

5. $C(6, 2) \rightarrow C'(x, y)$ ____________________

Draw the lines of symmetry for each figure. If there are no lines of symmetry, write *none*.

6. 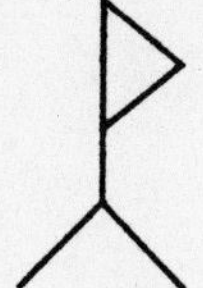

7. 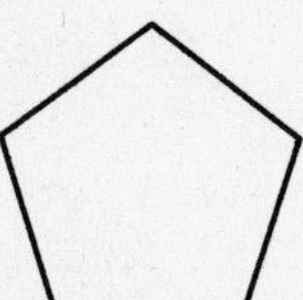

8. 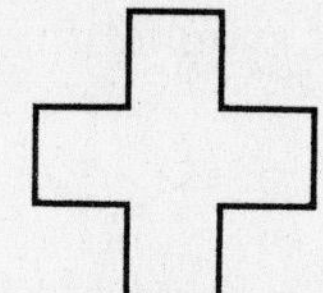

Graph the reflection of each point across the indicated axis. Write the coordinates of the reflected point.

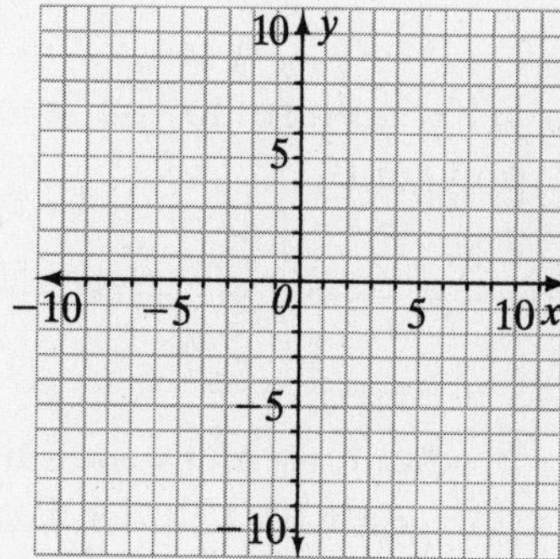

9. $X(-3, 4)$ across the y-axis ____________________

10. $Y(0, 3)$ across the x-axis ____________________

11. $Z(4, -6)$ across the y-axis ____________________

Name ______________________ Class ______________ Date ____________

Activity Lab 10-6

Line Symmetry and Reflections

Draw lines of symmetry for each regular polygon.

1. Lines of symmetry: ____________

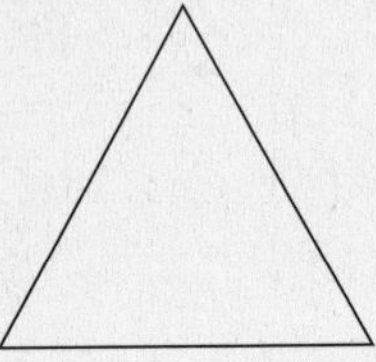

2. Lines of symmetry: ____________

3. Lines of symmetry: ____________

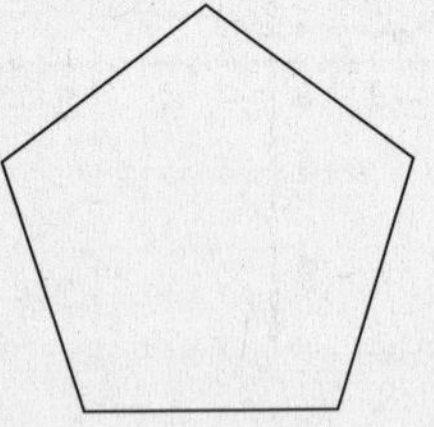

4. Lines of symmetry: ____________

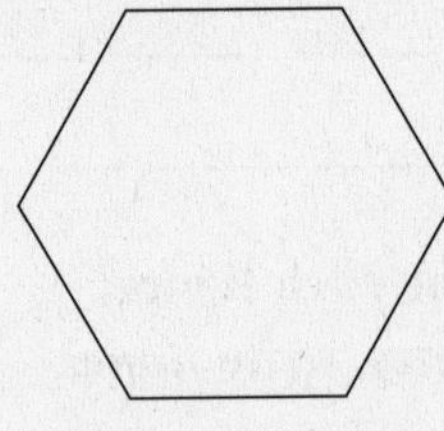

5. Lines of symmetry: ____________

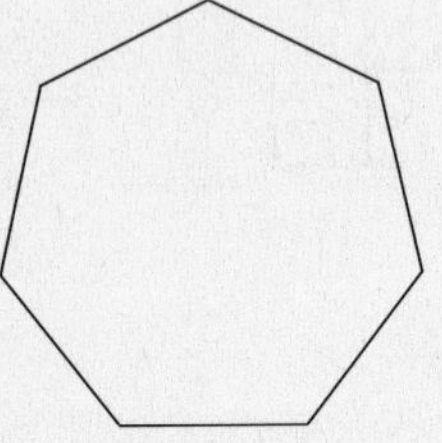

6. Lines of symmetry: ____________

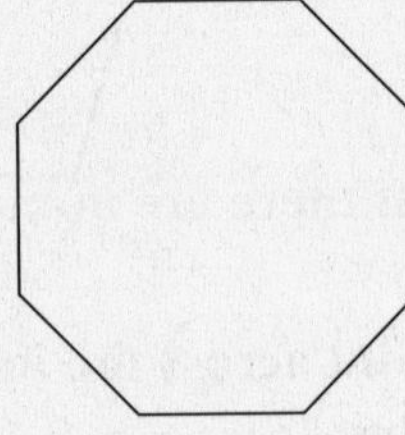

7. What pattern do you see in the lines of symmetry of the regular polygons?

____

____

8. Predict how many lines of symmetry you would find in a regular polygon with 12 sides. With 20 sides? With 100 sides?

____

____

9. Do you think this pattern will be true for irregular polygons? On another sheet of paper, sketch some irregular figures to support your answer. Write Yes or No below each drawing.

____

Name ______________________ Class ______________ Date ______________

Reteaching 10-6

Line Symmetry and Reflections

Symmetry

A figure is **symmetrical** if one side is a mirror image of the other. The line that divides a figure into two identical parts is called a **line of symmetry.**

The figure below has 2 lines of symmetry.

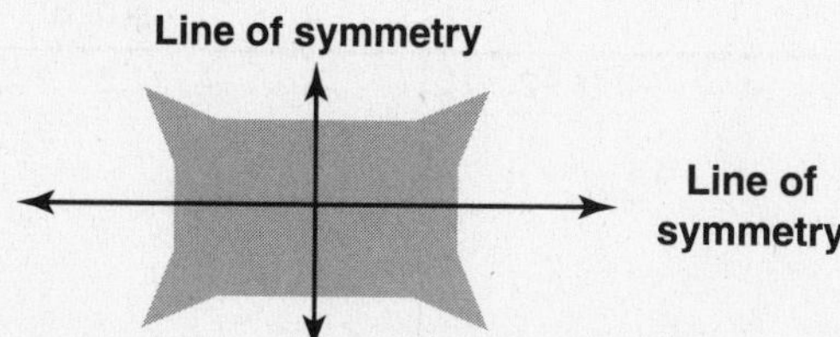

You can trace the figure and fold it along either line to see that the two halves match.

Reflections

A **reflection** is a transformation that creates a mirror image. $\triangle A'B'C'$ is the mirror image of $\triangle ABC$ across the x-axis. The x-axis is the **line of reflection.**

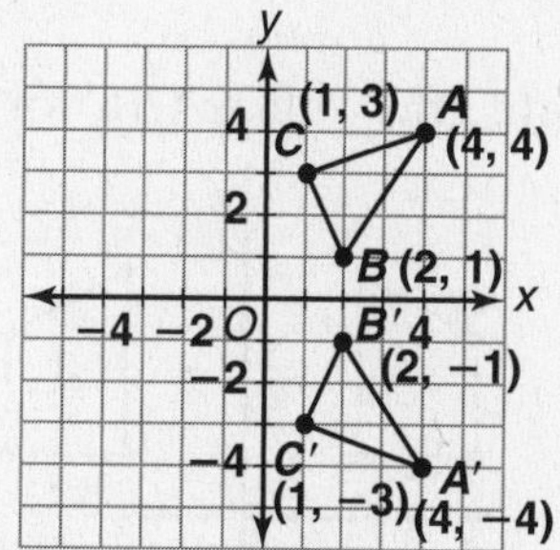

- When you reflect across the x-axis, the y-coordinates change sign.
- When you reflect across the y-axis, the x-coordinates change sign.
- When you reflect across a line of symmetry, the image is the figure itself.

Draw the line(s) of symmetry. If there are no lines of symmetry, write *none.*

1. 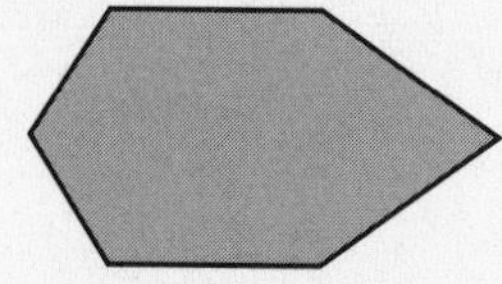

____

2. 

____

3. 

____

$\triangle ABC$ is shown. Draw $\triangle A'B'C'$ so it is a reflection of $\triangle ABC$ over the indicated axis. Then complete each statement.

4. over the x-axis

$A(-4, 4) \rightarrow A'$

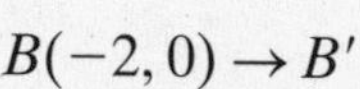

$B(-2, 0) \rightarrow B'$

____

$C(0, 2) \rightarrow C'$

____

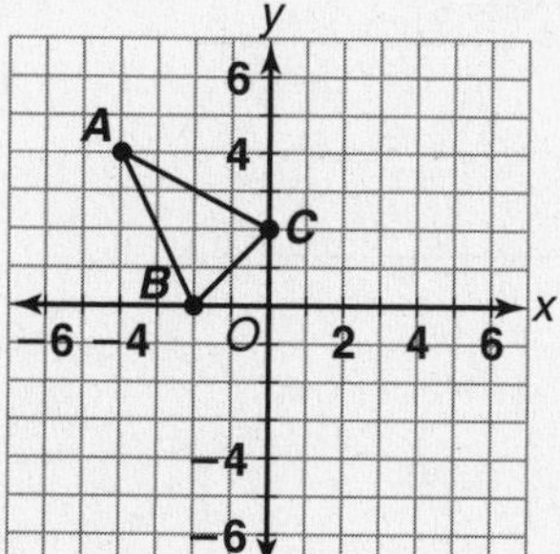

5. over the y-axis

$A(-4, 4) \rightarrow A'$

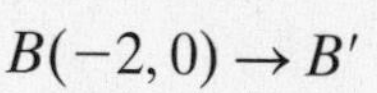

$B(-2, 0) \rightarrow B'$

____

$C(0, 2) \rightarrow C'$

____

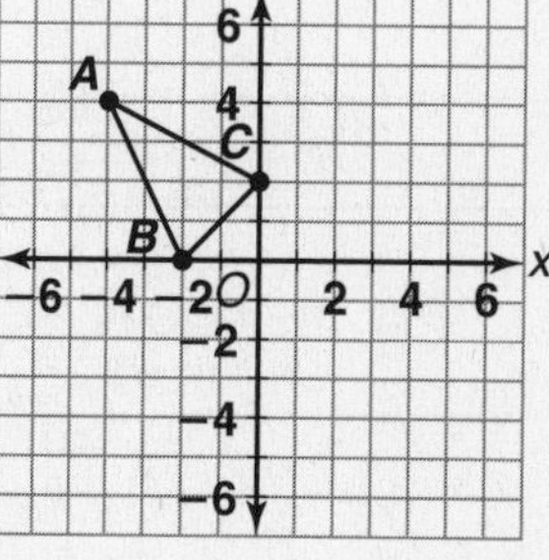

Enrichment 10-6

Line Symmetry and Reflections

Critical Thinking

Figure A, below, is a mirror image of Figure B. Mathematicians refer to a mirror image as a *reflection image.* In this case, the figure reflects over the y-axis.

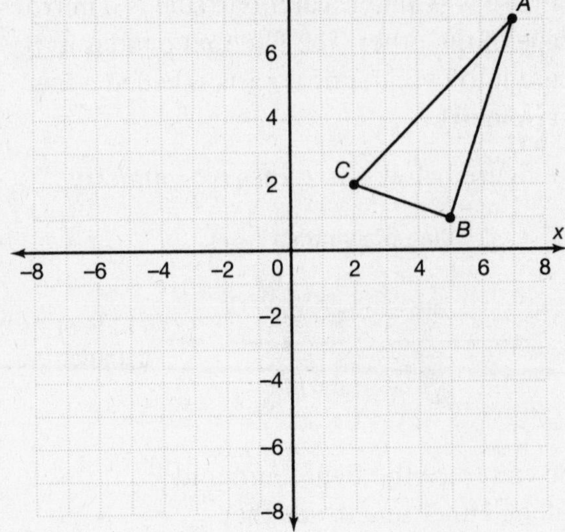

Use the coordinate grid with $\triangle ABC$ for Exercises 1–4.

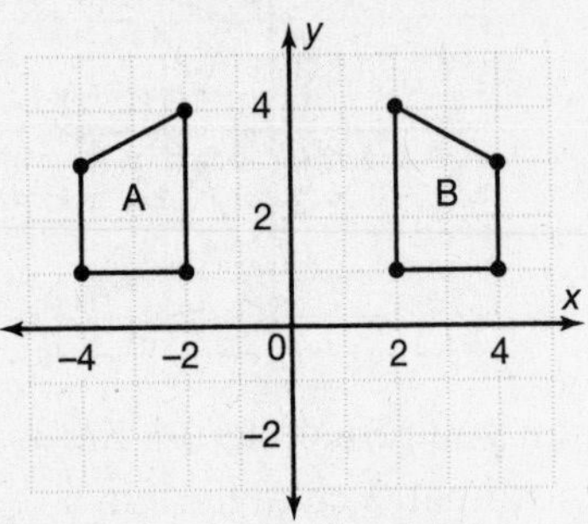

1. Give the coordinates of each point.

   a. A ____________ b. B ____________ c. C ____________

2. Change the sign of each x-coordinate—if positive, change to negative; and if negative, change to positive. Plot the new points and connect them. Describe the new figure.

   ____

   ____

3. Predict what will happen to the original figure if you change the signs of the y-coordinates. Plot the points to test your prediction.

   ____

   ____

4. Plot a mirror image of the original figure in Quadrant III. Give the coordinates of each point and describe what you did to find them.

   ____

   ____

   ____

Name ________________ Class ________________ Date ________________

10D: Visual Vocabulary Practice

For use after Lesson 10-6

Study Skill When a math exercise is difficult, try to determine what makes it difficult. Is it a word that you don't understand? Are the numbers difficult to use?

Concept List

linear equation	slope	origin
coordinate plane	reflection	translation
nonlinear equation	x-coordinate	y-coordinate

Write the concept that best describes each exercise. Choose from the concept list above.

1. (0, 0)

____

2. 2 for the ordered pair (4, 2)

____

3. $y = 2x - 3$

____

4.

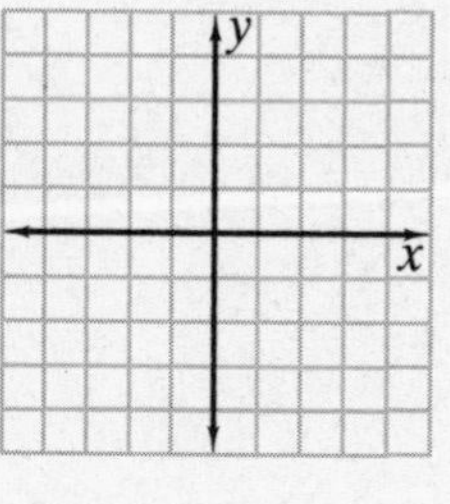

____

5.

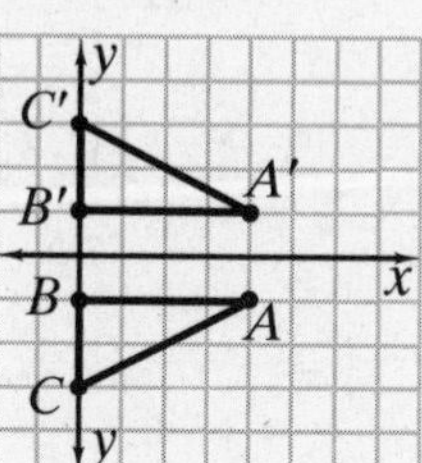

____

6.

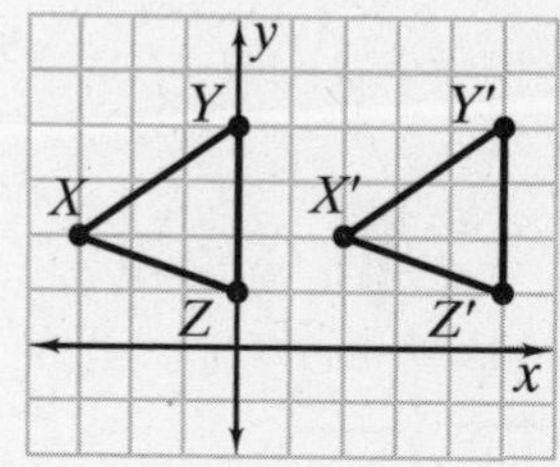

____

7.

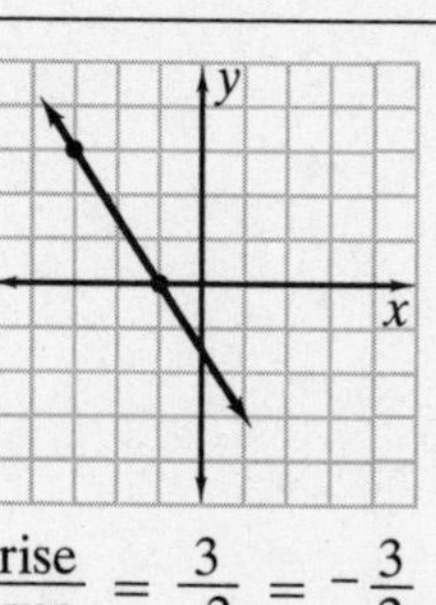

$\frac{\text{rise}}{\text{run}} = \frac{3}{-2} = -\frac{3}{2}$

____

8. $-\frac{1}{2}$ for the ordered pair

$(-\frac{1}{2}, 8)$

____

9. $y = -\frac{1}{2}x^2 + 5$

____

Name ________________ Class ________________ Date ________________

Puzzle 10-6

Write the letter of the figure on the right that shows the figure created by reflecting the given shape over the dashed line of symmetry.

1. ____

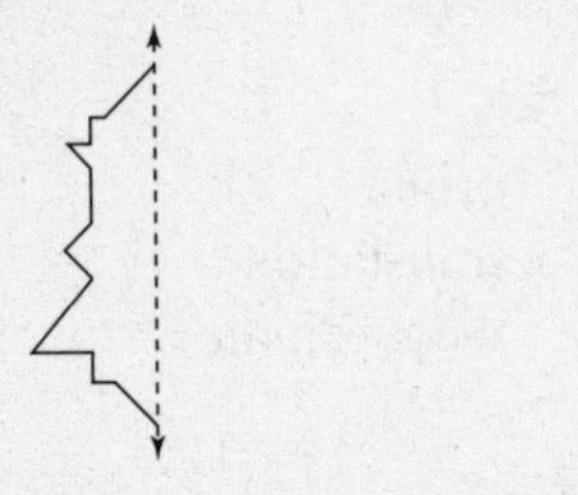

a.

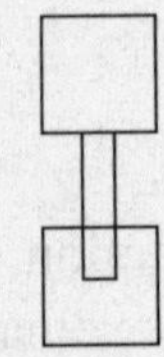

2. ____

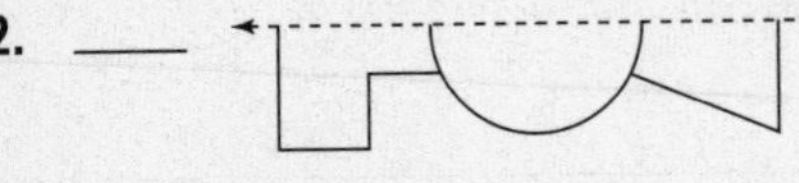

b.

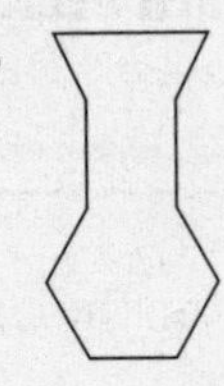

3. ____

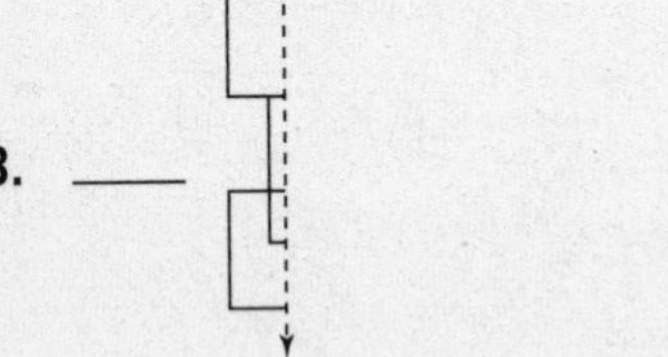

c.

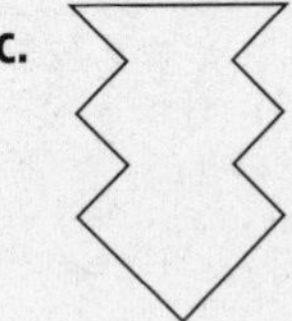

4. ____

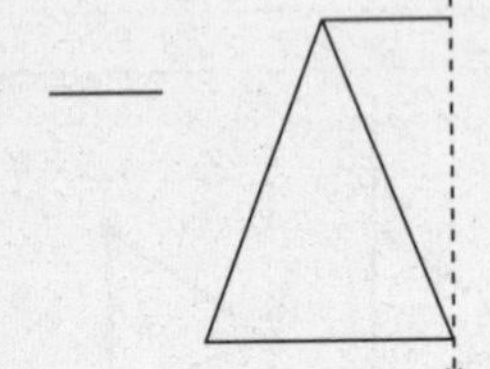

d.

5. ____

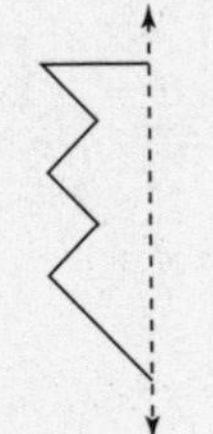

e.

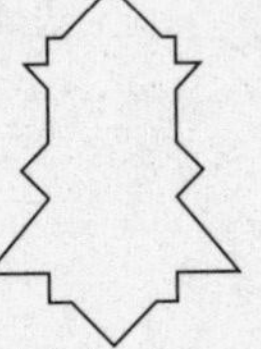

6. ____

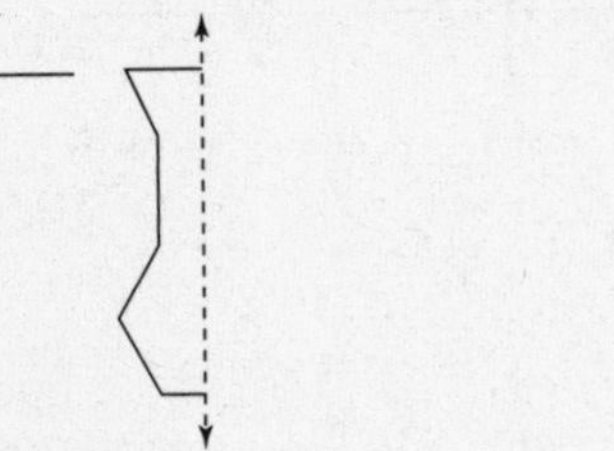

f.

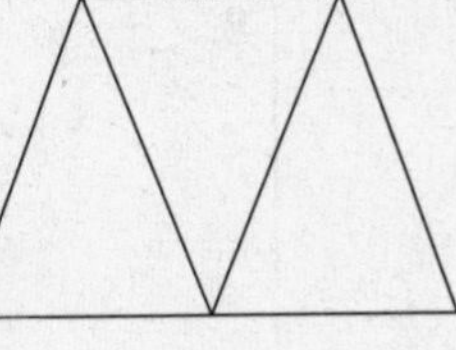

7. ____

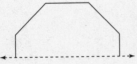

g.

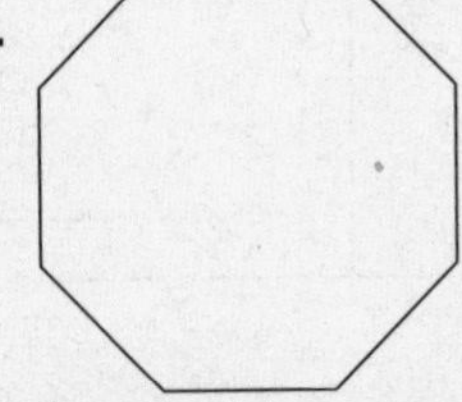

Name ______________________ Class ______________ Date ____________

Practice 10-7

Rotational Symmetry and Rotations

Does the figure have rotational symmetry? Explain.

1.

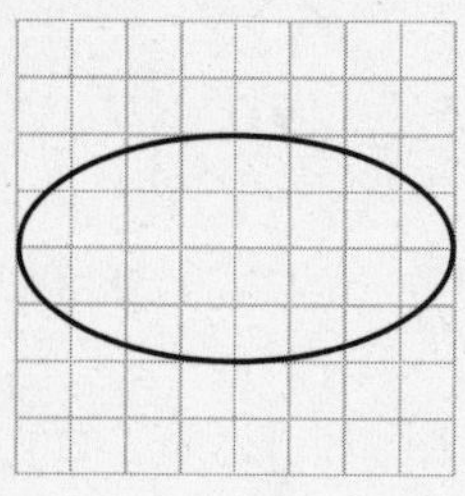

2.

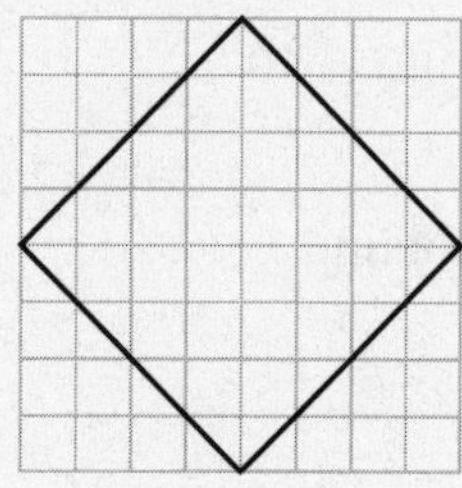

3.

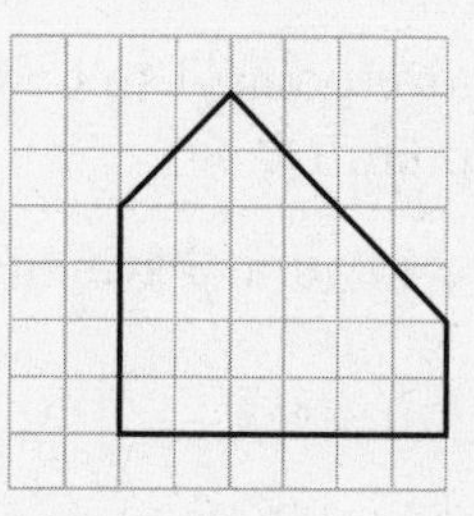

4.

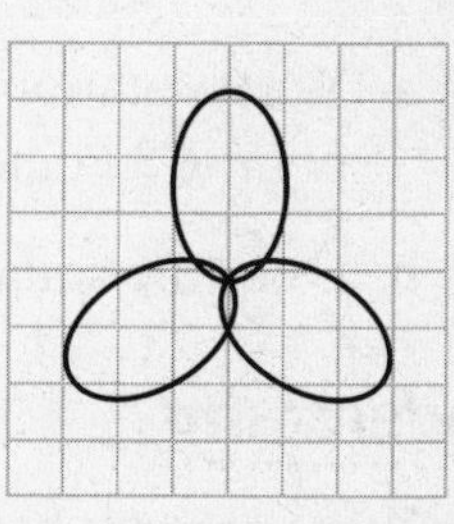

Draw the images of the figure after the given rotation about point *O*.

5. 90° rotation

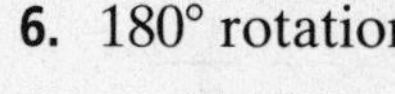

6. 180° rotation

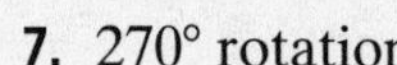

7. 270° rotation

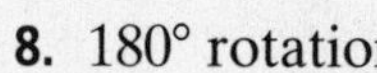

8. 180° rotation

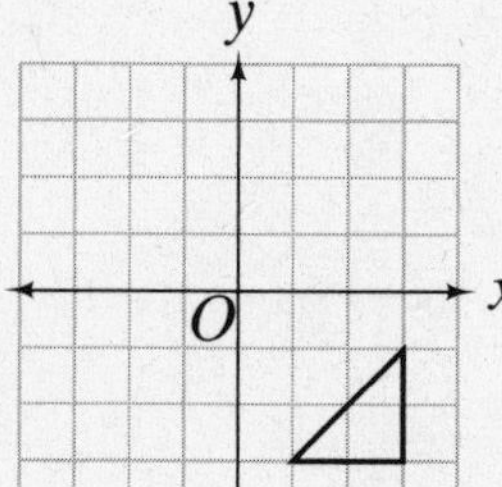

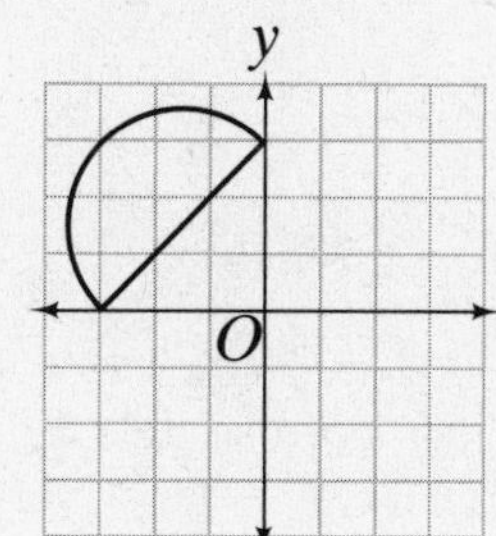

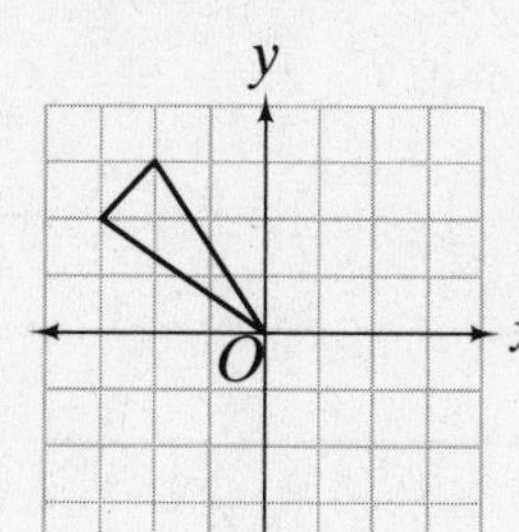

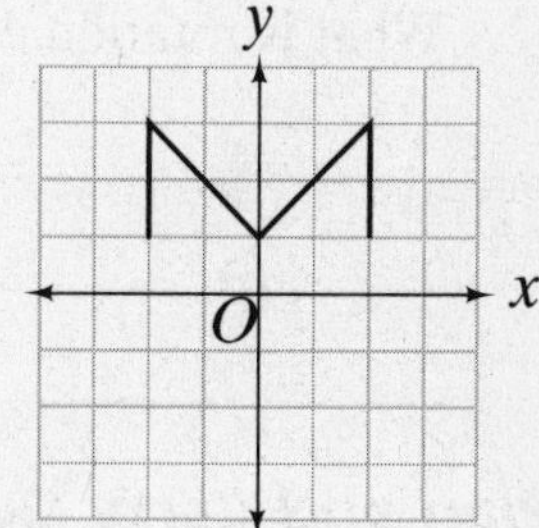

Figure II is the image of Figure I. Identify the transformation as a translation, a reflection, or a rotation.

9.

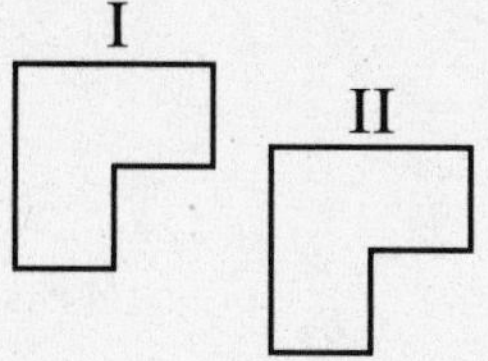

10.

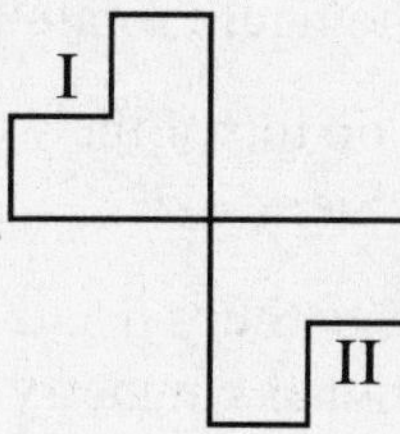

11.

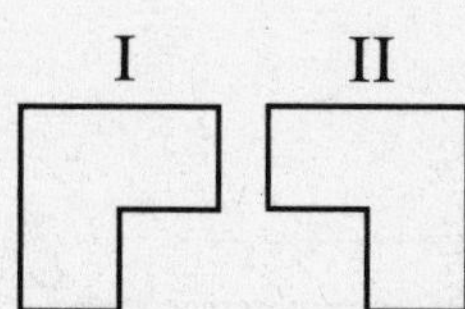

12.

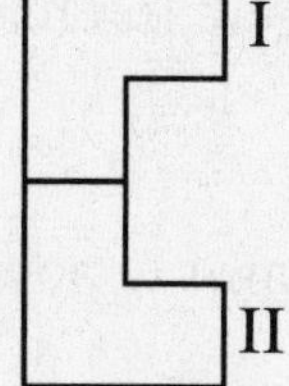

Name ______________________ Class ______________ Date ______________

10-7 • Guided Problem Solving

GPS Student Page 522, Exercise 23:

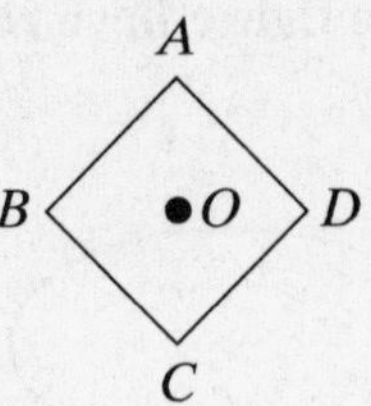

a. What rotation will move point A to point B? Point A to point C? Point A to point D?

b. Does the square have rotational symmetry? Explain.

Understand

1. What are you being asked to do?

____

____

____

2. What is rotational symmetry?

____

____

____

Plan and Carry Out

3. How many degrees does the figure rotate from A to B? ______
4. How many degrees does the figure rotate from A to C? ______
5. How many degrees does the figure rotate from A to D? ______
6. Does the figure fit exactly on top of the original in the rotations in Steps 3–5? ______
7. According to your answers to Steps 6 and 7, does the square have rotational symmetry? ______

Check

8. Are the rotations that make the figure fit exactly on top of the original figure less than 360°? ______

Solve Another Problem

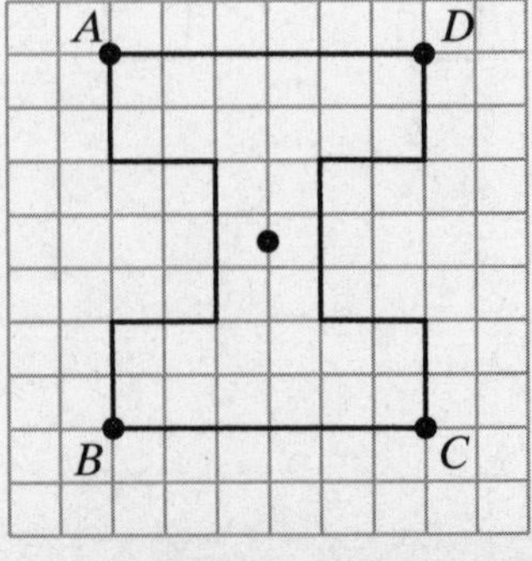

9. **a.** What rotation will move point A to point C? Point B to point D?

____

b. Does the figure have rotational symmetry? Explain.

____

Name ______________________ Class ______________ Date ______________

Practice 10-7

Rotational Symmetry and Rotations

Does the figure have rotational symmetry? Explain.

1. 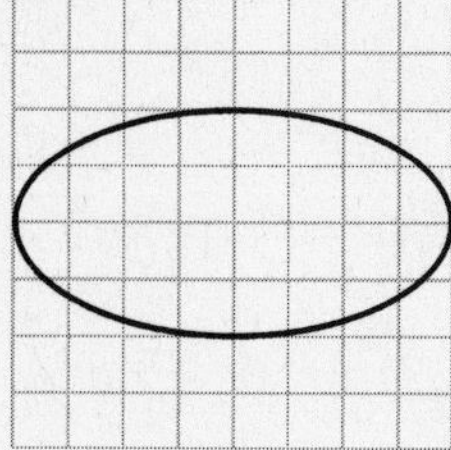

2. 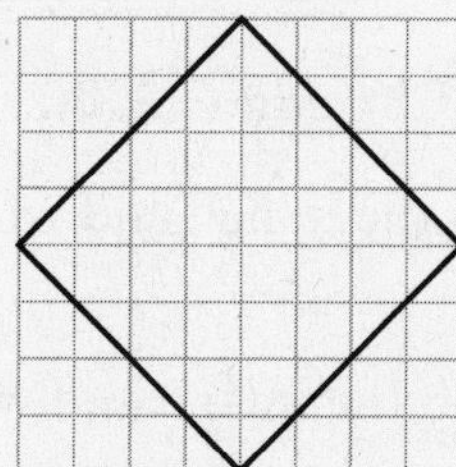

3. 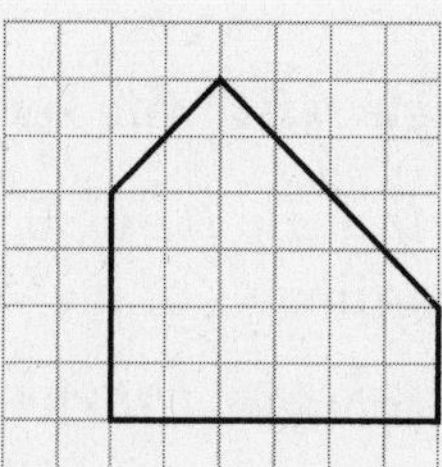

______________________ ______________________ ______________________

Draw the images of the figure after the given rotation about point *O*.

4. 90° rotation

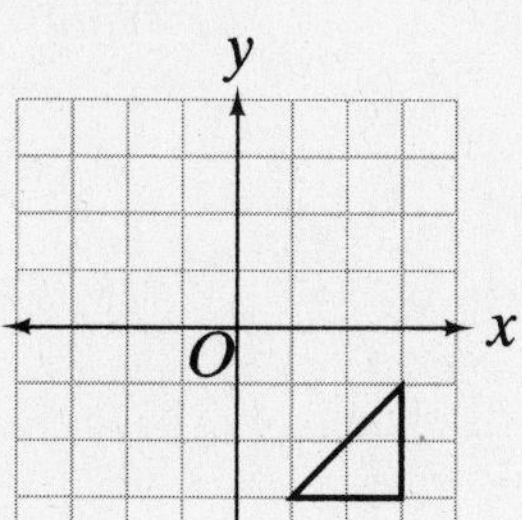

5. 180° rotation

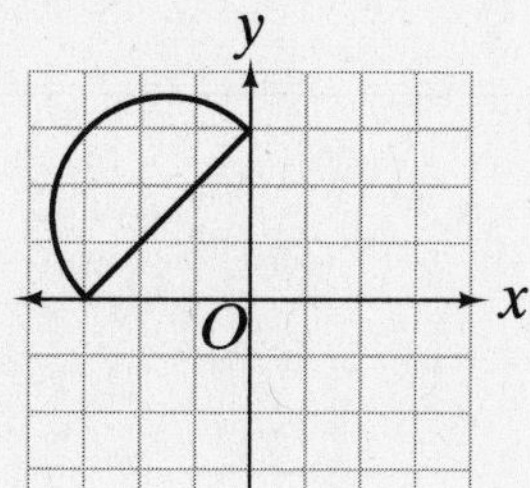

6. 270° rotation

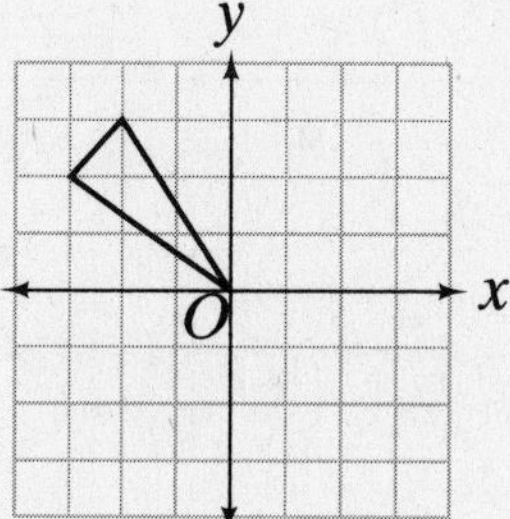

Figure II is the image of Figure I. Identify the transformation as a translation, a reflection, or a rotation.

7. 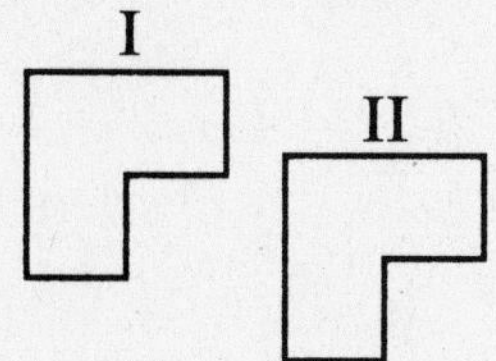

8. 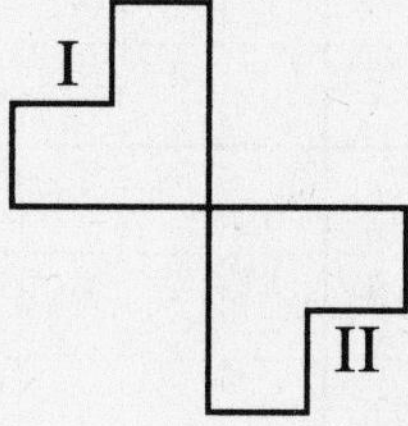

______________________ ______________________

9. 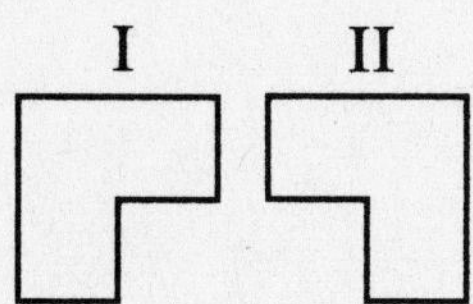

10. 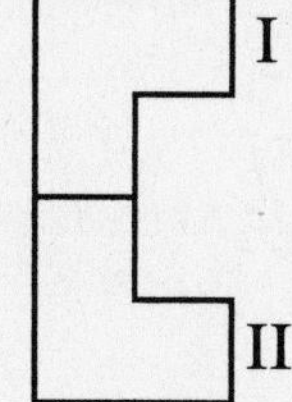

______________________ ______________________

Activity Lab 10-7

Rotational Symmetry and Rotations

Materials needed: pencil and ruler

Graph triangle *ABC* with vertices *A*(0, 0), *B*(0, 3), and *C*(3, 0).

1. Rotate triangle *ABC* 90° about *A*. Graph the image and write the new coordinates of the vertices.

2. Rotate triangle *ABC* 180° about *A*. Graph the image and write the new coordinates of the vertices.

3. Rotate triangle *ABC* 270° about *A*. Graph the image and write the new coordinates of the vertices.

4. Does the figure have rotational symmetry? ______________

5. Connect all points. What type of quadrilateral is formed?

____

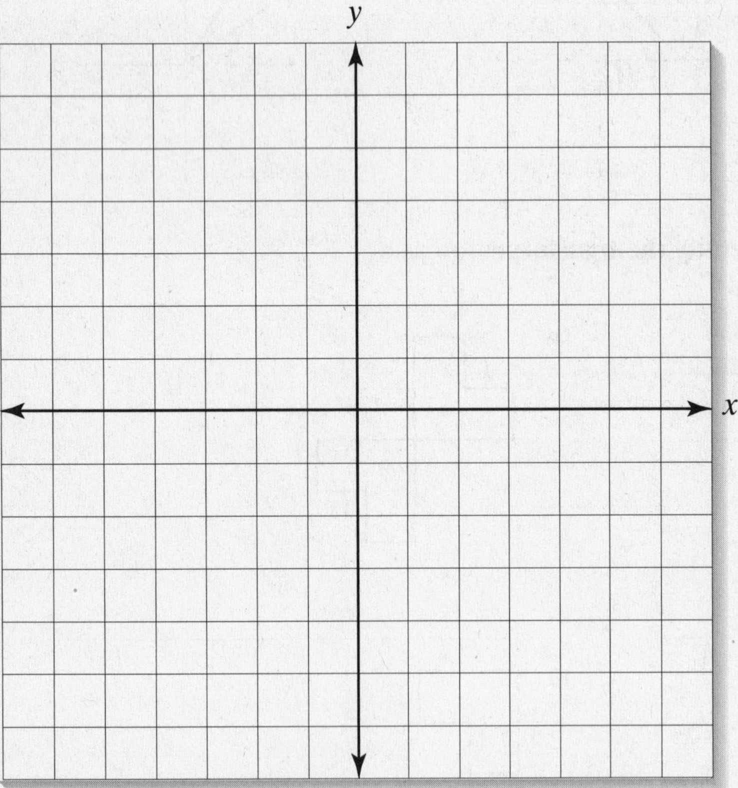

Name ______________________ Class ______________ Date ______________

Reteaching 10-7

Rotational Symmetry and Rotations

A **rotation** is a transformation that turns a figure about a fixed point. The fixed point is called the **center of rotation.**

If a figure has **rotational symmetry,** it can be rotated less than 360° and fit exactly on top of the original figure.

The figure below has rotational symmetry.

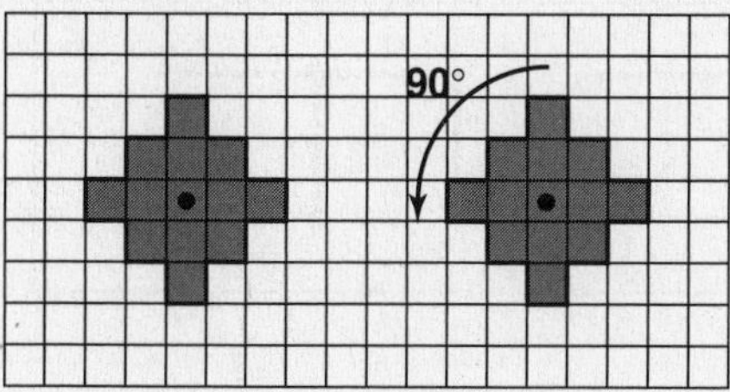

For a rotation of 90° or 180° about its center, the figure fits exactly on top of itself.

To draw a 180° rotation about point A, trace $\triangle ABC$. Place a pencil tip on point A and rotate the tracing 180°. Mark points A', B', and C'. Then draw $\triangle A'B'C'$.

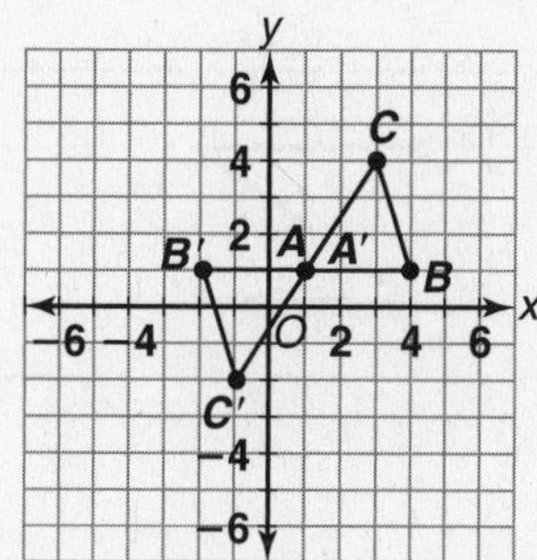

Does the figure have rotational symmetry?

1. 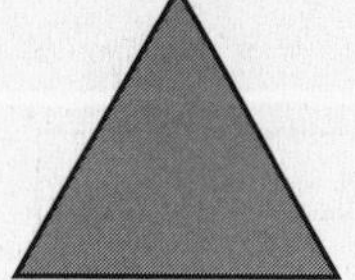

____

2. 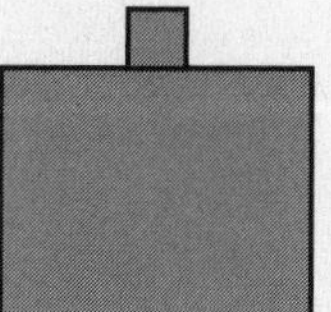

____

3. 

____

Draw the image of the figure after each rotation about point *O*.

4. rotation of 90°

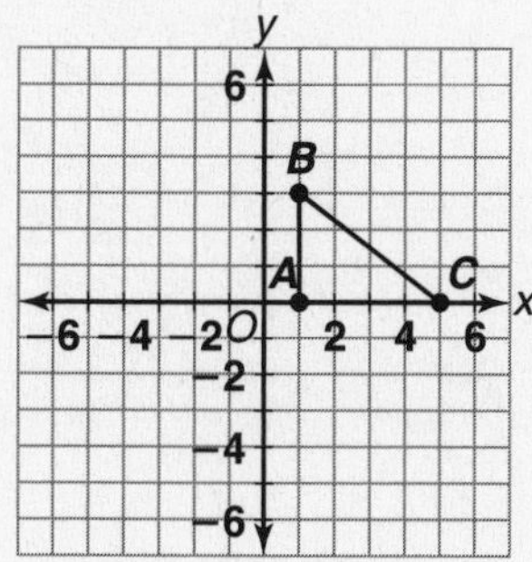

5. rotation of 180°

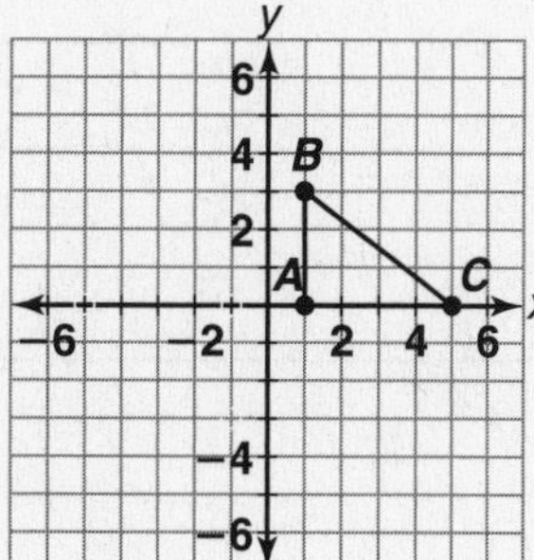

6. rotation of 270°

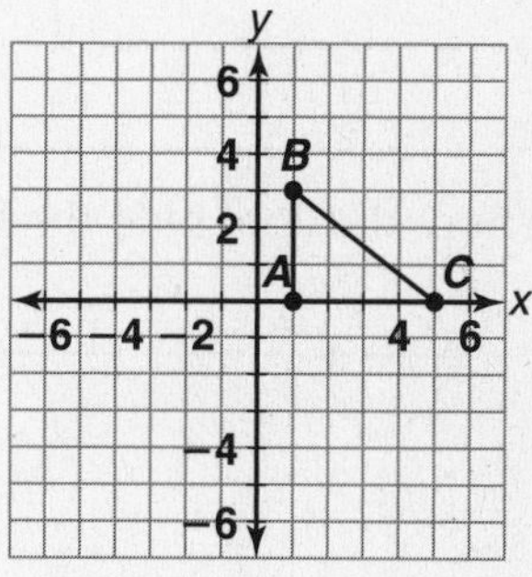

Enrichment 10-7

Rotational Symmetry and Rotations

Visual Thinking

Joel's brother is coming home from college for the weekend. Since Joel might not be home when his brother arrives, he decided to hide a front door key in a secret location. The grid below shows an encoded message that Joel taped to the front door for his brother. His brother must use his knowledge of rotations to determine where Joel hid the key.

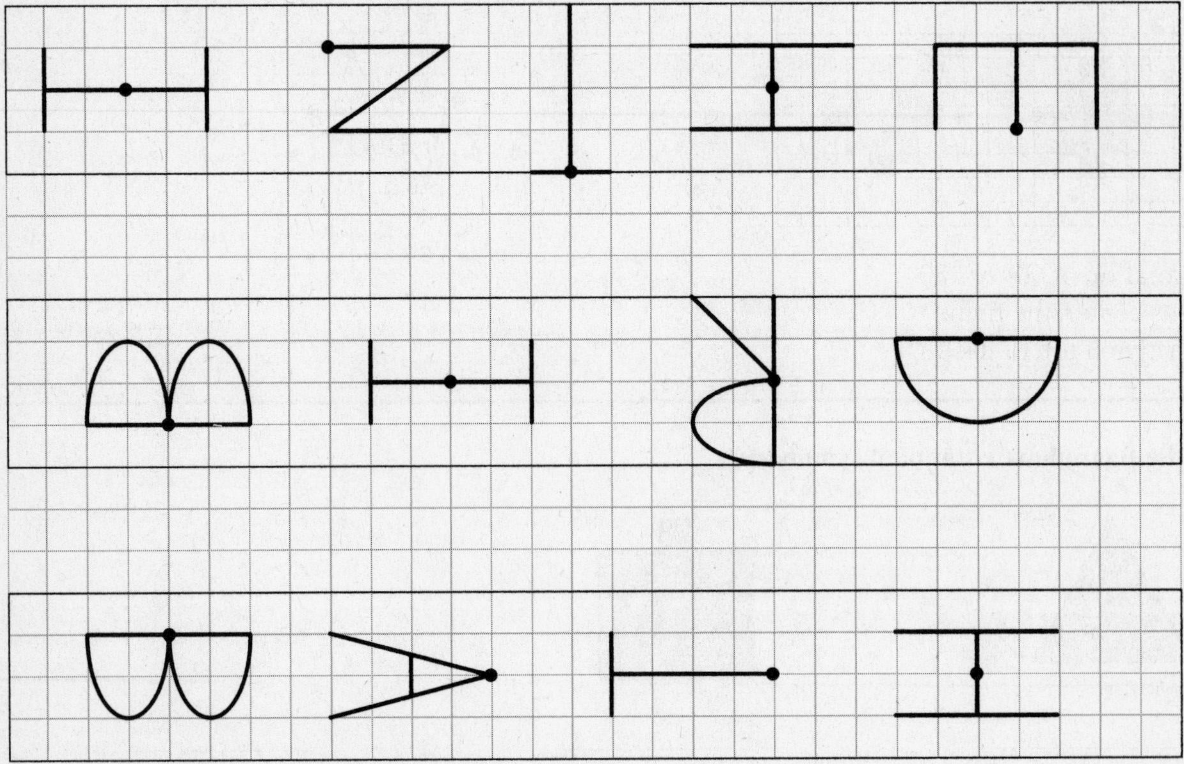

Decode the message and describe each rotation.

Where did Joel hide the key?

____

Name ____________________ Class ____________ Date ____________

10E: Vocabulary Check

For use after Lesson 10-7

Study Skill Strengthen your vocabulary. Use these pages and add cues and summaries by applying the Cornell Notetaking style.

Write the definition for each word or term at the right. To check your work, fold the paper back along the dotted line to see the correct answers.

____________________	line of symmetry
____________________	transformations
____________________	image
____________________	quadrants
____________________	rotation

Name ________________ Class ________________ Date ________________

10E: Vocabulary Check (continued)

or use after Lesson 10-7

Write the vocabulary word or term for each definition. To check your work, fold the paper forward along the dotted line to see the correct answers.

a line that divides a figure into mirror images ________________

a change in the position, shape, or size of a figure ________________

the result of a transformation of a point, line, or figure ________________

the four regions of the coordinate plane divided by the *x*- and *y*-axes ________________

a transformation that turns a figure about a fixed point ________________

Name ______________________ Class ______________ Date ______________

10F: Vocabulary Review

For use with the Chapter Review

Study Skill Use a highlighter to mark material that is important in your notes or on teacher handouts. When you review for tests, pay special attention to this highlighted information.

Match the term in Column A with its definition in Column B.

Column A	Column B
1. transformation	A. transformation that creates symmetry
2. decagon	B. polygon with 10 sides
3. reflection	C. segment that has both endpoints on the circle
4. chord	D. quadrilateral with four congruent sides
5. rhombus	E. change of position, shape, or size of a figure
6. slope	F. quadrilateral with exactly one pair of parallel sides
7. trapezoid	G. ratio that describes the steepness of a line

Match the term in Column A with its definition in Column B.

Column A	Column B
8. complementary	H. two angles whose sum is 180 degrees
9. rotation	I. identifies the location of a point
10. hypotenuse	J. one side of a figure is the mirror image of the other side
11. translation	K. transformation that moves points the same distance and in the same direction
12. symmetry	L. two angles whose sum is 90 degrees
13. ordered pair	M. the longest side of a right triangle
14. supplementary	N. transformation that turns a figure about a fixed point
15. radius	O. segment with one endpoint at the center and the other endpoint on the circle

Name ______________________ Class ______________ Date ____________

Puzzle 10-7

Rotational Symmetry and Rotations

Graph triangle ABC with vertices $A(0, 0)$, $B(3, 0)$, $C(3, 3)$ on the grid. Transform the triangle by rotations 1–8 consecutively, as described. Under each illustration is a letter. Write the letter of each image at the bottom of the page to find out which state is the birthplace of eight U.S. Presidents.

1. 135° about point A

2. 270° about point A

3. 135° about point A

4. 180° about point A

5. 45° about point A

6. 45° about point A

7. 315° about point A

8. 225° about point A

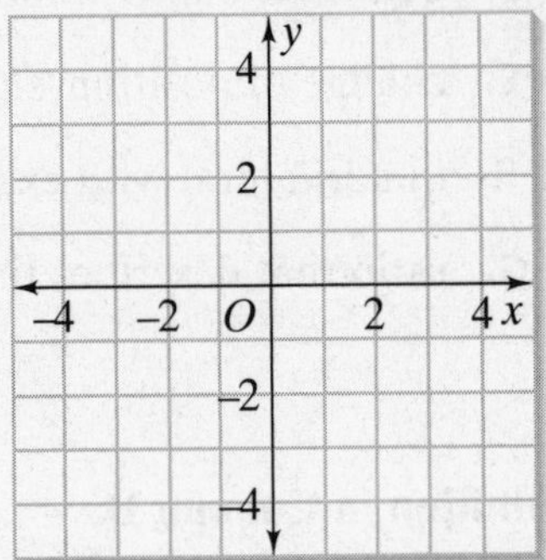

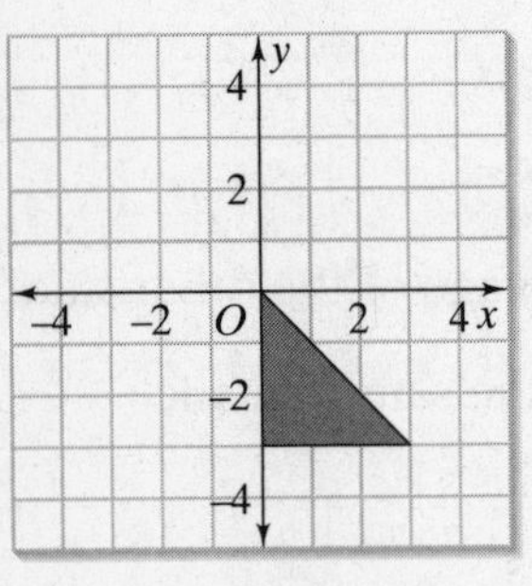
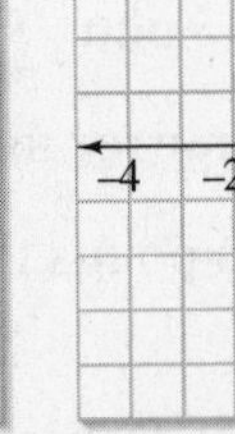

A

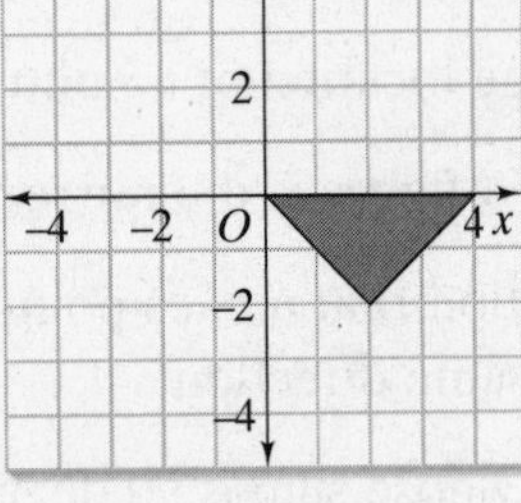

U

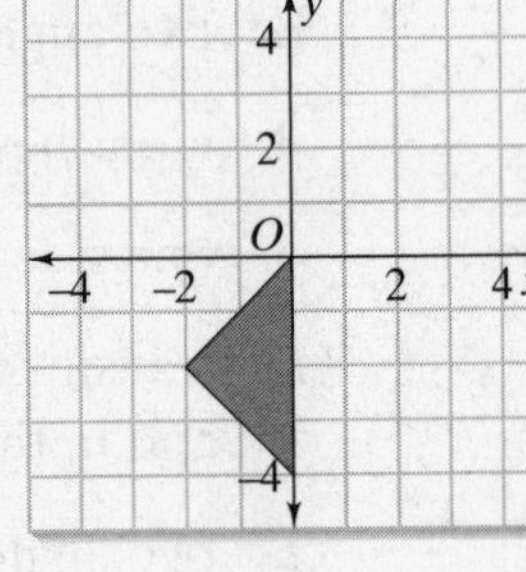

C

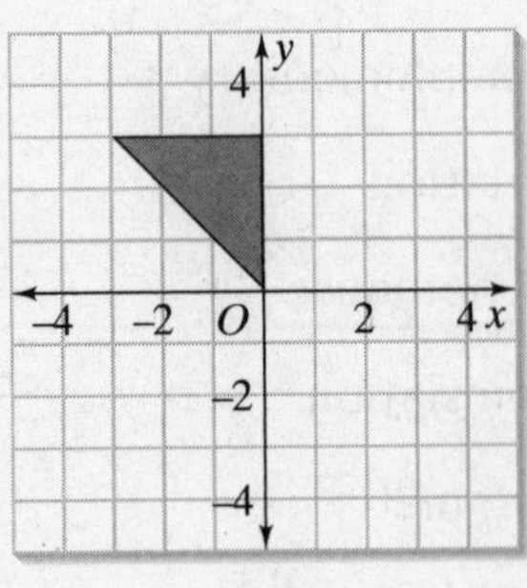

N

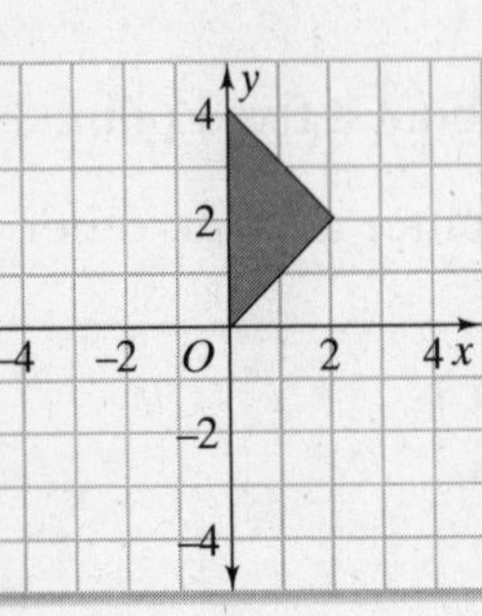

I

V

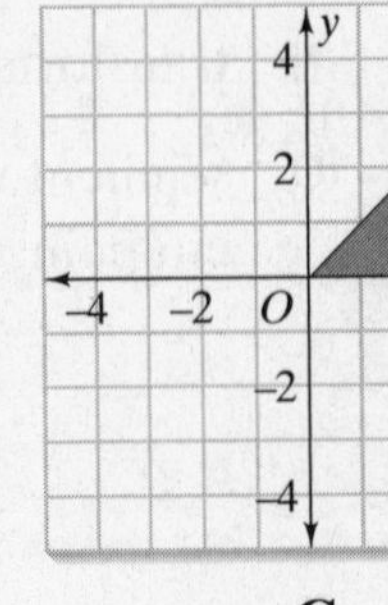

G

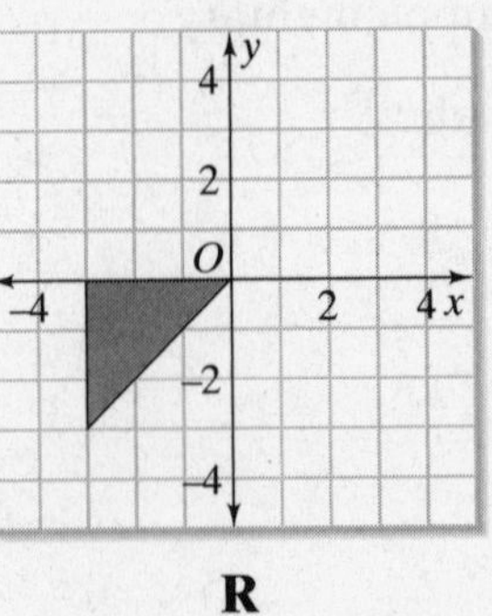

R

_____ _____ _____ _____ _____ _____ _____ _____

1 2 3 4 5 6 7 8

Name ______________________ Class ______________ Date ______________

Chapter 10 Project: People's Choice

Find a Sample Size

Beginning the Chapter Project

You are an advertising executive, and you want to know which of three television shows is the most popular. So you plan to conduct a poll of viewers.

But how many viewers do you survey? Polling is expensive, so you don't want to poll too many. Polling too few viewers might give you the wrong information. Here's your chance to explore the process.

In this chapter project, you will fill a container with three different kinds of beans. Use the beans to find the ample size that best predicts the percent of each kind of bean in the container.

Activities

Activity 1: Collecting Data

Sample the beans in the container ten times. Make each sample larger than the previous one. Remember to mix the sampled beans back into the container each time. Keep track of the size of each sample and the percent of each type of bean.

Activity 2: Graphing

For each type of bean, make a graph relating the different sample sizes to the percents you found in each sample. Put sample size on the x-axis and percent on the y-axis. Use your graphs to decide the smallest sample size you need to predict the percent of each kind of bean in the jar.

Activity 3: Writing

Connect your findings about sample sizes to a real situation. Do you need to survey everyone who watches television to get an idea about which shows are most popular? Explain.

Name ______________________ Class ______________ Date ______________

Chapter 10 Project: People's Choice (continued)

Finishing the Project

Plan a presentation to show your results. Explain the connection between the size of a sample and how accurately that sample represents the container of beans.

Reflect and Revise

Ask a classmate to review your graphs with you and practice your presentation. If necessary, make revisions that make your ideas more forceful or your graphs more clear.

Extending the Project

Use the information from the project to create a survey for the students in your school.

Visit PHSchool.com for information and links you might find helpful as you complete your project.

Name ______________________ Class ______________ Date ______________

Chapter Project Manager

Getting Started

Read about the project. As you work on it, you will need several sheets of paper. If available, a spreadsheet program also can be used. Keep all your work for the project in a folder, along with this Project Manager.

Checklist

Checklist	Suggestions
❑ Activity 1: collecting data	❑ Keep track of the sample and the percent of each type of bean with a table or chart.
❑ Activity 2: graphing	❑ Choose your intervals for your graphs so that all the data is presented correctly.
❑ Activity 3: writing	❑ Look in the newspaper for ideas of real situations with surveys.
❑ Recommendations	❑ Decorate your graph with the different types of beans you sampled.

Scoring Rubric

3 For each of ten samples, you provide a table listing the number and percentage of each bean type in the sample. For each type of bean, you draw a graph of percent versus sample size. You write a paragraph describing how sample size affects the accuracy of the survey results. Your work is clear and provides convincing evidence to support the statements you make in your paragraph.

2 You collect data and calculate percentages accurately for at least seven sample sizes. You provide percentage versus sample size graphs for at least two of the bean types, and you write a brief conclusion to your investigation.

1 Your data, your graphs, and your conclusions are incomplete or do not provide a clear picture of your work or your findings.

0 You omit important parts of the project.

Your Evaluation of Project Evaluate your work, based on the Scoring Rubric.

Teacher's Evaluation of Project

Name ______________________ Class ______________ Date ______________

Chapter Project Teacher Notes

About the Project

Students will apply their knowledge of graphing in the coordinate plane to conduct a poll.

Introducing the Project

Ask students:

- Have you ever been included in a market survey?
- How can market surveys be used to help develop something new to sell?
- How might a survey be used to help make a product more successful?

Activity 1: Collecting Data

You may want to use a coffee scoop or teaspoon to help students select their samples. Each sample then can be one scoop larger than the previous one.

Activity 2: Graphing

Encourage students to consider the size of their largest sample before choosing intervals for the *x*-axis. For example: If their largest sample was 40 beans, they may want to use intervals of 5 rather than 2.

Activity 3: Writing

Ask: What might make it difficult to ask everyone's opinion?

Finishing the Project

You may wish to plan a project day on which students share their completed projects. Encourage students to explain their process as well as their products.

Visit PHSchool.com for information and links you might find helpful as you complete your project.

Name ______________________ Class ______________ Date ______________

✔ Checkpoint Quiz 1

Use with Lessons 10-1 through 10-3.

Identify the quadrant in which each point lies.

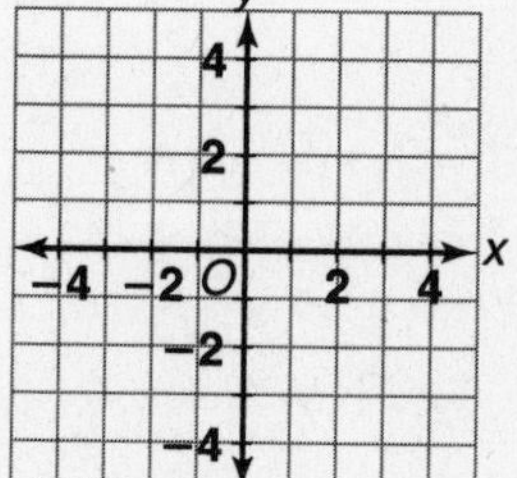

1. (–4, 3) ____ **2.** (5, –2) ____ **3.** (–3, –2) ____ **4.** (3, 2) ____

5. a. Graph $y = 2x + 1$ **b.** What is the slope? ____

Draw a line with the given slope through the given point.

6. $Q(3, -4)$, slope $= -3$ **7.** $Z(0, 2)$, slope $= \frac{2}{3}$ **8.** $T(3, 2)$, slope $= 1$

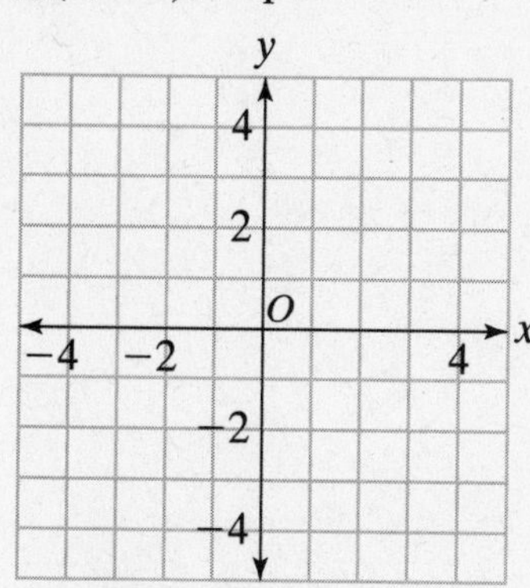

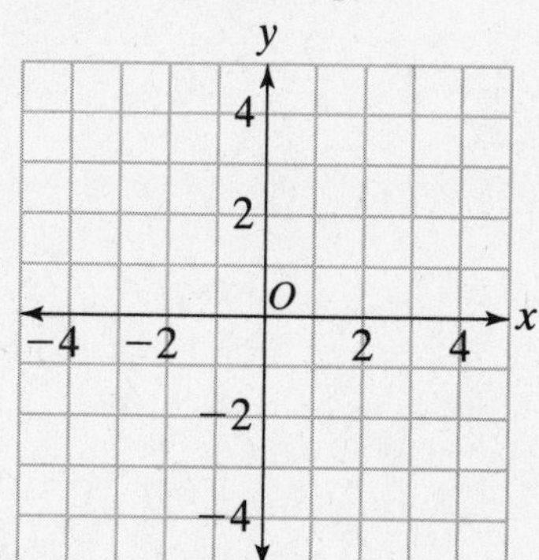

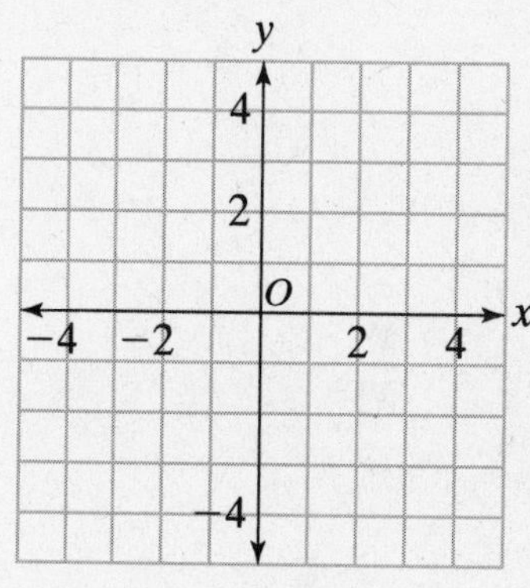

Name ______________________ Class ______________ Date ______________

✔ Checkpoint Quiz 2

Use with Lessons 10-4 through 10-6.

Graph each equation.

1. $y = x^2 + 2$ **2.** $y = 3x - 4$ **3.** $y = |x| + 1$ **4.** $y = 2x^2$

5. Is (3, 12) a solution of $y = 3x^2$? Explain.

____

Translate each point left 1 unit and down 3 units. Write the new coordinates.

6. (1, 1) **7.** (−3, 5) **8.** (0, 6) **9.** (5, −7)

10. Write the rule for the translation of point $A(-1, 4)$ to $A'(6, 2)$.

____

11. Draw the line(s) of symmetry.
$y = x^2 + 2$

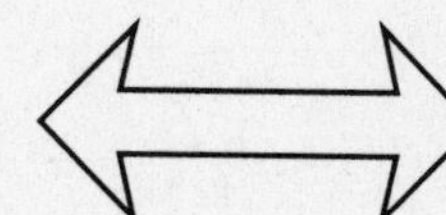

Name ______________________ Class ______________ Date ______________

Chapter Test

Form A

Chapter 10

Graph each point on the same coordinate plane.

1. $(0, 3)$

2. $(1, -3)$

3. $(-3, -1)$

4. $(-2, 4)$

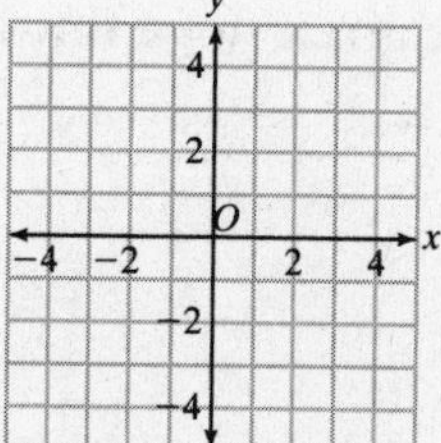

Graph each polygon. Use (–3, –3) as one vertex and label all vertices.

5. a rectangle with vertical length 2 units and horizontal length 6 units

____

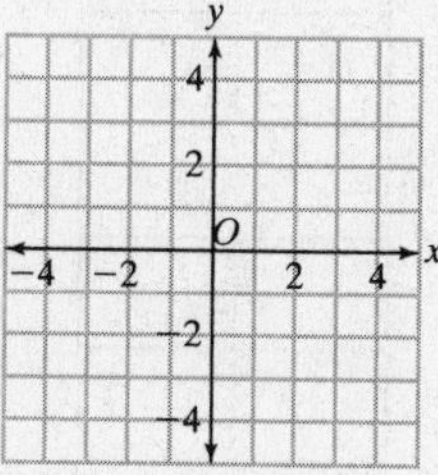

6. a square with side length 5 units

____

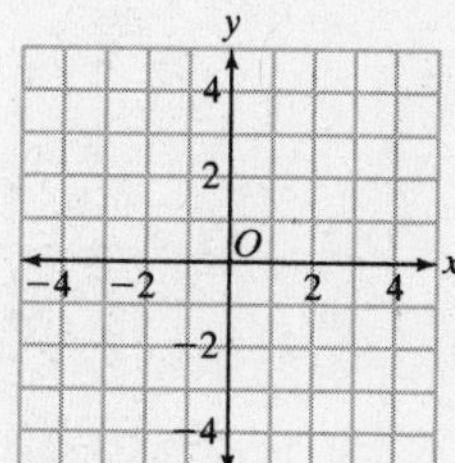

7. an equilateral triangle with side length 6 units

____

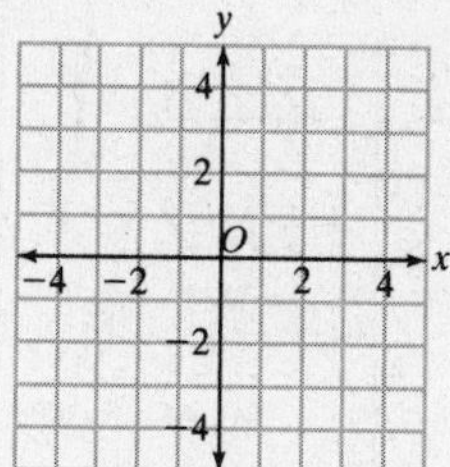

Determine whether each ordered pair is a solution of $y = 6 - x$.

8. $(-2, 8)$ ______________

9. $(4, 2)$ ______________

10. $(7, 1)$ ______________

Graph each linear equation.

11. $y = \frac{3}{2}x - 1$

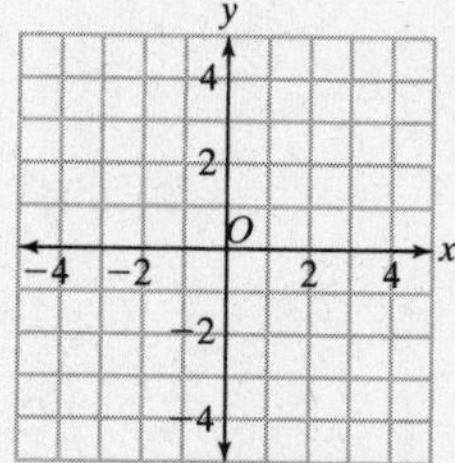

12. $y = -x + 3$

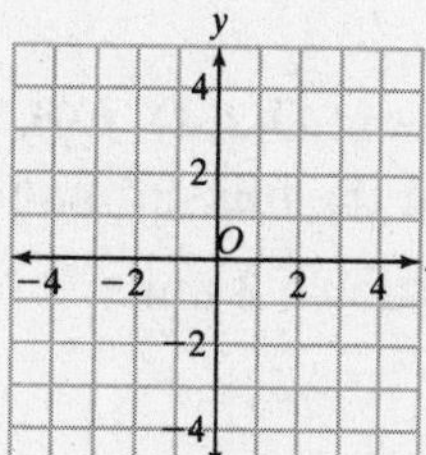

Graph each pair of points. Determine the slope of the line through the points.

13. $A(-2, 4), B(0, 2)$ ______________

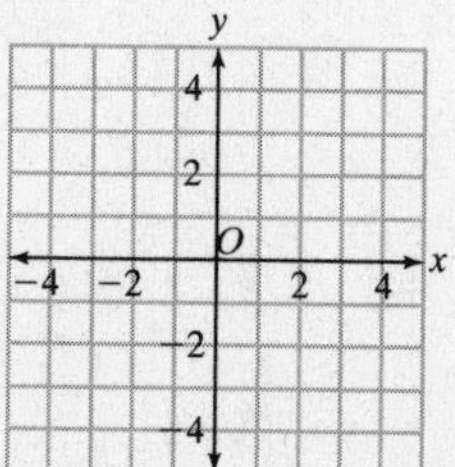

14. $C(3, 5), D(0, -4)$ ______________

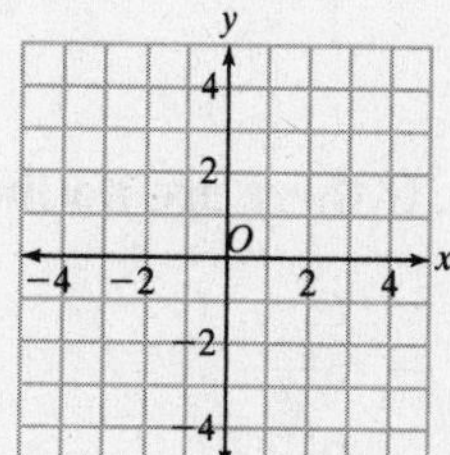

Chapter Test (continued) Form A

Chapter 10

Draw a line with the given slope through the given point.

15. $E(-2, 4)$ slope $-\frac{1}{3}$

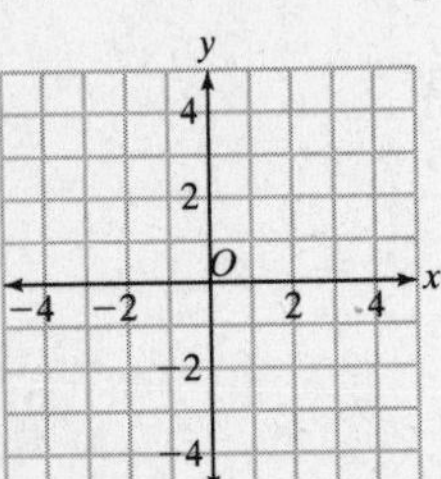

16. $F(3, 5)$, slope 2

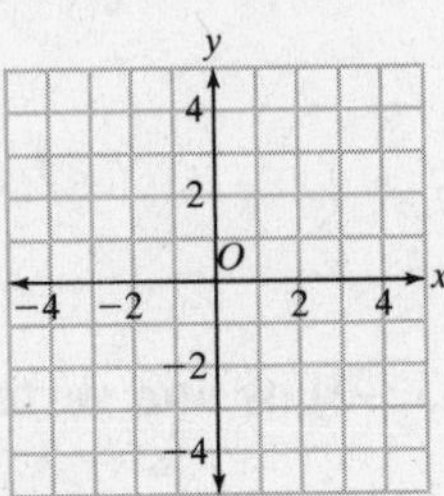

Make a table of values for each equation. Use integer values of x from -3 to 3. Then graph the equation.

17. $y = -2|x| - 1$

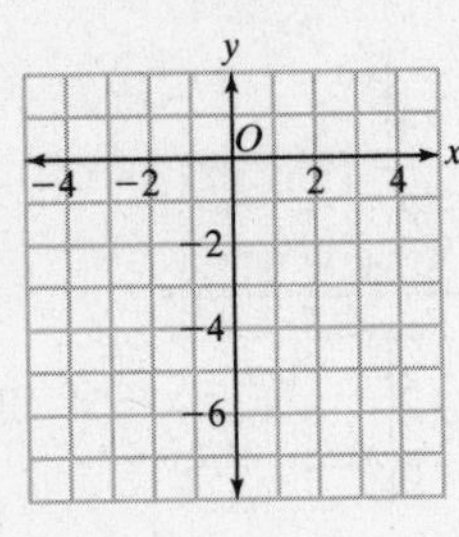

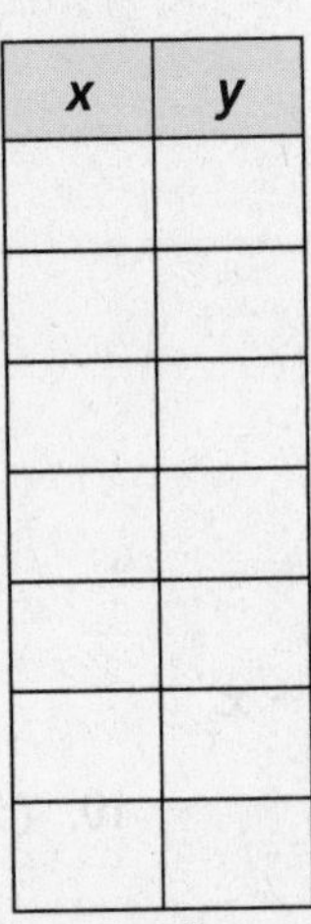

x	y

18. $y = -x^2 + 4$

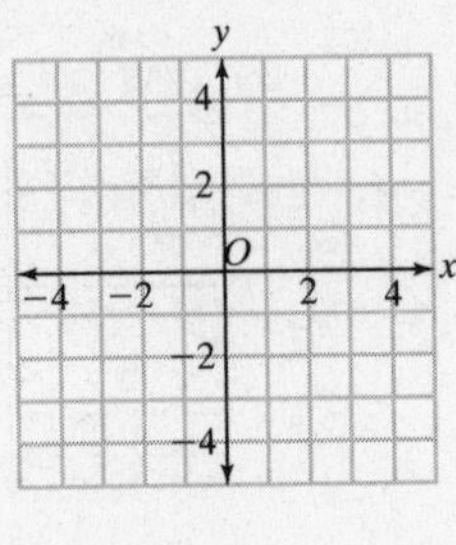

x	y

19. Draw the image of the figure after a counterclockwise rotation of 90° about the point shown.

The graph of $\triangle DEF$ has vertices at $D(2, 4)$, $E(0, 1)$, and $F(5, 0)$. Graph each image of $\triangle DEF$ for the transformation described.

20. translated left 2 units and down 3 units

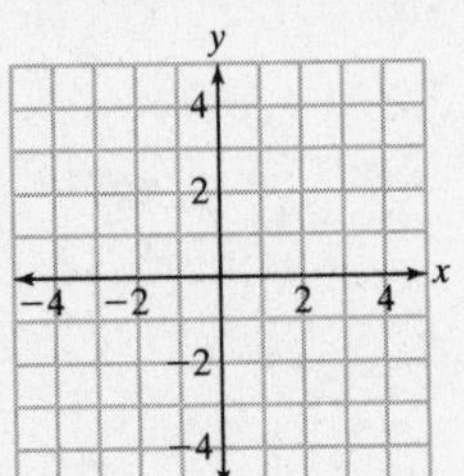

21. reflected over the y-axis

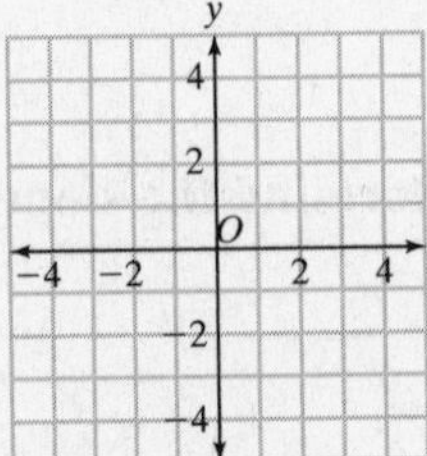

Draw the line(s) of symmetry. If there are no lines of symmetry, write *none*.

22.

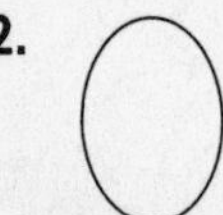

23.

24.

25.

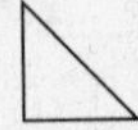

Name ________________________ Class ________________ Date ______________

Chapter Test

Form B

Chapter 10

Graph each point on the same coordinate plane.

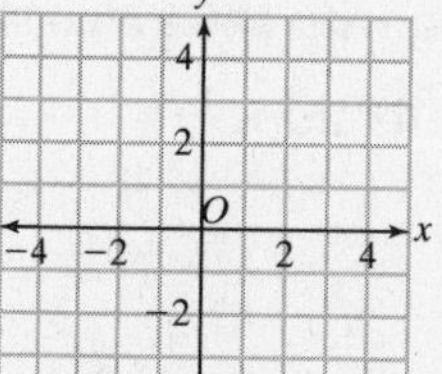

1. $(0, 3)$

2. $(1, -3)$

3. $(-3, -1)$

4. $(-2, 4)$

Graph each polygon. Use (–3, –3) as one vertex and label all vertices.

5. a rectangle with vertical length 2 units and horizontal length 6 units

____

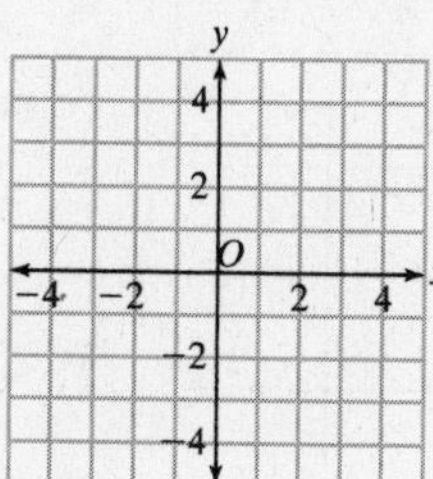

6. an equilateral triangle with side length 6 units

____

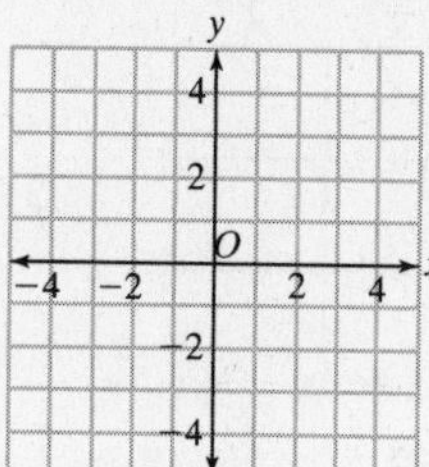

Determine whether each ordered pair is a solution of $y = 6 - x$.

7. $(-2, 8)$ ____________

8. $(7, 1)$ ____________

Graph each linear equation.

9. $y = \frac{3}{2}x - 1$

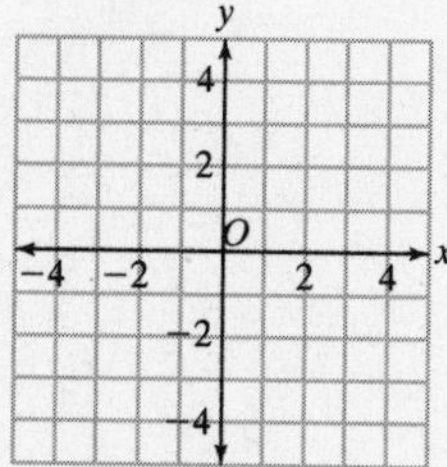

10. $y = -x + 3$

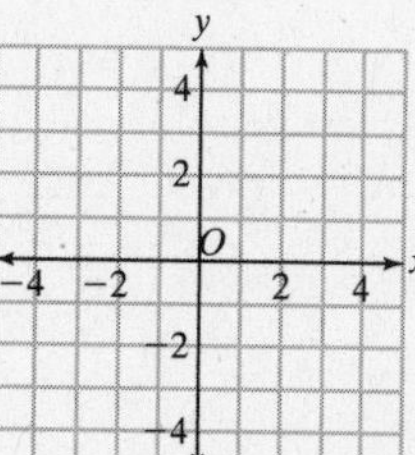

Graph each pair of points. Determine the slope of the line through the points.

11. $A(-2, 4), B(0, 2)$ ____________

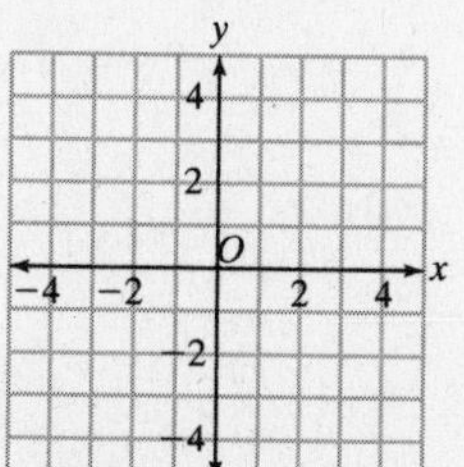

12. $C(3, 5), D(0, -4)$ ____________

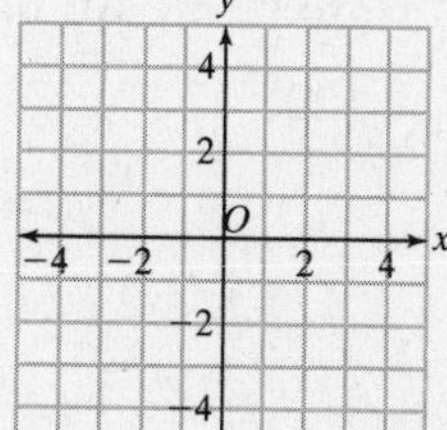

Chapter Test (continued) Form B

Chapter 10

Draw a line with the given slope through the given point.

13. $E(-2, 4)$ slope $-\frac{1}{3}$

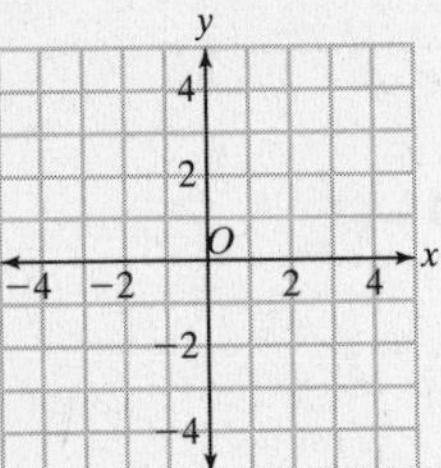

14. $F(3, 5)$, slope 2

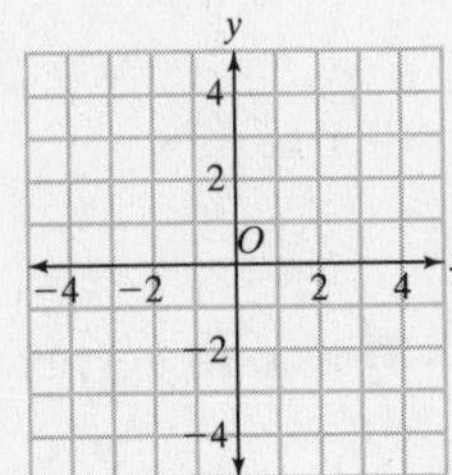

Make a table of values for each equation. Use integer values of x from -3 to 3. Then graph the equation.

15. $y = -2|x| - 1$

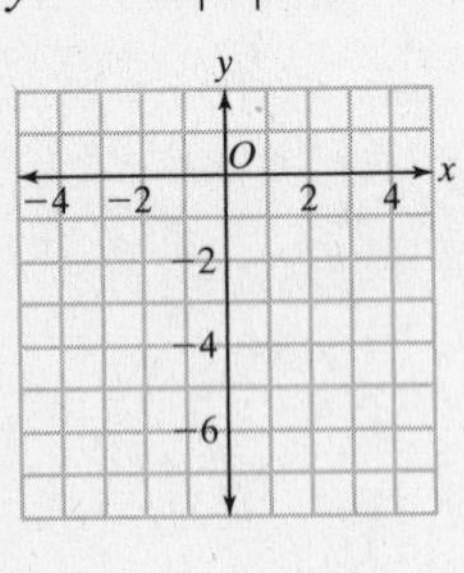

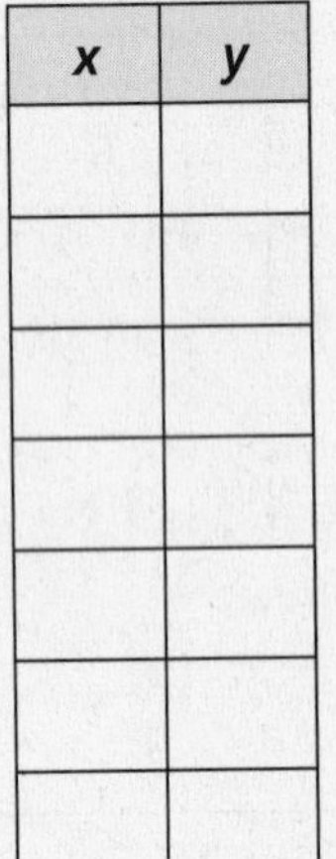

x	y

16. $y = -x^2 + 4$

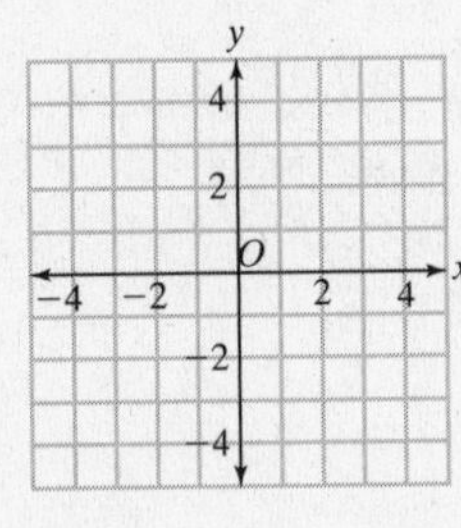

x	y

The graph of $\triangle DEF$ has vertices at $D(2, 4)$, $E(0, 1)$, and $F(5, 0)$. Graph each image of $\triangle DEF$ for the transformation described.

17. translated left 2 units and down 3 units

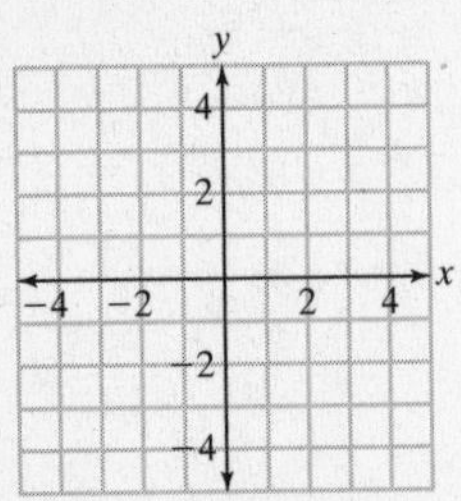

18. reflected over the y-axis

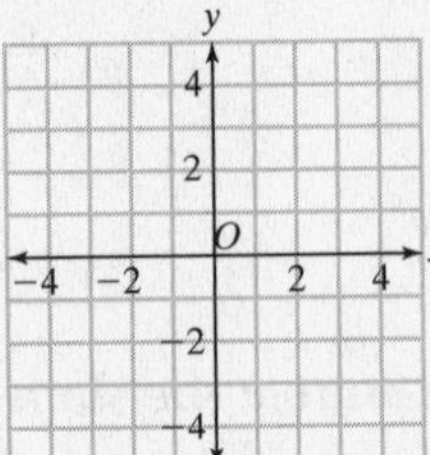

Draw the line(s) of symmetry. If there are no lines of symmetry, write *none*.

19. 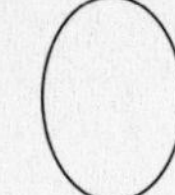

20. 

21. 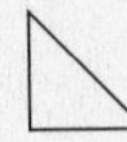

Name ______________________ Class ______________ Date ____________

Alternative Assessment **Form C**

Chapter 10

HIT THE SLOPES

Did you ever consider the fun that you can have on a mountain? Going up mountains is fun for hikers. Going down mountains is fun for skiers.

Show all of your work on a separate sheet of paper.

1. The steeper a mountain is, the harder it is to climb up or down. Look at these two mountain profiles and decide which one looks harder to climb. Explain.

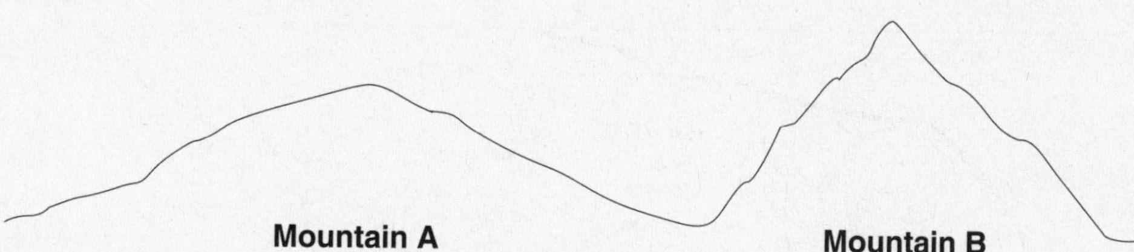

2. Ski resorts mark their trails with symbols that show the levels of difficulty of the trails. Circles represent the easiest trails, squares represent somewhat harder trails, and diamonds represent the most difficult. The map below shows several trails at Mount Ski. Choose one circle trail, one square trail, and one diamond trail. Circle the trails you choose and give them each an appropriate name.

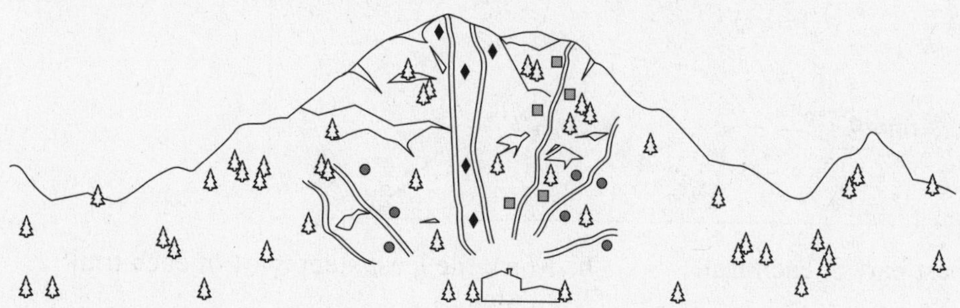

3. Copy the chart below. Draw the profile of each of your three trails in the chart. (A profile of a ski trail shows how steep it is.) A sample profile of the beginner trail appears on the chart.

Profile Chart		
Type of trail	**Name**	**Profile**
Beginner	Easy as Pie	

Alternative Assessment (continued) Form C

Chapter 10

4. The map below shows two hiking trails on Mount Monadnock in southern New Hampshire. The names of the trails are the Marlboro Trail and the Dublin Trail. A hiking guidebook shows each trail is 2.2 mi long; the trip to the top of the mountain takes about 2 h on each trail.

The lines on the map are called contour lines. A contour line labels height, or elevation. Every point on the contour line has the same elevation. There is a 100-ft difference in elevation between any two adjacent lines. The closer the lines are to each other, the steeper the slope. Make a copy of the map.

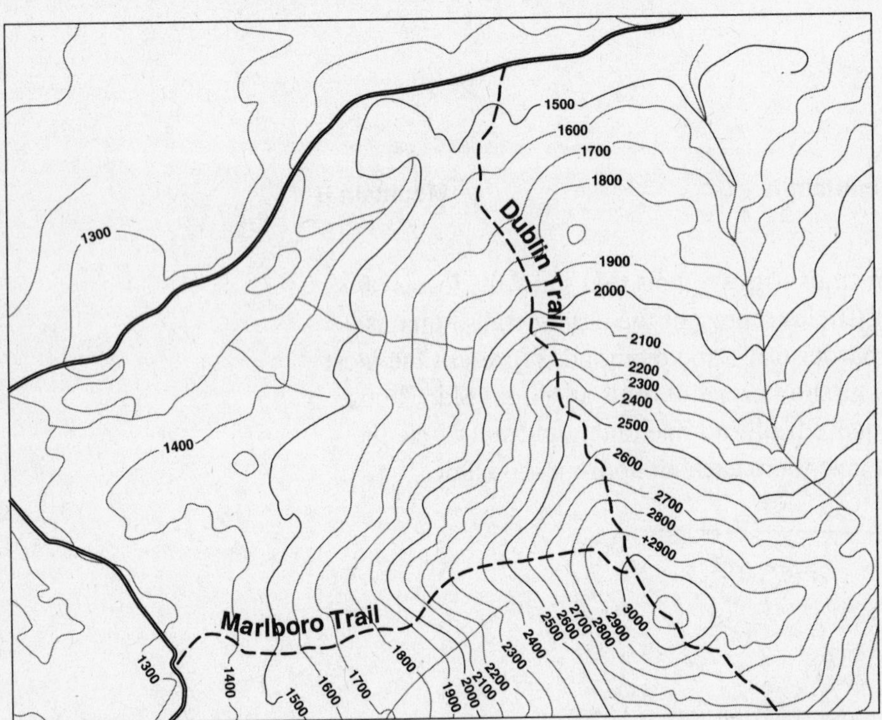

a. Mark the steepest part of each trail in red.

b. Mark the least steep part of each trail in blue.

c. What can you say about the slope of the two trails? Explain.

d. If you were choosing between these trails, which one would you choose? Explain.

Excursion

Where can you find slopes near you? List at least four possibilities. The slopes you think of could be outside or inside, natural or made by people. Rate each slope as gentle, medium, steep, or very steep. Then look at your list and place a star next to the slope you think is steepest. Explain.

Name ______________________ Class ______________ Date ______________

Cumulative Review

Chapters 1–10

Multiple Choice. Choose the letter of the best answer.

1. What is the next term in this pattern?
500, 250, 125, . . .

A. 100 B. 75
C. 62.5 D. 50

2. What is 1.47×10^8 written in standard notation?

F. 14,700,000 G. 147,000,000
H. 1,470,000,000 J. 14,700,000,000

3. Use the formula $B = p(1 + r)^t$ to find the amount of money in your savings account after ten years if you deposited $100 at an interest rate of 5% compounded annually.

A. $111.01 B. $112.74
C. $150.00 D. $162.89

4. Find the circumference of a circle with a diameter of 10 cm. Use 3.14 for π.

F. 15.7 cm G. 31.4 cm
H. 78.5 cm J. 314 cm

5. Which of the situations below could this graph describe?

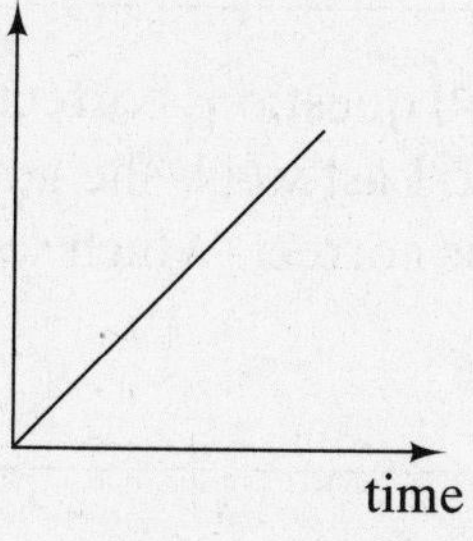

A. distance traveled on a train
B. height of a baseball after a pitch
C. weight of a person on a diet
D. amount of money after paying bills

6. What is the approximate unit price of a lemon if a bag of 15 lemons costs $2?

F. $0.075 G. $0.13
H. $0.15 J. $0.30

7. A map of a city has a scale of 2 in. : $\frac{1}{2}$ mi. The distance on the map from the school to your house is $5\frac{1}{2}$ in. What is the actual distance from the school to your house?

A. $13\frac{3}{4}$ mi B. 11 mi
C. $5\frac{1}{2}$ mi D. $1\frac{3}{8}$ mi

8. How far apart are the 12 posts used to fence in a region with a perimeter of 96 ft if they are at equal intervals?

F. 12 ft G. 10 ft
H. 8 ft J. 6 ft

9. Which proportion will help you find 36% of 90?

A. $\frac{90}{60} = \frac{n}{100}$
B. $\frac{n}{90} = \frac{36}{100}$
C. $\frac{90}{100} = \frac{36}{n}$
D. $\frac{100}{n} = \frac{36}{90}$

10. The sale price of a TV is $279. This is 80% of the original price. What was the original price?

F. $55.80 G. $286.74
H. $348.75 J. $400

11. In which quadrant is the point A (3, −1) located?

A. I B. II
C. III D. IV

Name ______________________ Class ______________ Date ______________

Cumulative Review (continued)

Chapters 1–10

12. What is the slope of the line shown?

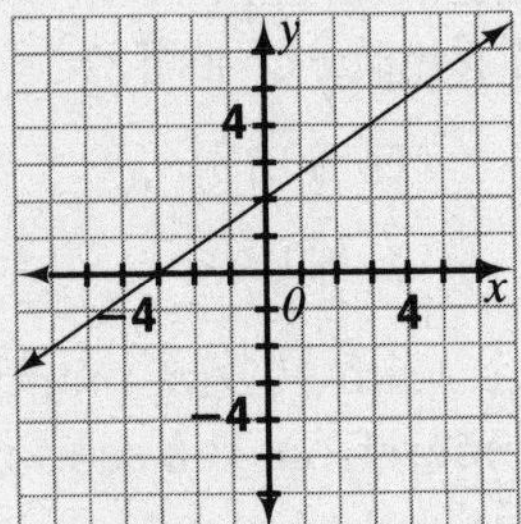

F. $\frac{3}{2}$ **G.** $\frac{2}{3}$

H. $-\frac{3}{2}$ **J.** 3

13. Which equation is a linear equation?

A. $y = 3x + 4$ **B.** $y = x^3 + 2$

C. $y = x^2 - 3$ **D.** $y = |x - 1|$

14. Jay has two more quarters than dimes in his pocket. He has a total of 20 dimes and quarters. Which equation could you use to find how many of each coin Jay has?

F. $x + 2 = 20$

G. $20 - x = 2x$

H. $x + (x + 2) = 20$

J. $\frac{20}{2} = x$

15. What are the coordinates of the image of point $D(-2, 3)$ after reflecting D across the x-axis?

A. $(3, -2)$ **B.** $(-2, -3)$

C. $(2, 3)$ **D.** $(-3, 2)$

16. A right triangle has legs of 12 ft and 16 ft. Find the longest side of the triangle. Use the Pythagorean theorem.

F. 20 ft   **G.** 28 ft

H. 400 ft   **J.** not here

17. Two ladders are leaning against a wall at the same angle as shown.

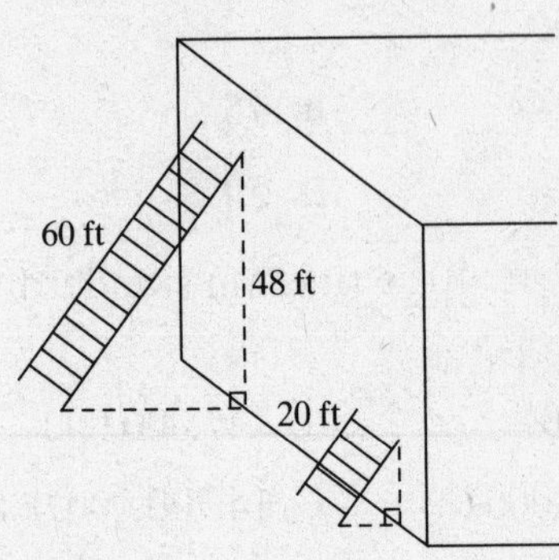

How far up the wall does the shorter ladder reach?

____

Extended Response

18. Explain the rule for multiplying two negative integers. Use a number line or algebra tiles to illustrate three examples. Make a sketch of your work.

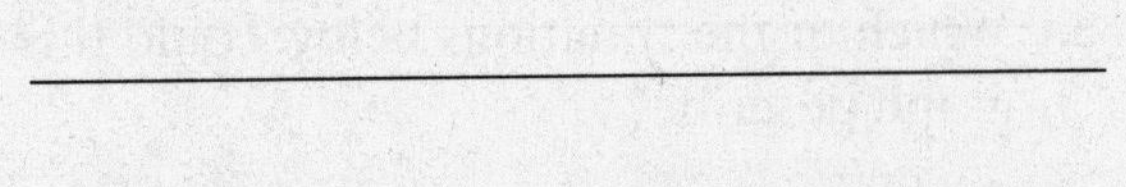

____

____

19. Casey got 32 out of 40 questions correct on her social studies test. Last week she got 24 out of 30 questions correct. Which score was better? Explain.

____

____

____

Name ______________________ Class ______________ Date ______________

Practice 11-1

Reporting Frequency

Make a frequency table and a line plot for the data.

1. boxes of juice sold per day:
   26 21 26 24 27 23 24 22
   26 21 23 26 24 26 23

Ms. Makita made a line plot to show the scores her students got on a test. At the right is Ms. Makita's line plot.

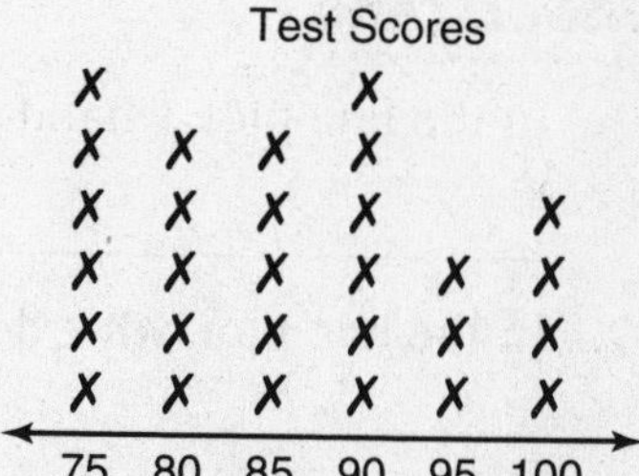

2. What does each data item or ✗ represent?

   ____

3. How many more students scored 75 than scored 95?

   ____

4. How many students scored over 85?

   ____

5. What scores did the same number of students get?

   ____

Nathan asked 24 classmates to estimate the total number of hours (to the nearest quarter hour) they spend doing homework Monday through Thursday. The frequency table below shows their responses.

Hours Spent Doing Homework

Number of Hours	Frequency
1–1.75	1
2–2.75	1
3–3.75	2
4–4.75	6
5–5.75	8
6–6.75	3
7–7.75	2
8–8.75	1

6. Can you tell from the table how many students do homework for two hours or less? Explain.

   ____

7. How many more students do homework for at least 5 hours than do homework for less than 4 hours?

   ____

8. Make a histogram for the data. Use the intervals in the table.

Name ______________________ Class ______________ Date ______________

11-1 • Guided Problem Solving

GPS Student Page 535, Exercise 12:

Books The line plot shows the number of books each bookstore customer bought. How many customers bought more than three books?

Number of Books Purchased

1	2	3	4	5	6
	x				
x	x				
x	x	x			
x	x	x			x
x	x	x	x	x	x

Understand

1. In the line plot, what do the numbers at the bottom represent?

____

2. In the line plot, what do the X's represent?

____

____

Plan and Carry Out

3. To find the number of customers who bought more than three books, in which columns do you have to look?

____

4. How many customers bought 4 books?

____

5. How many customers bought 5 books?

____

6. How many customers bought 6 books?

____

7. How many customers bought more than 3 books?

____

Check

8. Why do you not include the customers who bought 3 books?

____

____

Solve Another Problem

9. The line plot shows how many CDs each customer in a music store bought. How many customers bought two or fewer CDs?

____

Number of CDs Purchased

0	1	2	3	4
	x			
	x			
x	x	x		
x	x	x	x	x

Name ______________________ Class ______________ Date ______________

Practice 11-1

Reporting Frequency

Make a frequency table and a line plot for the data.

1. boxes of juice sold per day:
   26 21 26 24 27 23 24 22
   26 21 23 26 24 26 23

Ms. Makita made a line plot to show the scores her students got on a test. At the right is Ms. Makita's line plot.

Test Scores

X			X		
X	X	X	X		
X	X	X	X		X
X	X	X	X	X	X
X	X	X	X	X	X
X	X	X	X	X	X
75	80	85	90	95	100

2. What does each data item or ✗ represent?

   ____

3. How many more students scored 75 than scored 95?

   ____

4. How many students scored over 85?

   ____

Nathan asked 24 classmates to estimate the total number of hours (to the nearest quarter hour) they spend doing homework Monday through Thursday. The frequency table below shows their responses.

Hours Spent Doing Homework

Number of Hours	Frequency
1–1.75	1
2–2.75	1
3–3.75	2
4–4.75	6
5–5.75	8
6–6.75	3
7–7.75	2
8–8.75	1

5. Make a histogram for the data. Use the intervals in the table.

Name ______________________ Class ______________ Date ______________

Activity Lab 11-1

Reporting Frequency

Materials needed: standard number cube, paper

Part 1: Number Cube Line Plot

Work in groups of three or four. Take turns rolling a number cube. Record the results using tally marks in the table below for each roll. Continue until the cube has been rolled twenty-four times. Complete the table by filling in the "Frequency" row.

Number	1	2	3	4	5	6
Tally						
Frequency						

On a separate sheet of paper, draw a number line with the least value 1 and the greatest value 6. Use your number line to create a line plot for the data you collected by rolling the number cube.

Part 2: Classroom Survey

Estimate the time it takes for you to travel from your home to school each morning. As a class, collect and compare your estimations by creating a list of values on the chalkboard.

1. What is the shortest travel time recorded? What is the longest?
2. Complete the frequency table below. As a class, decide what interval values should be used to organize the data into five equal-sized intervals.

Travel Time	Tally	Frequency

3. Use the frequency table to create a Histogram. Label the horizontal axis "Travel Time (minutes)" and the vertical axis "Frequency." Draw your histogram below the line plot you created in Part 1.

Name ______________________ Class ______________ Date ______________

Reteaching 11-1

Reporting Frequency

Aimee asked students in her grade how many CDs they own. She displayed her data in a **frequency table.** Each tally stands for 1 CD.

Students' CD Collections

Number of CDs	17	18	19	20	21	22	23	24
Tally	𝍸 I	I	𝍸	III	I	IIII	II	IIII
Frequency	6	1	5	3	1	4	2	4

She displayed the same data in a **line plot.** Each ✗ stands for 1 CD.

Number of CDs Students Own

✗							
✗		✗					
✗		✗			✗		✗
✗		✗	✗		✗		✗
✗		✗	✗		✗	✗	✗
✗	✗	✗	✗	✗	✗	✗	✗
17	**18**	**19**	**20**	**21**	**22**	**23**	**24**

She also made a **histogram** to show the frequencies. The bars represent intervals of equal size. The height of each bar gives the frequency of the data.

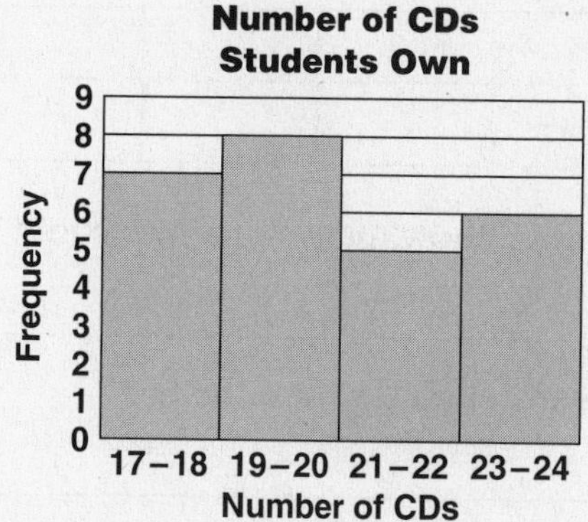

Use the frequency table for Exercises 1–3.

1. Ms. Ortiz's class is planning a school garden. She asked her students how many rosebushes they want in the garden. She recorded the data in a frequency table. Complete the table.

Number of Rosebushes	1	2	3	4	5	6
Tally	I	IIII	III	𝍸 I	I	I
Frequency						

2. Use the frequency table to make a line plot for the data.

3. Draw a histogram of the students' data.

Name ________________ Class ________________ Date ________________

Enrichment 11-1

Reporting Frequency

Recording and Organizing Data

Mr. Ishii made a histogram showing his students' performance on a recent English test.

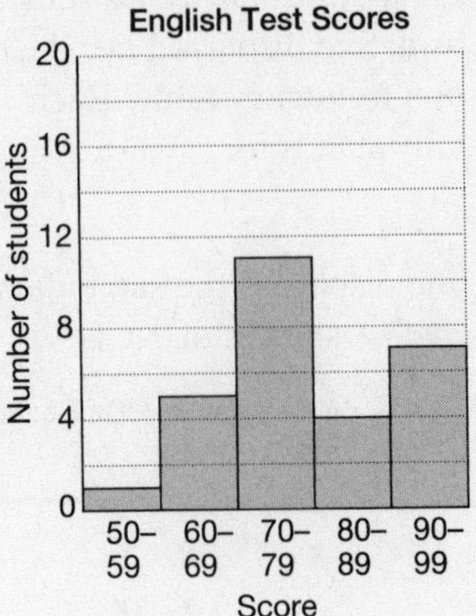

1. What is the interval width in this histogram?

____

2. How many students scored between 80 and 89 points?

____

3. Make a frequency table for the histogram.

Score					
Students					

4. Can you tell how many students scored 73 points? Explain.

____

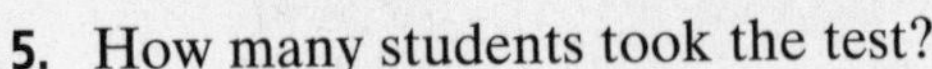

5. How many students took the test?

____

6. Mr. Ishii has 32 students in his class. He gave a makeup test to the absent students one week after these test scores were plotted. The four students received the following points on the test: 58, 100, 43, 78. Describe how you would change the intervals in the frequency table to reflect these new scores.

____

____

7. Create a new frequency table to include these new test scores.

Score							
Students							

8. How many bars will the histogram have if you plot the new data?

____

9. Create a new histogram to reflect the new test scores.

10. Mr. Ishii gave every student who scored between 70 and 79 a C on their progress report. What percent of students received a grade lower than a C? Show your work.

____

Name ______________________ Class ______________ Date ______________

11A: Graphic Organizer

For use before Lesson 11-1

Study Skill As your teacher presents new material in the chapter, keep a paper and pencil handy to write down notes and questions. If you miss class, borrow a classmate's notes so you will not fall behind.

Write your answers.

1. What is the chapter title?

____

2. How many lessons are there in this chapter?

____

3. What is the topic of the Test-Taking Strategies page?

____

4. Complete the graphic organizer below as you work through the chapter.
   - In the center, write the title of the chapter.
   - When you begin a lesson, write the lesson name in a rectangle.
   - When you complete a lesson, write a skill or key concept in a circle linked to that lesson block.
   - When you complete the chapter, use this graphic organizer to help you review.

Name ____________________ Class ____________ Date ____________

Puzzle 11-1

Reporting Frequency

The line plot and histogram below show the results of a survey regarding catalogs and unwanted advertisements (or "junk mail") received in the mail during the course of a month. Use the line plot to answer Exercises 1–5, and the histogram to answer Exercises 6–10. When you have completed the Exercises, use the letter code to complete the sentence.

Number of Catalogs Received By 20 People in One Month

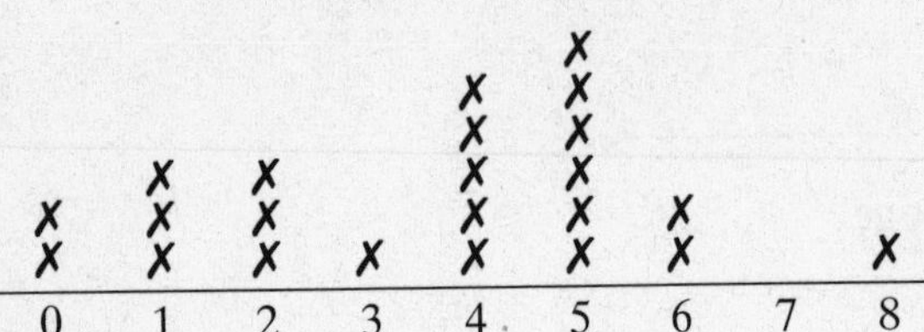

Number of Unwanted Advertisements Received in One Month

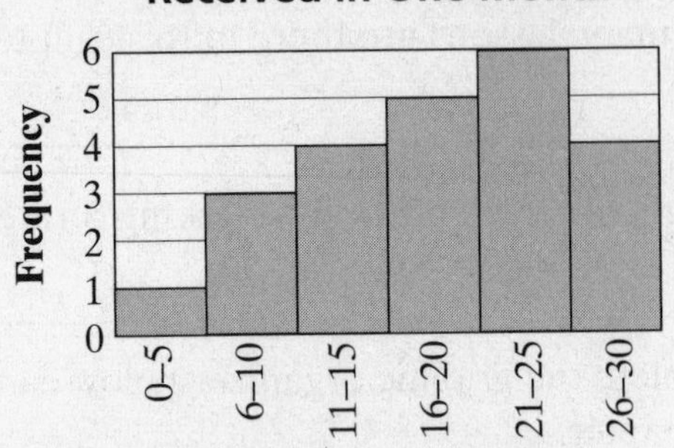

1. How many people received three catalogs in the mail? ______

2. How people received at least one but fewer than four catalogs? ______

3. The number of people who received more than one catalog: ______

4. How many people received either two or six catalogs? ______

5. The number of people who received more than six catalogs: ______

6. The number of people who did *not* receive between six and ten pieces of "junk mail": ______

7. How many people received more than five pieces? ______

8. The number of people who received between eleven and twenty unwanted advertisements: ______

9. How many people received fewer than five or more than twenty-five pieces of "junk mail"? ______

10. What was the total number of people surveyed? ______

Complete by writing the letter for each answer above the exercise numbers:

Histograms and line plots give:

Letter Code: 1 = A
2 = B
3 = C
.
.
.
26 = Z

___ ___ ___ ___ ___ ___ ___ ___ ___ ___
1 2 3 4 5 6 7 8 9 10

Name ____________________ Class ____________ Date ____________

Practice 11-2

Spreadsheets and Data Displays

Use the spreadsheet at the right for Exercises 1–4.

Tickets Sold to Concert Performances

	A	B	C
1	Performance	Adult Tickets	Student Tickets
2	Thursday	47	65
3	Friday	125	133
4	Saturday	143	92

1. What is the value in cell B3?

____

2. Which cell shows 65 tickets sold?

____

3. How many more adult tickets than student tickets were sold on Saturday?

____

4. The concert producer thought she would have the greatest attendance on Saturday. Compare the data with her expectation.

____

____

____

Decide whether a double bar graph or a double line graph is more appropriate for the given data. Draw the graph.

5. students taking foreign language classes

Year	Boys	Girls
2003	45	60
2004	50	55
2005	70	60
2006	55	75

6. extracurricular sport activities

Sport	Boys	Girls
basketball	40	30
volleyball	30	40
soccer	40	25

Name ______________________ Class ______________ Date ______________

11-2 • Guided Problem Solving

GPS Student Page 541, Exercise 23:

Writing in Math Describe how you would display measurements of a pet's growth over several years. What measurements would you use? How would you display them?

Understand

1. What ways of displaying data have you learned?

____

2. Which of these could you use to show the growth of an animal?

____

Plan and Carry Out

3. Which type of data display or graph provides the most detail about representing changes over time?

____

4. What kind of growth patterns or information about your pet would you want to know?

____

5. What units of measurement would you use in your graph to determine these growth patterns? What time units and limits would you use to analyze your data?

____

6. Explain your steps in constructing this data display.

____

Check

7. Follow the steps you wrote in Step 6. Does your data display clearly show units of measure and time to provide you with the information you wanted? Can you draw accurate conclusions about the growth of your pet over time from the display?

____

Solve Another Problem

8. Olivia wants to know which band that students in each of the four grades prefer. They must decide between a salsa band and a rock band. Describe how you would gather and display this information. What type of graph would be the best choice to represent this data? Explain.

____

Name ____________________ Class ____________ Date ____________

Practice 11-2

Spreadsheets and Data Displays

Use the spreadsheet at the right for Exercises 1–3.

Tickets Sold to Concert Performances

	A	B	C
1	Performance	Adult Tickets	Student Tickets
2	Thursday	47	65
3	Friday	125	133
4	Saturday	143	92

1. What is the value in cell B3?

   ____

2. Which cell shows 65 tickets sold?

   ____

3. How many more adult tickets than student tickets were sold on Saturday?

   ____

Decide whether a double bar graph or a double line graph is more appropriate for the given data. Draw the graph.

4. students taking foreign language classes

Year	Boys	Girls
2003	45	60
2004	50	55
2005	70	60
2006	55	75

5. extracurricular sport activities

Sport	Boys	Girls
basketball	40	30
volleyball	30	40
soccer	40	25

Name ____________________ Class ______________ Date ______________

Activity Lab 11-2

Spreadsheets and Data Displays

Materials needed: graph paper

The spreadsheet below shows the number of gold medals and the total number of medals won by six countries in the 2006 Winter Olympics in Torino, Italy.

	A	B	C
1	Country	Gold Medals	Total Medals
2	U.S.	9	25
3	Russia	8	22
4	Italy	5	11
5	China	2	11
6	Australia	1	2
7	Estonia	3	3

1. What is the entry for B2? What does it represent?

____

2. What is the entry for C3? What does it represent?

____

3. Use the data in the spreadsheet to create a double bar graph. Label the vertical axis "Number of Medals." Your graph should include a bar for gold medals, and a bar for total medals for each country. Draw your graph on a sheet of graph paper.

4. How does your graph help you compare the United States' gold medals with its total medals?

____

5. How does your graph help you compare the number of medals won by athletes from the United States with the number of medals won by athletes from Italy?

____

6. During the 2006 Winter Olympics, athletes from France won 9 medals, 3 of which were gold. Describe what changes you would make to the spreadsheet in order to include this additional information. Copy the double bar graph you created for Exercise 3. Modify the graph to incorporate the number of gold medals, and total number of medals won by French athletes.

Reteaching 11-2

Spreadsheets and Data Displays

A **spreadsheet** is one way to organize data.

Columns are labeled A, B, C, and so on. Rows are numbered 1, 2, 3, and so on. The box where column B and row 3 meet is called **cell** B3. The *value* in cell B3 is 10.

Weekly Butter and Margarine Sales

	A	B	C
1	Day	Butter	Margarine
2	Monday	9	7
3	Tuesday	10	9
4	Wednesday	7	6
5	Thursday	9	6
6	Friday	10	8
7	Saturday	11	9

- Spreadsheet column A gives the labels for the horizontal axis.
- Spreadsheet column B gives the heights for one set of bars and one set of points.
- Spreadsheet column C gives the heights for another set of bars and another set of points.

You can use the data from this spreadsheet to make a **double bar graph.** A double bar graph compares two sets of data. The **legend,** or key, tells what kinds of data the graph is comparing.

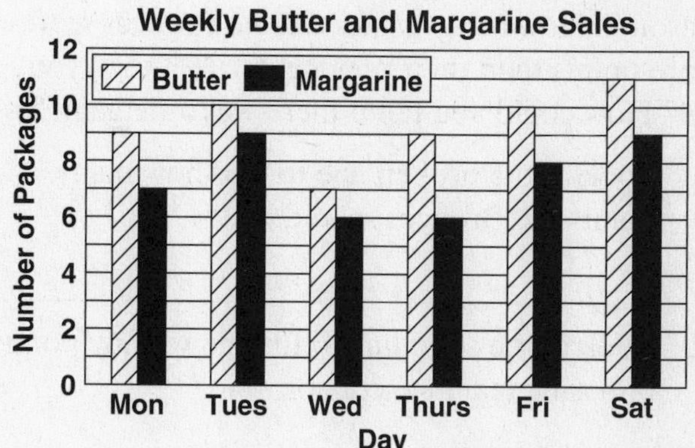

You can compare changes over time of two sets of data with a double line graph.

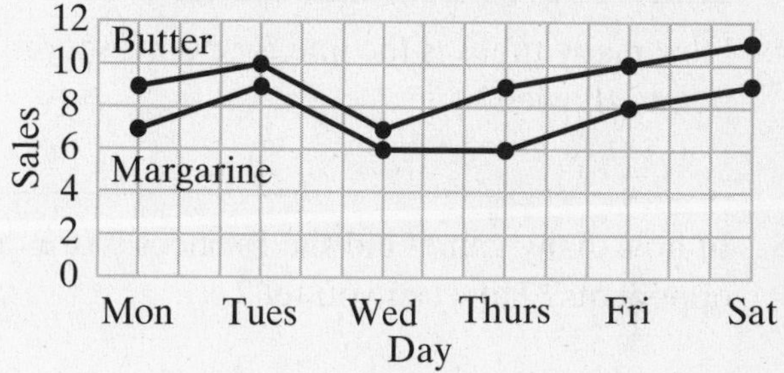

Use the data in the spreadsheet for Exercises 1–4.

1. What is the value in cell B4? cell C2?

____

2. In which cell is the year 2006? 2003?

____

Percents of Families Who Prefer Frozen and Fresh Vegetables

	A	B	C
1	Year	Frozen	Fresh
2	2003	61	39
3	2004	70	30
4	2005	78	22
5	2006	84	16

3. Make a double bar graph from the spreadsheet. Include a legend.

4. Make a double line graph from the spreadsheet. Include a legend.

Name ______________________ Class ______________ Date ______________

Enrichment 11-2

Spreadsheets and Data Displays

Analyzing Data

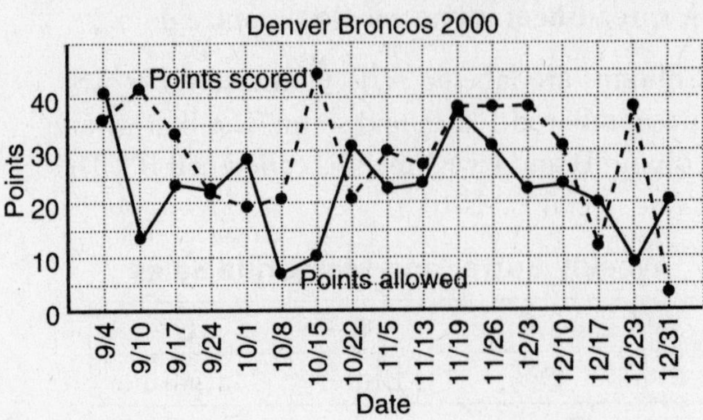

The double-line graph shows the number of points scored and allowed by the National Football League's Denver Broncos during the 2000 football season. In how many games did the Broncos score more points than their opponents? How can you tell? How could you tell if there was a tie game?

1. Look at the broken line to find how many points the Broncos scored on 9/4.

____

2. Look at the solid line to find how many points they allowed the opposing team to score on 9/4.

____

3. If the line for points scored is below the line for points allowed, did the Broncos win or lose?

____

4. How many times is the line for points scored above the line for points allowed?

____

5. In how many games did the Broncos score more points than their opponents? How can you tell?

____

____

____

6. Suppose both teams score 10 points. Describe what happens to the lines. Who wins the game?

____

____

7. Write a number sentence to show that the Bronco wins and the Bronco losses equal the total games played.

____

8. In how many games did the Broncos score 10 or more points fewer than their opponents? Give the dates of these games.

____

Name ____________________ Class ____________ Date ____________

Puzzle 11-2

Spreadsheets and Data Displays

Choose the correct tool for the job. The letter of each correct answer choice will help you answer the question at the bottom of the page.

Problem	Best Tool for Solving
1. Victor wants to keep track of the amount of money he spends each month for a year on CDs.	**A.** spreadsheet **C.** word processor **L.** calculator
2. Victor has a paper to write for his English class and his teacher wants it typed with no spelling errors.	**C.** word processor **L.** calculator **R.** ruler
3. Victor wants to check his arithmetic homework for mistakes in addition and subtraction.	**S.** spreadsheet **A.** word processor **E.** calculator
4. Victor has a job that pays $7 an hour. He needs to keep track of his hours for every week he works.	**T.** calculator **H.** ruler **L.** spreadsheet
5. Victor is measuring a board to cut for a step to the treehouse he is building. It needs to be 12 inches long.	**S.** spreadsheet **L.** ruler **E.** calculator

____ ____ ____ ____ ____ is a box in a spreadsheet where a specific row and column meet.

Name ____________________ Class ____________ Date ____________

Practice 11-3

Stem-and-Leaf Plots

The stem-and-leaf plot at the right shows the number of baskets scored by one of ten intramural teams last season. Use it for Exercises 1–4.

5	2	6	9
6	0	4	6
7	1	5	
8	4	8	

8|4 means 84

1. How many data items are there?

2. What is the least measurement given?

3. What is the greatest measurement given?

4. In how many games did the team score less than 70 baskets?

5. Draw a stem-and-leaf plot for the set of data.

science test scores:	83	73	78	60	85
	92	95	85	99	68

Use the stem-and-leaf plot from Exercise 5 to answer Exercises 6–8.

6. Find the mode of the test scores.

7. How many data items are in the set?

8. Find the mean of the test scores.

9. You have a spreadsheet showing how many DVDs people bought in 1998, 2000, and 2002. The spreadsheet also shows how many videocassettes were bought in 1998, 2000, and 2002. Which is the most effective data display choice: a double line graph or a stem-and-leaf plot? Explain your answer.

Name ____________________ Class ____________ Date ____________

11-3 • Guided Problem Solving

GPS Student Page 546, Exercise 8:

Height How many males are 65 in. tall?

Student Height (in.)

Female	Stem	Male
7 4 3 1 0 0	5	6 7
8 5 4 1 0	6	2 3 5 5 6 7 9
0	7	1 2 3 4 6

Key: 61 ← 1 | 6 | 3 → 63

Understand

1. What data does the stem-and-leaf plot display?

2. What is the question asking you to find?

Plan and Carry Out

3. Circle the part of the stem-and-leaf plot that pertains to males.
4. According to the key, what place value do the numbers on the right have?

5. According to the key, what place value do the numbers between the stems have?

6. Underline the row that has a 6 in the tens place.
7. Circle the fives in the row you underlined in Step 6.
8. Count the number of fives you circled in the male half of the stem-and-leaf plot. How many males are 65 in. tall?

Check

9. Write out the heights of all of the males in the stem-and-leaf plot. Count the number of males who are 65 in. tall.

Solve Another Problem

10. In the stem-and-leaf plot at the right, how many female students scored 91 on their test?

Test Scores

Female	Stem	Male
0	5	
7	6	1 3
9 4	7	6 8
9 6 1 1	8	2 8 8 9 9
3 1 1 1 1 0	9	2 2 9

Key: 79 ← 9 | 7 | 3 → 73

Name ______________________ Class ______________ Date ______________

Practice 11-3

Stem-and-Leaf Plots

The stem-and-leaf plot at the right shows the number of baskets scored by one of ten intramural teams last season. Use it for Exercises 1–3.

5	2	6	9
6	0	4	6
7	1	5	
8	4	8	

8|4 means 84

1. How many data items are there?

____

2. What is the least measurement given?

____

3. In how many games did the team score less than 70 baskets?

____

4. Draw a stem-and-leaf plot for the set of data.

science test scores:	83	73	78	60	85
	92	95	85	99	68

Use the stem-and-leaf plot from Exercise 4 to answer Exercises 5–7.

5. Find the mode of the test scores.

____

6. Find the mean of the test scores.

____

7. You have a spreadsheet showing how many DVDs people bought in 1998, 2000, and 2002. The spreadsheet also shows how many videocassettes were bought in 1998, 2000, and 2002. Which is the most effective data display choice: a double line graph or a stem-and-leaf plot? Explain your answer.

____

____

____

____

Name ______________________ Class ______________ Date ______________

Activity Lab 11-3

Stem-and-Leaf Plots

Jackie is training for a triathlon. Each day she bikes in the morning and runs in the evening. She created a stem-and-leaf plot showing the distances she ran and biked for the past 12 days.

Distance (miles) Traveled in Workout

Running		Cycling
5 4 2 0	1	7 8 9
2 1 0 0 0	2	0 1 3 3 5
3 2 1	3	0 4 5
	4	2

Key: 4.3 ← 3 | 4 | 1 → 4.1

1. In the plot above, what do the stem values represent? What do the leaf values represent?

____

2. What is the greatest distance Jackie bicycled in a day? __________

3. What is the least distance she ran in one day? __________

4. Examine the data for Jackie's cycling workouts. What is the mode of this data set?

____

5. What is the mean distance traveled during Jackie's running workouts?

____

6. What is the range of the entire data set? __________

7. What are some advantages to organizing data in a stem-and-leaf plot? Explain.

____

____

8. Jackie created the stem-and-leaf plot from the data below. Think of another way she could have organized and displayed the data. What are the advantages and disadvantages of your method? Explain.

____

____

	Day 1	Day 2	Day 3	Day 4	Day 5	Day 6	Day 7	Day 8	Day 9	Day 10	Day 11	Day 12
Running (miles)	1.2	1.0	1.4	1.5	2.2	2.0	2.0	2.1	3.1	2.0	3.2	3.3
Cycling (miles)	1.8	1.9	2.3	2.0	1.7	2.1	2.3	3.0	2.5	3.5	3.4	4.2

Name ______________________ Class ______________ Date ______________

Reteaching 11-3

Stem-and-Leaf Plots

Make a **stem-and-leaf plot** of the summer earnings data.

① Make a column of the tens digits of the data in order from least to greatest. These are the stems.

② Record the ones digits for each tens digit in order from least to greatest. These are the leaves.

③ Make a *key* to explain what the stems and leaves represent.

Summer Earnings					
$35	$35	$38	$15	$52	$40
$20	$23	$56	$12	$14	$58

① stems

```
1 |
2 |
3 |
4 |
5 |
```

② leaves

```
1 | 2 4 5
2 | 0 3
3 | 5 5 8
4 | 0
5 | 2 6 8
```

③ 1 | 2 means 12

---

1. Complete the stem-and-leaf plot of this set of data.

24	36	64	42	59
61	16	63	54	39
36	45	15	27	51

```
1 | _ _
2 | 4 _
3 | 6 _ _
4 | _ _
5 | _ _ _
6 | _ _ _
```

1 | 5 means ___

Use the stem-and-leaf plot from Exercise 1 to answer Exercises 2–5.

2. What place value are the stems?

____

3. What place value are the leaves?

____

4. What is the highest value of the data set?

____

5. What is the lowest value of the data set?

____

6. Brandy recorded these high temperatures for two weeks in July. Make a stem-and-leaf plot of her data.

92	86	91	90	85
82	84	78	79	83
84	89	86	87	

Name ______________________ Class ______________ Date ______________

Enrichment 11-3

Stem-and-Leaf Plots

Critical Thinking

This back-to-back stem-and-leaf plot shows the average daily April temperatures for Boston, MA, and Portland, OR. Use the plot to compare the pattern of April temperatures in the two cities.

Boston, MA		Portland, OR
	7	1
2 2	6	0 0 0 1 1 1 1 2 3 3 4 5
9 8 7 7 7 5 3 3 1 1 1 0	5	2 5 5 5 6 6 6 7 8 9 9
8 8 8 7 4 4 2 2 0 0	4	2 2 3 4 4 5
6 6 4 3 3 0	3	

1. What do the digits in the stem represent?

____

2. Which leaves, those on the right or those on the left, show temperatures for each city?

   a. Portland ____________ b. Boston ____________

3. The lowest temperature for Boston was 30°. The highest temperature was 62°. For Portland, what was the

   a. lowest temperature? ____________ b. highest temperature? ____________

4. How many more days was the temperature in the 60s and 70s in Portland than in Boston?

____

5. Write a sentence comparing the temperature patterns for the two cities.

____

____

6. How can you compare the pattern without comparing the actual temperatures?

____

____

____

____

Name ______________________ Class ______________ Date ______________

11B: Reading Comprehension

For use after Lesson 11-3

Study Skill Take short breaks between assignments.

Read the paragraph and answer the questions.

In 1945, the first electronic computer was built. ENIAC, which stands for Electronic Numerical Integrator and Calculator, was able to do 5,000 additions per second. Current computers are capable of doing 100,000 times as many additions per second. ENIAC weighed approximately 30 tons and had a length of 40 feet and a width of 45 feet. Present-day computer notebooks weigh about 3 pounds. Unlike modern computers, which use microprocessors composed of thousands or millions of transistors, ENIAC used vacuum tubes to process data. It had about 18,000 tubes, each the size of a small light bulb.

1. What does the acronym ENIAC stand for?

____

2. How many years ago was ENIAC built?

____

3. How many additions could ENIAC perform per second?

____

4. How many additions per second do current computers perform?

____

5. How much area did ENIAC cover?

____

6 How many pounds did ENIAC weigh?

____

7. How many times more does ENIAC weigh than today's notebook computers?

____

8. What do today's modern computers use to process data?

____

9. **High-Use Academic Words** In Exercise 1, what does the word *acronym* mean?

   a. a certain way in which something appears

   b. a word formed from the first letters of several other words

Name ________________________ Class ________________ Date ______________

Puzzle 11-3

Stem-and-Leaf Plots

Jonas is an avid birdwatcher. During his last 16 birding adventures, he has kept track of the number of birds he has seen each day:

Day	1	2	3	4	5	6	7	8	9	10	11	12	13	14	15	16
Number of birds observed	15	33	16	26	23	51	47	32	37	40	55	15	53	56	32	28

Organize this data in the stem-and-leaf plot below. Then write the values recorded in the □ boxes to discover an interesting state fact.

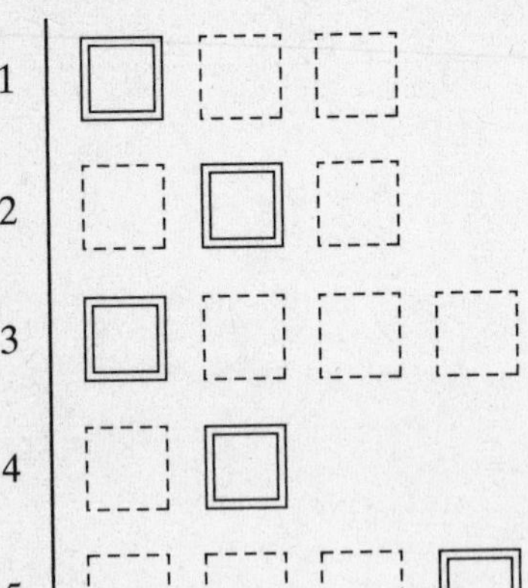

Key 1|5 = 15 birds

The area of the state of Iowa is ______ ______ ______ ______ ______ mi^2.
Leaf 1 Leaf 2 Leaf 3 Leaf 4 Leaf 5

Name ____________________ Class ____________ Date ____________

Practice 11-4

Random Samples and Surveys

You want to survey students in your school about their exercise habits. Tell whether the situations described in Exercises 1 and 2 are likely to give a random sample of the population. Explain.

1. You select every tenth student on an alphabetical list of the students in your school. You survey the selected students in their first-period classes.

2. At lunchtime you stand by a vending machine. You survey every student who buys something from the vending machine.

Is each question *biased* or *fair*? Rewrite biased questions as fair questions.

3. Do you think bike helmets should be mandatory for all bike riders?

4. Do you prefer the natural beauty of hardwood floors in your home?

5. Do you exercise regularly?

6. Do you eat at least the recommended number of servings of fruits and vegetables to ensure a healthy and long life?

7. Do you prefer the look and feel of thick lush carpeting in your living room?

8. Do you take a daily multiple vitamin to supplement your diet?

9. Do you read the newspaper to be informed about world events?

10. Do you feel that the TV news is a sensational portrayal of life's problems?

Name ____________________ Class ______________ Date ______________

11-4 • Guided Problem Solving

GPS Student Page 553, Exercise 19:

Parks Suppose you are gathering information about visitors to Yosemite National Park. You survey every tenth person entering the park. Would you get a random sample of visitors? Explain.

Understand

1. What is a random sample?

____

____

2. What are you being asked to do?

____

____

Plan and Carry Out

3. What is the population you are surveying?

____

4. Does every person in the population have an equal chance of being surveyed?

____

5. Is this a random sample? Why or why not?

____

____

Check

6. How else could you randomly survey the people at Yosemite National Park?

____

____

Solve Another Problem

7. You want to survey the people at the local pool about the food served in the snack shack. You decide to walk around the kiddy pool and survey parents. Is this a random sample? Why or why not?

____

____

Name ______________________ Class ______________ Date ______________

Practice 11-4

Random Samples and Surveys

You want to survey students in your school about their exercise habits. Tell whether the situations described in Exercises 1 and 2 are likely to give a random sample of the population. Explain.

1. You select every tenth student on an alphabetical list of the students in your school. You survey the selected students in their first-period classes.

____

____

2. At lunchtime you stand by a vending machine. You survey every student who buys something from the vending machine.

____

____

Is each question *biased* or *fair*? Rewrite biased questions as fair questions.

3. Do you think bike helmets should be mandatory for all bike riders?

____

____

4. Do you prefer the natural beauty of hardwood floors in your home?

____

____

5. Do you exercise regularly?

____

____

6. Do you eat at least the recommended number of servings of fruits and vegetables to ensure a healthy and long life?

____

____

7. Do you prefer the look and feel of thick lush carpeting in your living room?

____

____

Name ______________________ Class ______________ Date ______________

Activity Lab 11-4

Random Samples and Surveys

Sample size may influence the predictions you make.

Suppose your class is asked to choose the type of music to play after school over the PA system. As a leader of the group, you appoint Jeff and Carla to survey students in the middle school to find what type of music they prefer.

Jeff surveyed 4 students. Of these students, 3 out of 4 preferred country music and 1 preferred rock music. So Jeff reported: $P(\text{country music}) = \frac{3}{4}$ and $P(\text{rock music}) = \frac{1}{4}$.

Carla surveyed 35 students. Of these students, 10 students chose country music, 13 chose rock, 9 chose rhythm and blues, and 3 chose jazz. So Carla reported: $P(\text{country music}) = \frac{2}{7}$, $P(\text{rock music}) = \frac{13}{35}$, $P(\text{rhythm and blues}) = \frac{9}{35}$, and $P(\text{jazz}) = \frac{3}{35}$.

1. Which survey do you think is a more accurate reflection of the preferences of students in the school? Explain.

____

____

____

2. What could you do to ensure a more accurate survey?

____

____

____

3. Which type of music would you recommend to be played after school?

____

____

____

4. Suppose the principal authorizes you to buy 100 music CDs. About how many of each type would you buy, based on Carla's survey?

____

____

Name ______________________________ Class ____________________ Date ____________________

Reteaching 11-4

Random Samples and Surveys

Carlos is curious about sports that students in his school like best. He cannot interview every student in the school. But he could interview a sample of the school **population.**

Carlos wants a **random sample.** A sample is random if everyone has an equal chance of being selected. How will Carlos get a random sample? He considers two possibilities:

- He can interview 30 students at a soccer game.
- He can interview 5 students in each of 6 class changes.

Carlos realizes that students at a soccer game probably like soccer better than other sports. That would not be a random sample. He decides on the interviews during class changes.

What question will he ask? He considers two possibilities:

- "Which sport do you prefer, football, soccer, baseball, or tennis?"
- "Which do you enjoy most, the slow sport of baseball or one of the more exciting sports like football, soccer, or tennis?"

The second question is **biased.** It makes one answer seem better than another. Carlos decides to ask the first question.

---

1. You want to find how many people in your community are vegetarian. Where would be the best place to take a survey?

   ____

Is each question biased or fair?

2. Will you vote for the young, inexperienced candidate, Mr. Soong, or the experienced candidate, Ms. Lopez? ____________________

3. Will you vote for Mr. Soong or Ms. Lopez? ____________________

You plan to survey people to see what percent own their home and what percent rent. Tell whether the following will give a random sample. Explain.

4. You interview people outside a pool supply store in the suburbs.

   ____

5. You interview people in the street near an apartment complex.

   ____

6. You mail a survey to every 20th person in the telephone book.

   ____

Name ______________________ Class ______________ Date ____________

Enrichment 11-4

Random Samples and Surveys

Designing a Survey

The organizers of a youth troop in Dallas, Texas, plan to print some brochures to target young people in their community. To find out what images and activities appeal to the young people, the youth group plans to take a survey.

1. Who is the population of the survey?

____

2. Why do the organizers want to know which images and activities appeal to the target population?

____

____

3. The organizers discover that a similar survey has already been taken in a rural Pennsylvania community. Should they use the results of that survey instead of taking a new survey? Explain.

____

____

4. The survey needs to be fair and not biased. Write two possible survey questions that might suggest bias.

____

____

____

____

5. Suggest two ways that the organizers can survey a random sample of the intended population.

____

____

____

6. From the data, can the organizers make exact conclusions about the population, or estimate conclusions? Explain.

____

____

____

Name ______________________ Class ______________ Date ______________

11C: Reading/Writing Math Symbols

For use after Lesson 11-4

Study Skill Make a realistic study schedule. Plan ahead when your teacher assigns a long-term project.

Some mathematical symbols have multiple meanings. Explain the meaning of the bar (–) in each of the following.

1. $2.\overline{3}$ ______________________
2. $11 - 15$ ______________________
3. $\overline{GH}$ ______________________
4. $3 + (-7)$ ______________________
5. $\frac{1}{5}$ ______________________

The bar (–) takes on different meanings when used with other symbols. Explain the meaning of each symbol below.

6. $=$ ______________________
7. $\leq$ ______________________
8. $\cong$ ______________________
9. $\overset{?}{=}$ ______________________
10. $\neq$ ______________________

When they are vertical, the bars also take on different meanings. Explain the meaning of these symbols.

11. $|\ \ |$, as in $|-3| = 3$

____

12. $\|$, as in $m \parallel n$

____

Name ______________________ Class ______________ Date ____________

Puzzle 11-4

Random Samples and Surveys

Match each set of surveys and questions on the left with the descriptions on the right. Then use your answers to solve each puzzle.

(8) You survey 200 7th graders to find out how tall the average 7th grade student is.	A. Uses a random sample
(7) Do you prefer shiny blond hair or plain brown hair?	B. Does not use a random sample
(1) You survey the 7th grade basketball team to find out how tall the average 7th grade student is.	C. This question is biased
(7) Whom do you admire?	D. This question is not biased

Delaware, the first of the original thirteen colonies, became the first state on December 7, ___ ___ ___ ___.
B C A D

(3) The art club wants to find out what kind of art 8th grade students like. They survey the students in the 5th period art class.	A. Uses a random sample
(1) Do you admire tall people or ordinary short people?	B. Does not use a random sample
(8) The art club wants to find out what kind of art 8th grade students like. They survey half the students at the 8th grade assembly.	C. This question is biased
(6) What kind of art do you like the least?	D. This question is not biased

The twenty-fifth state, Arkansas, became a state on June 15, ___ ___ ___ ___.
C A B D

(9) You want to know how 7th grade students spend their free time. You ask 6 of your friends to survey at least 5 people they know.	A. Uses a random sample
(9) What do you usually do on Saturday?	B. Does not use a random sample
(1) You want to know how 7th grade students spend their free time. You ask 6 of your teachers to survey at least 5 of their classes.	C. This question is biased
(5) Do you watch TV on Saturday like everyone else?	D. This question is not biased

Hawaii, the 50th state, joined the union on August 21, ___ ___ ___ ___.
A D C B

Name ______________________ Class ______________ Date ______________

Practice 11-5

Estimating Population Size

Workers at a state park caught, tagged, and set free the species shown at the right. Later that same year, the workers caught the number of animals shown in the table below and counted the tagged animals. Use a proportion to estimate the park population of each species.

Tagged Animals

Bears	12
Squirrels	50
Raccoons	23
Rabbits	42
Trout	46
Skunks	21

	Caught	Counted Tagged	Estimated Population
1. Bears	30	9	
2. Squirrels	1,102	28	
3. Raccoons	412	10	
4. Rabbits	210	2	
5. Trout	318	25	
6. Skunks	45	6	

A park ranger tags 100 animals. Use a proportion to estimate the total population for each sample.

7. 23 out of 100 animals are tagged

____

8. 12 out of 75 animals are tagged

____

9. 8 out of 116 animals are tagged

____

10. 5 out of 63 animals are tagged

____

11. 4 out of 83 animals are tagged

____

12. 3 out of 121 animals are tagged

____

13. 83 out of 125 animals are tagged

____

14. 7 out of 165 animals are tagged

____

Use a proportion to estimate each animal population.

15. Total ducks counted: 1,100
Marked ducks counted: 257
Total marked ducks: 960

____

16. Total alligators counted: 310
Marked alligators counted: 16
Total marked alligators: 90

____

Name ______________________ Class ______________ Date ______________

11-5 • Guided Problem Solving

GPS Student Page 556, Exercise 19:

Sharks A biologist is studying the shark populaton off the Florida coast. He captures, tags, and sets free 38 sharks. A week later, 8 out of 25 sharks captured have tags. He uses the proportion $\frac{25}{8} = \frac{38}{x}$ to estimate that the population is about 12.

a. **Error Analysis** Find the error in the biologist's proportion.

b. Estimate the shark population.

Understand

1. What are you being asked to do?

____

Plan and Carry Out

2. If x represents all the sharks off the coast of Florida, write the ratio of the sharks the biologist originally tagged to the number of all the sharks off the coast of Florida. ________

3. How many sharks did the biologist capture the second time? How many were tagged? ____________

4. Write a ratio comparing the sharks the biologist found tagged and the number that were captured the second time. ______

5. Set the ratios from Steps 2 and 4 equal to form the correct proportion. ____________

6. What is wrong with the biologist's proportion? ____________

7. Solve this proportion to find the correct estimate. ____________

Check

8. Explain why the biologist should have known the estimate was wrong.

____

____

Solve Another Problem

9. A ranger traps, tags, and releases 32 jackrabbits. Later she captures 12 jackrabbits, of which 4 are tagged. The ranger estimates that there are 96 jackrabbits in the area. Write a proportion and check the ranger's estimate. Is she correct?

____

Name ______________________ Class ______________ Date ______________

Practice 11-5

Estimating Population Size

Workers at a state park caught, tagged, and set free the species shown at the right. Later that same year, the workers caught the number of animals shown in the table below and counted the tagged animals. Use a proportion to estimate the park population of each species.

Tagged Animals

Bears	12
Squirrels	50
Raccoons	23
Rabbits	42
Trout	46

	Caught	Counted Tagged	Estimated Population
1. Bears	30	9	
2. Squirrels	1,102	28	
3. Raccoons	412	10	
4. Rabbits	210	2	
5. Trout	318	25	

A park ranger tags 100 animals. Use a proportion to estimate the total population for each sample.

6. 23 out of 100 animals are tagged

____

7 12 out of 75 animals are tagged

____

8. 8 out of 116 animals are tagged

____

9. 5 out of 63 animals are tagged

____

10. 4 out of 83 animals are tagged

____

11. 3 out of 121 animals are tagged

____

Use a proportion to estimate each animal population.

Use a proportion to estimate each animal population.

12. Total ducks counted: 1,100
Marked ducks counted: 257
Total marked ducks: 960

____

13. Total alligators counted: 310
Marked alligators counted: 16
Total marked alligators: 90

____

Name ______________________ Class ______________ Date ______________

Activity Lab 11-5

Estimating Population Size

Materials needed: 100 beads in 4 colors, paper bag

1. Copy the table below. List the colors of your beads in place of the labels Color A, Color B, Color C, and Color D.

	10 Beads	First Prediction	25 Beads	Second Prediction	50 Beads	Third Prediction	Actual Amount
Color A							
Color B							
Color C							
Color D							

2. a. Place all the beads in the paper bag. These beads represent the population. Without looking, draw 10 beads from the bag. The 10 beads are a random sample of the population.

b. Record the number of beads of each color in the column labeled "10 Beads."

c. Based on the number of beads of each color in your sample, predict the number of beads of each color in the population. Since there are 100 beads in the population, multiply the numbers in your sample by 10. For example, if there are 3 beads of Color A in your sample, you can predict that there are 3×10, or 30 beads of Color A in the population. Write your predictions in the column labeled "First Prediction."

d. Put all the beads back in the bag.

3. a. Without looking, draw 25 beads from the bag as a random sample. Record the amount of each color in the table.

b. Fill in the column labeled "Second Prediction" by multiplying each amount by 4. For example, if there are 3 beads of Color A in your sample, you can predict that there are 3×4, or 12 beads of Color A in the population.

c. Return all the beads to the bag.

4. Repeat Step 3, drawing 50 beads from the bag. Fill in the column labeled "Third Prediction" by multiplying the amounts by 2.

5. Which of your predictions would you expect to be closest to the actual total? Explain.

6. a. Fill in the last column in the table by counting the number of beads of each color in the population.

b. How do your predictions compare to the actual total?

c. What are some of the reasons you might want to draw a large, random sample to make predictions about a population? What are some disadvantages of a large random sample?

Name ______________________ Class ______________ Date ______________

Reteaching 11-5

Estimating Population Size

Researchers tagged 100 fish in a pond and then released them back into the pond. Later they captured 60 fish and found that 3 were tagged. Estimate the number of fish in the pond.

① Write a proportion of tagged fish to total fish.

$$\frac{\text{tagged fish (pond)}}{\text{total fish (pond)}} = \frac{\text{tagged fish (sample)}}{\text{total fish (sample)}}$$

$$\frac{100}{n} = \frac{3}{60}$$

② Write cross products. $3n = 6{,}000$

③ Solve. $n = 2{,}000$

There are about 2,000 fish in the pond.

Complete to estimate the number of deer in the woods.

1. One year researchers tagged 80 deer. They later captured 15 deer and found 5 were tagged. Estimate the number of deer in the woods.

   $\frac{80}{n} = \frac{\square}{\square}$

   $5n = 15 \cdot$ __________

   $n =$ __________

   There are about __________ deer.

2. Two years later, researchers tagged 45 deer. They later captured 20 and found 3 were tagged. Estimate the number of deer in the woods then.

   $\frac{\square}{n} = \frac{\square}{20}$

   $3n =$ __________

   $n =$ __________

   There are about __________ deer.

Use a proportion to estimate each animal population.

3. In another project, researchers caught and tagged 85 sea lions in a bay. Later they caught and released 50 sea lions. Of those, 9 had tags. Estimate the sea lion population in the bay.

   ____

4. Other researchers caught and tagged 5 spotted owls. Later they caught 7 owls. Of those, 4 were tagged. Estimate the number of spotted owls in that forest.

   ____

5. An ecology class helped researchers determine the rabbit population in a nature preserve. One weekend, the students captured, tagged, and set free 32 rabbits. A month later, they captured 27 rabbits, including 16 with tags. Estimate the number of rabbits in the nature preserve.

   ____

Name ______________________ Class ______________ Date ______________

Enrichment 11-5

Estimating Population Size

Visual Thinking

The main purpose of the United States Census Bureau is to collect and secure general statistical information. The first U.S. census was taken in 1790. The census counted 3.9 million people.

The table to the right shows the population of people residing in the states in 2000. In the year 2000, the census estimated the total population within the United States at 281,421,906.

U.S. Resident Population 2000	
Iowa	2,926,324
Kansas	2,688,418
Kentucky	4,041,769
Louisiana	4,468,976
Maine	1,274,923
Maryland	5,296,486
Massachusetts	6,349,097
Michigan	9,938,444
Minnesota	4,919,479
Mississippi	2,844,658

1. Suppose that in Michigan, 450 16-year-old students were given an identification card. A month later, at a public gathering of 200 students, only 3 had identification cards. Estimate the number of 16-year-old students in the state of Michigan.

   ____

2. From 1990 to 2000, census officials saw a population growth of about 5.9% in the state of Louisiana. If the growth rate for Louisiana stays about the same for the next decade, estimate the population of Louisiana in 2010.

   ____

3. From 1990 to 2000, census officials saw a population growth of about 12.4% in the state of Minnesota. Estimate the population of Minnesota in 1990.

   ____

4. In the year 1990, the population of the United States was recorded as 32,712,033 fewer people than in the year 2000. What was the total population recorded in 1990? Use this information to calculate a percent increase and then estimate the population size of the U.S. in 2010.

   ____

   ____

   ____

Name ________________ Class ________________ Date ________________

Puzzle 11-5

Estimating Population Size

Marine biologists at Inlet Bay keep data on the groups, or pods, of dolphins that visit the Bay. The Bay water is murky and since the dolphins in a pod do not surface to breathe at the same time, getting an accurate count is difficult. By attaching electronic tags to some members of each pod, the biologists are able to get more accurate counts. The table below shows data from observations of nine pods. Use the information to estimate the population of each pod.

Pod	Dolphins Sighted	Tagged Dolphins Sighted	Total Tagged Dolphins	Population Estimate for Pod
1	8	5	10	____ h
2	10	6	12	____ o
3	4	3	9	____ e
4	6	3	9	____ a
5	6	2	7	____ l
6	5	3	9	____ c
7	4	2	11	____ n
8	12	8	16	____ i
9	4	2	7	____ t

Use your answers to find out how dolphins navigate.

Dolphins navigate by using __ __ __ __ __ __ __ __ __ __ __ __ .

12 15 16 20 21 20 15 18 14 24 20 22

Name ______________________ Class ______________ Date ______________

Practice 11-6

Using Data to Persuade

The table below shows the number of students enrolled in swimming classes for 2001 to 2003.

1. Use the data to create a double line graph that emphasizes the increase in the number of students enrolled in summer swim classes.

Swim Class Enrollment

Year	Boys	Girls
2001	375	360
2002	400	395
2003	410	420

2. Use the data again to create a second double line graph that does not emphasize the increase in the number of students enrolled in the summer swim classes.

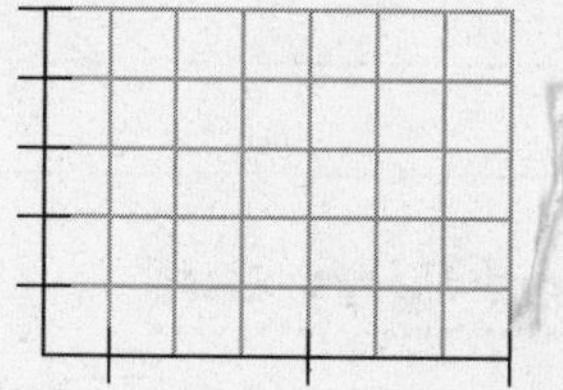

3. Which graph could be used to request additional reserved times for swim classes at the pool?

____

____

Vince has the following scores on chapter tests in his math class. Use this data in Exercises 4–6.

95 89 83 90 83

4. Find the mean, median, and mode of his test scores.

____

5. Should Vince describe his tests using the mean, the median, or the mode to show his ability to do well in math?

____

____

6. Should his teacher use the mean, the median, or the mode to encourage Vince to check his work carefully on the next test?

____

____

Name ____________ Class ____________ Date ____________

11-6 • Guided Problem Solving

GPS Student Page 564, Exercise 19:

Writing in Math Spotless Cleaners sends out 200 customer surveys. The company gets 100 replies with 97 customers saying they are satisfied. In an ad, Spotless Cleaners says that 97% of its customers are satisfied. Is this statement misleading? Explain.

Understand

1. What statement does Spotless Cleaners make?

____

2. What are you being asked to do?

____

____

Plan and Carry Out

3. How many surveys did Spotless Cleaners send out? ____________

4. How many replies did Spotless Cleaners get back? ____________

5. Did Spotless Cleaners represent all of the surveys they sent out in their ad? ____________

6. How many surveys did Spotless Cleaners not report? ____________

7. Is this statement misleading? Why? ____________

____

Check

8. Using the correct sample size, 200, what percentage of customers does the data represent? ____________

Solve Another Problem

9. Students can receive either Advanced, Proficient, or Basic on the state standardized test. The local newspaper reports that only 30% of the students passed the state standardized test at the proficient level. How does this statement mislead its readers?

____

____

____

Name ______________________ Class ______________ Date ______________

Practice 11-6

Using Data to Persuade

The table below shows the number of students enrolled in swimming classes for 2001 to 2003.

1. Use the data to create a double line graph that emphasizes the increase in the number of students enrolled in summer swim classes.

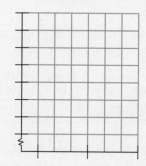

Swim Class Enrollment

Year	Boys	Girls
2001	375	360
2002	400	395
2003	410	420

2. Use the data again to create a second double line graph that does not emphasize the increase in the number of students enrolled in the summer swim classes.

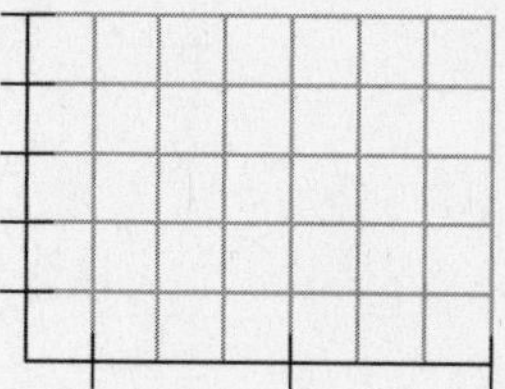

Vince has the following scores on chapter tests in his math class. Use this data in Exercises 3 and 4.

95 89 83 90 83

3. Find the mean, median, and mode of his test scores.

____

4. Should Vince describe his tests using the mean, the median, or the mode to show his ability to do well in math?

____

____

Name ______________________ Class ______________ Date ______________

Activity Lab 11-6

Using Data to Persuade

Population Growth

The table below shows the population of the United States that was recorded in each national census from 1950 to 2000.

Year	1950	1960	1970	1980	1990	2000
Population (millions)	151	179	203	226	248	281

1. Using the data in the table, create a bar graph below. Your horizontal scale should start with 1950 and increase in increments of 10 years. Your vertical scale should start at zero and increase in increments of 50.

2. Using the data in the table, construct another bar graph. This time, begin your vertical scale at 150 and increase in increments of 30.

3. Which graph seems to show a more rapid increase in population between 1950 and 2000? Why is this?

____

____

____

____

Name ______________________ Class ______________ Date ____________

Reteaching 11-6

Using Data to Persuade

There are 3 ways that graphs can be drawn to be misleading.

1. The interval on the vertical axis may not start at zero.
2. There may be a break in the graph.
3. The intervals on the horizontal or vertical axis may be unequal.

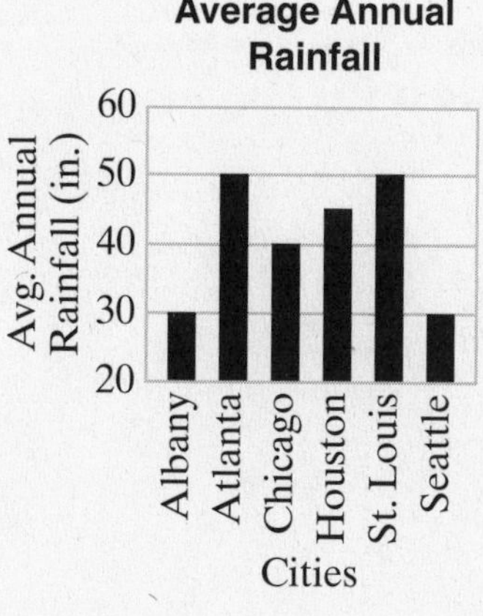

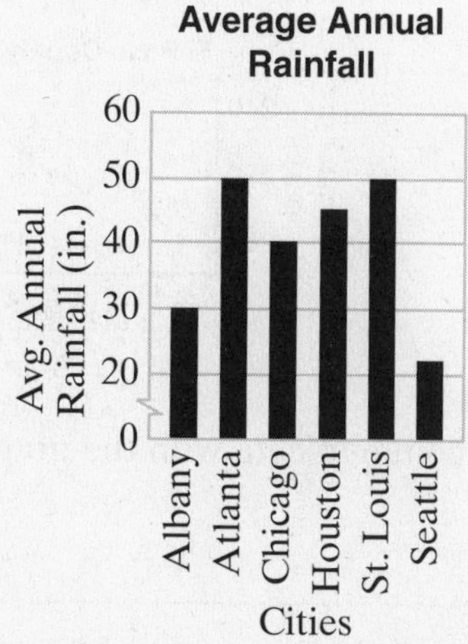

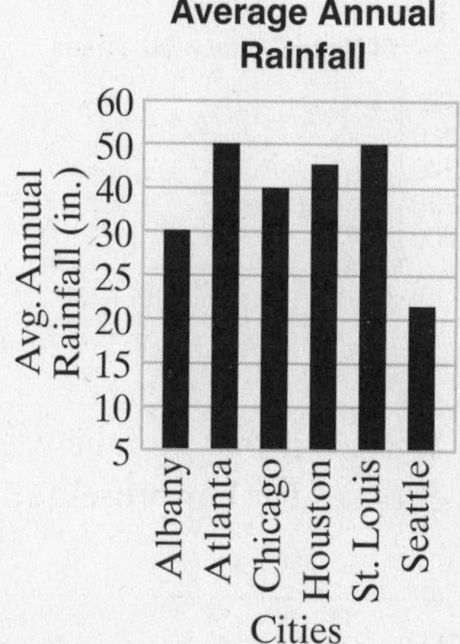

Mean, median, and mode can also be used to mislead. Consider a set of data where most of the numbers are in a certain range. There are a few numbers that are either way above or way below the range. The mean is not a good measure of the data in this case.

For each graph, do the following:
(a) Tell what the graph shows. (b) What can you say about the graph?

1.

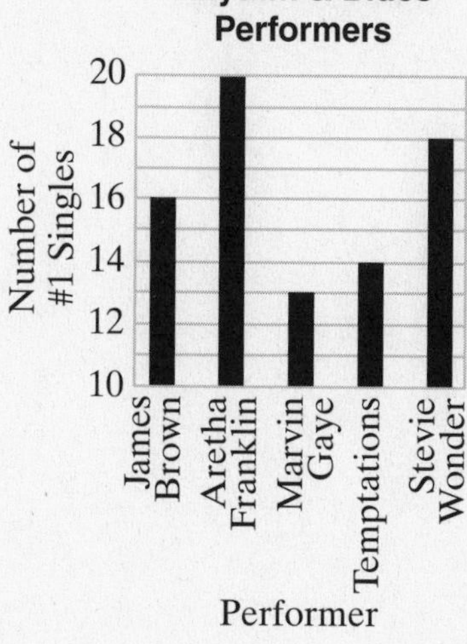

2.

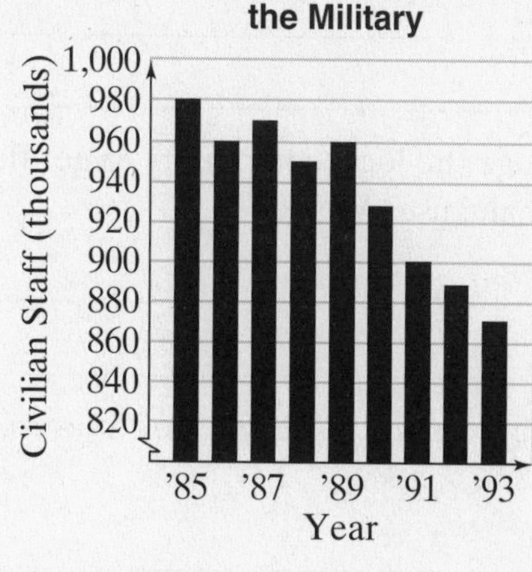

______________________ ______________________

______________________ ______________________

______________________ ______________________

______________________ ______________________

______________________ ______________________

Name ______________________ Class ______________ Date ______________

Enrichment 11-6

Using Data to Persuade

Decision Making

Amalia Ruiz works for the El Paso County Health Department. Each of the graphs below shows the number of reported flu cases during a ten-year period. Which of the graphs should she use to encourage getting flu shots? Why?

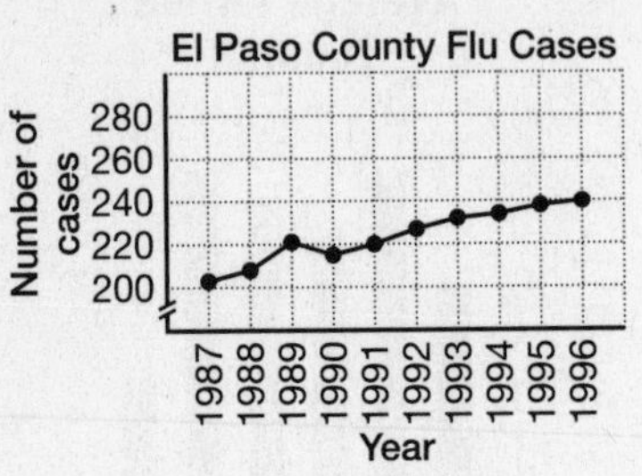

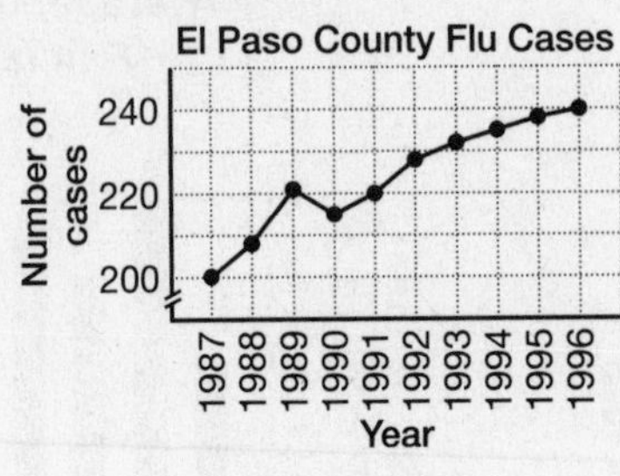

1. What is it that Amalia wishes to communicate with the graph she chooses for her presentation?

   ____

2. What type of change does the graph on the left show?

   ____

3. What type of change does the graph on the right show?

   ____

4. Which graph would tend to imply that the incidence of flu is increasing dramatically? Why?

   ____

   ____

5. To encourage the local community to get flu shots, which graph should Amalia use? Why?

   ____

   ____

6. In reality, how many more cases of flu were reported in 1996 than in 1987?

   ____

7. Explain why the second graph appears to show more of a dramatic increase than the first graph.

   ____

   ____

   ____

Name ______________________ Class ______________ Date ______________

Puzzle 11-6

Using Data to Persuade

The graph below shows the average high temperature for four weeks in September at a beach resort.

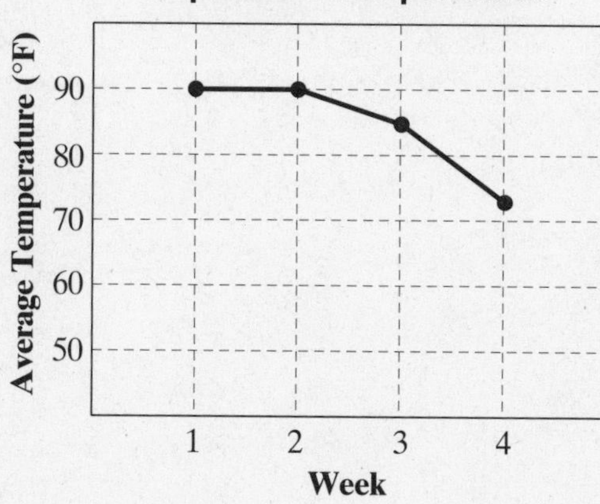

Read the situations shown in the first column below and match each situation to a misleading use of the information from the graph, shown in the second column.

1. A prospective client enjoys the beach when the temperature is in the nineties.
2. A potential client likes the beach when the temperature is neither too hot nor too cool.
3. A client is looking for a vacation where the temperature will reflect the changing season.
4. A client would like a vacation where the average temperature is less than 80°F.

A. The sales agent mentions the mean temperature for all of September.

B. The sales agent uses only the data for Week 4.

C. The sales agent uses the mode to describe the average daily temperature.

D. The sales agent uses the downward trend of the data on the graph to represent the approach of cooling temperatures.

Name ______________________ Class ______________ Date ______________

Practice 11-7

Exploring Scatter Plots

Tell what trend you would expect to see in scatter plots comparing the sets of data in Exercises 1–4. Explain your reasoning.

1. a person's height and the person's shoe size

____

____

2. the age of a child and amount of weekly allowance that the child receives

____

____

3. the distance one lives from school and the length of the school day

____

____

4. the average number of hours a child sleeps and the age of the child

____

____

5. Make a scatter plot of the following data. Does the scatter plot show any trend? If so, what?

____

Number of Hours of Practice	Number of Successful Free Throws out of 10
6	3
7	5
8	6
9	6
10	7
11	7
12	6
13	7

Describe the trend in each scatter plot.

6.

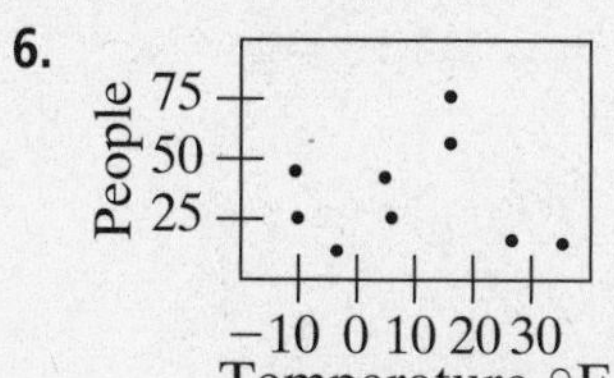

____

7.

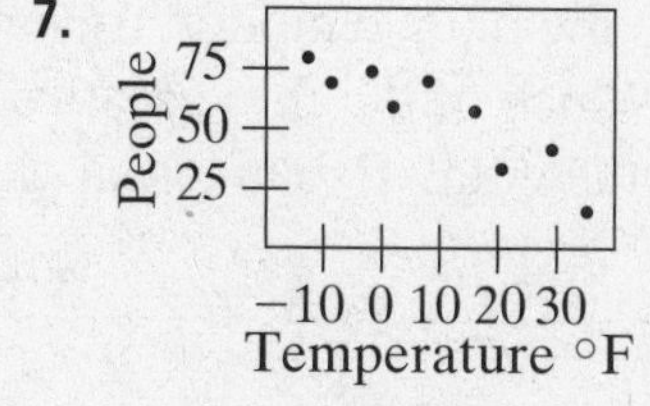

____

8.

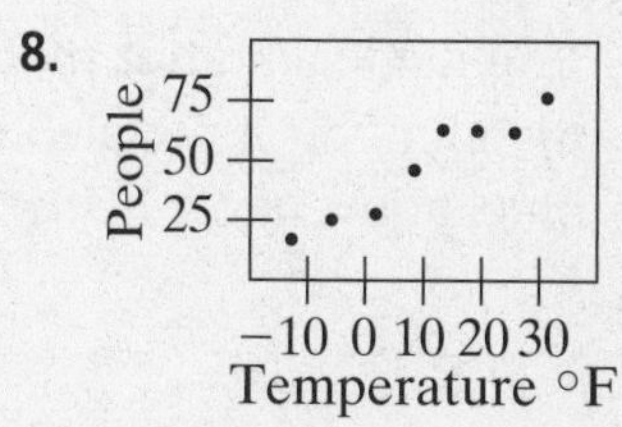

____

Name ______________________ Class ______________ Date ______________

11-7 • Guided Problem Solving

GPS Student Page 570, Exercise 16:

Carmella made a scatter plot comparing the daily temperature and the number of people at a beach. Which of the three scatter plots most likely represents the data? Explain your choice.

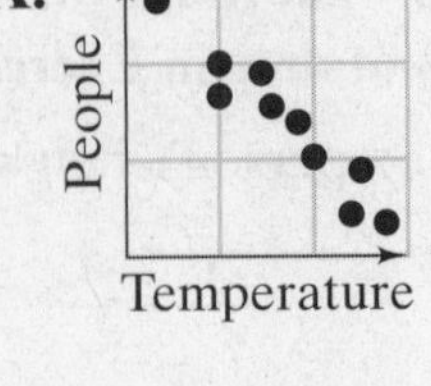

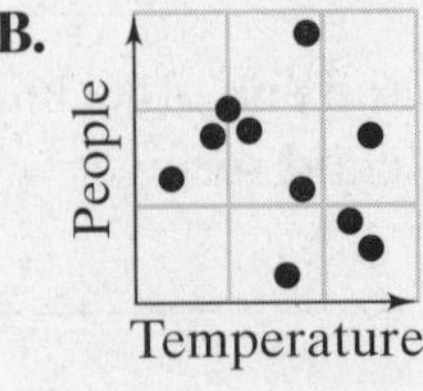

C.
People
Temperature

Understand

1. What two variables do the scatter plots relate?

____

2. What are you asked to do?

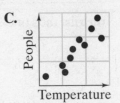

____

____

Plan and Carry Out

3. What does the scatter plot in choice A indicate?

____

4. What does the scatter plot in choice B indicate?

____

____

5. What does the scatter plot in choice C indicate?

____

6. Which of the three choices most likely represents the data?

____

Check

7. Explain your answer to Step 6.

____

____

Solve Another Problem

8. You made a scatter plot comparing the daily temperature and the number of people at the mall. Which of the three scatter plots above most likely represents the data? Explain your choice.

____

____

Name ______________________ Class ______________ Date ______________

Practice 11-7

Exploring Scatter Plots

Tell what trend you would expect to see in scatter plots comparing the sets of data in Exercises 1–3. Explain your reasoning.

1. a person's height and the person's shoe size

____

____

2. the age of a child and amount of weekly allowance that the child receives

____

____

4. the average number of hours a child sleeps and the age of the child

____

____

5. Make a scatter plot of the following data. Does the scatter plot show any trend? If so, what?

____

Number of Hours of Practice	Number of Successful Free Throws out of 10
6	3
7	5
8	6
9	6
10	7
11	7
12	6
13	7

Describe the trend in each scatter plot.

5.

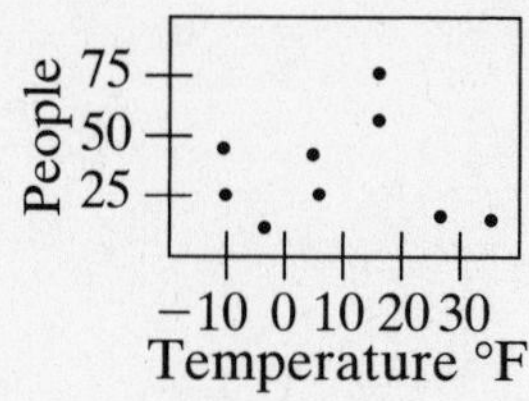

____

6.

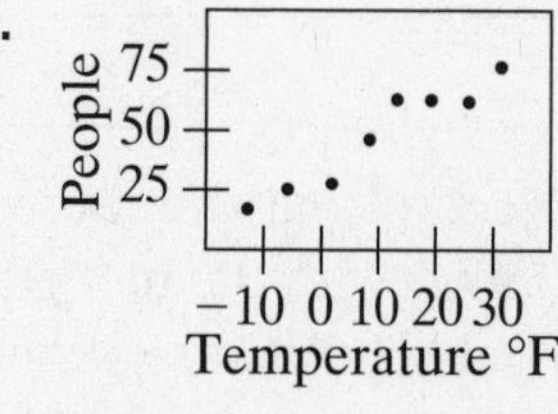

____

Name ______________________ Class ______________ Date ______________

Activity Lab 11-7

Exploring Scatter Plots

Materials needed: graph paper

The data in the table at right can be graphed in a scatter plot.

Hours Worked vs. Money Earned

Hours Worked	Money Earned
1	$5.50
2	$11.15
3	$16.40
4	$22.10
5	$27.35

1. On a sheet of graph paper, create a scatter plot with "Hours Worked" on the horizontal axis, and "Money Earned" on the vertical axis.

2. Describe the trend you notice in the scatter plot.

____

____

3. Create a scatter plot for the second set of data with "Computer Processor Speed" on the horizontal axis, and "Time Required to Load a Graphic" on the vertical axis.

CPU Speed vs. Time Required to Load a Graphic

Computer Processor Speed	Time Required to Load a Graphic
500	1
750	0.7
1000	0.5
1500	0.3
2000	0.2

4. Does the trend you notice in the scatter plot match your expectations about the relationship between processor speed and time required to load a graphic? Explain.

____

____

5. You are assigned a project to compare the weight of various cars and trucks (measured in kg) with the fuel efficiency each receives (measured in miles per gallon). What relationship do you expect to find between these two measurements? After you have collected data for the project, how will you display your findings? Why?

____

____

Name ______________________ Class ______________ Date ______________

Reteaching 11-7

Exploring Scatter Plots

Gilbert is investigating the relationship between the number of credit cards a person has and the amount of credit card debt.

First, he made a table from his data. Then he plotted the data in a scatter plot.

Credit Cards and Credit Card Debt

Number of Cards	Amount of Debt
1	$0
1	$1,000
1	$5,000
2	$3,000
2	$5,000
3	$10,000
3	$5,000
3	$8,000
4	$10,000
5	$19,000

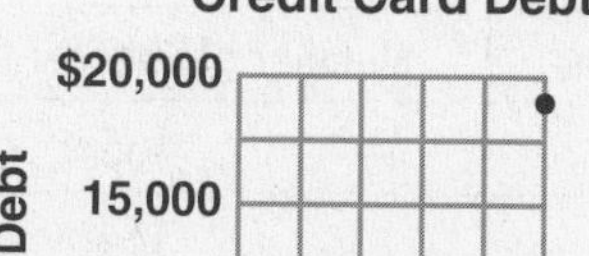

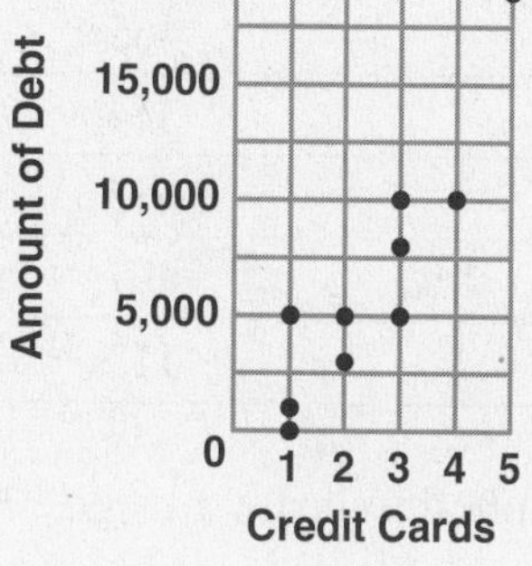

Gilbert's scatter plot shows a **positive trend** in the data. That means as the number of credit cards goes up, so does the amount of debt. As one value goes up, so does the other.

In a **negative trend,** one value goes up while the other goes down.

Complete the scatter plot for the data.

1. Dana surveyed her friends about how much TV they watch and their average test scores. Her results are shown below.

Test Scores and TV

TV Hours Per Day	Average Test Score	TV Hours Per Day	Average Test Score
1	98	3	79
1	86	3	73
2	90	3	75
2	82	4	62
2	85	5	68

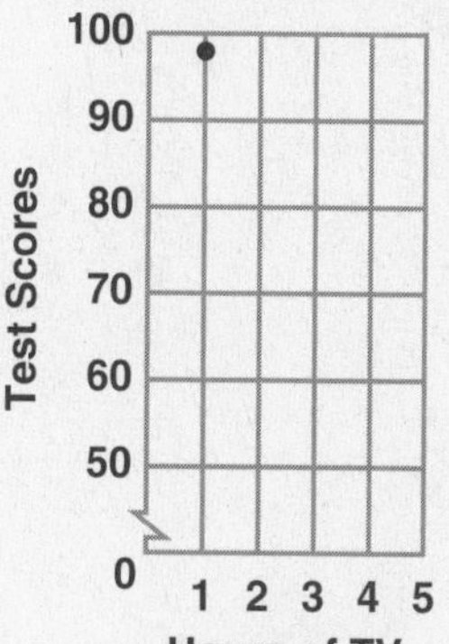

2. Is the trend in the data negative or positive? Explain.

____

____

3. Describe the relationship Dana likely found between test scores and TV time.

____

Name ______________________ Class ______________ Date ______________

Enrichment 11-7

Exploring Scatter Plots

Scatter plots can help identify trends in data. Use graph paper to plot the relationship between movie show times and the number of theater patrons described in the table below. Answer the questions that follow.

Movie Show Time	Number of Theater Patrons
3 P.M.	465
5 P.M.	354
7 P.M.	652
9 P.M.	497
11 P.M.	112

1. Do the points you graphed indicate a trend? Explain.

____

____

2. If you were the manager of a movie theater, how could finding trends in movie-going help you make employee schedules?

____

____

3. If you were a movie-goer, how could you use trends in movie attendance to your advantage?

____

Name ______________________ Class ______________ Date ______________

11E: Vocabulary Check

For use after Lesson 11-7

Study Skill Strengthen your vocabulary. Use these pages and add cues and summaries by applying the Cornell Notetaking style.

Write the definition for each word or term at the right. To check your work, fold the paper back along the dotted line to see the correct answers.

______________________	biased question
______________________	legend
______________________	positive trend
______________________	cell
______________________	random sample

Name ______________________ Class ______________ Date ______________

11E: Vocabulary Check (continued)

For use after Lesson 11-7

Write the vocabulary word or term for each definition. To check your work, fold the paper forward along the dotted line to see the correct answers.

a question that makes an unjustified assumption or makes one answer appear better than the other ______________________

something that identifies data that are compared ______________________

when one set of values increases, the other tends to increase ______________________

a box where a row and a column meet ______________________

a sample where each member of the population has an equal chance of being selected ______________________

Name ______________________ Class ______________ Date ______________

11D: Visual Vocabulary Practice

For use after Lesson 11-7

Study Skill When interpreting an illustration, notice the information that is given and also notice what is not given. Do not make assumptions.

Concept List

biased question	double bar graph	histogram
frequency table	line plot	population
sample	no trend	negative trend

Write the concept that best describes each exercise. Choose from the concept list above.

1.

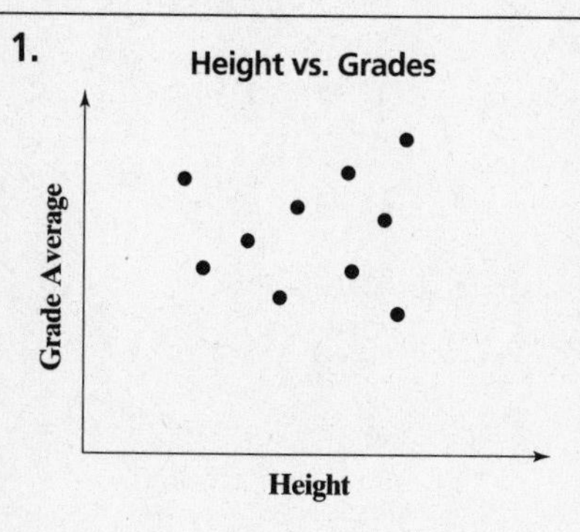

____

2. Number of Sports Played by Students

Sports	Tally	Frequency
0	~~IIII~~	5
1	II	2
2	III	3
3	~~IIII~~ II	7

____

3. Sandy conducted a survey at her college. She chose a random sample from all freshmen and asked how much time they study each week. The freshmen class represents this for the survey.

____

4.

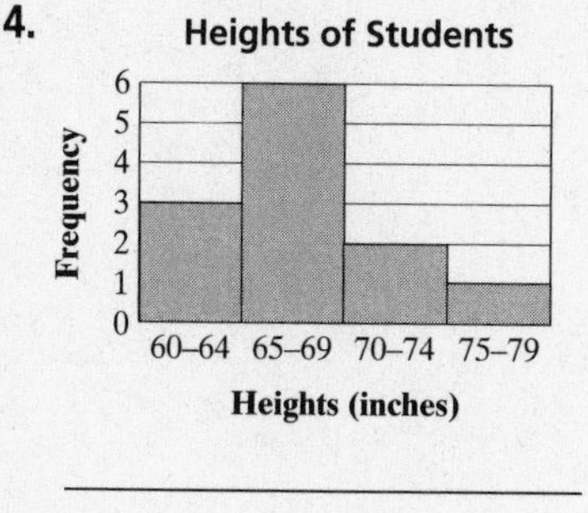

____

5.

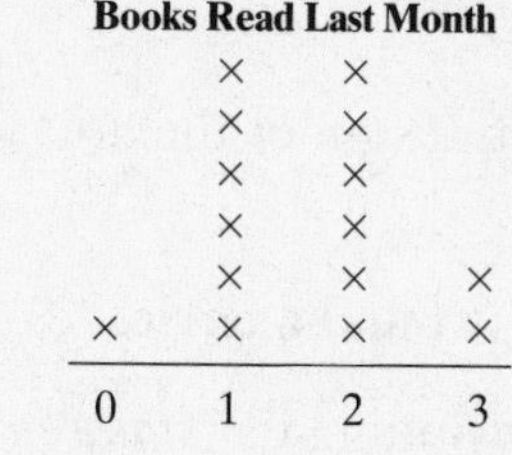

____

6.

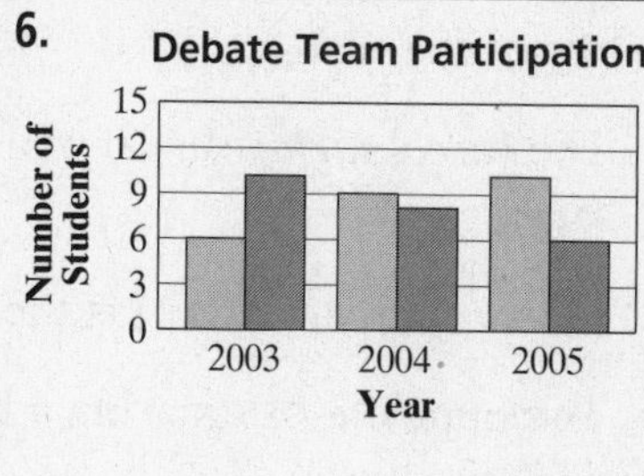

____

7. "Do you prefer lovable dogs or lazy cats?"

____

8.

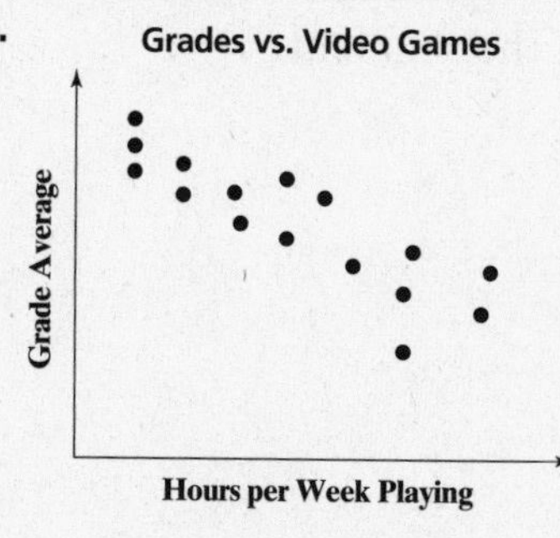

____

9. Derrick conducted a survey using the customers at a local ice cream shop. Derrick chose every 5th and 8th customer entering the shop to represent this.

____

Name ____________ Class ____________ Date ____________

11F: Vocabulary Review

For use with the Chapter Review

Study Skill Take notes while you study. Use a highlighter to emphasize important material in your notes.

Circle the term that correctly completes each sentence.

1. A flip that creates symmetry is a (*translation, reflection*).
2. The first number in an ordered pair is the (*x, y*) coordinate.
3. Lines in a coordinate plane that are parallel to the *y*-axis are (*horizontal, vertical*).
4. A (*line plot, frequency table*) uses a number line with "x" marks to represent each data item.
5. You can use a (*bar, circle*) graph to easily compare amounts.
6. The (*mean, median*) is the middle number in a data set when the values are written in order from least to greatest.
7. The (*mode, range*) of a data set is the difference between the greatest and least data values.
8. A (*line graph, scatter plot*) can be used to investigate the relationship between two sets of data.
9. A sequence is (*arithmetic, geometric*) if each term is found by adding the same number to the previous term.
10. (*Principal, Interest*) is the amount of money borrowed or deposited.
11. The (*area, surface area*) of a prism is the sum of the areas of the faces.
12. (*Circumference, Area*) is the distance around a circle.
13. The opposite of squaring a number is finding its (*square root, perfect square*).
14. The (*slope, bisector*) of a line segment is a line, segment, or ray, that goes through the midpoint of the segment.

Name ______________________ Class ______________ Date ______________

Puzzle 11-7

Exploring Scatter Plots

Make a scatter plot for each set of data. Use your scatter plot to describe each relationship as *positive, negative, or no trend.* Fill in your responses in the crossword puzzle at the bottom of the page.

Elevation	5,312 ft	8,641 ft	103 ft	3,500 ft	2,466 ft	4,385 ft	1,097 ft
Average Yearly Rainfall	32.4	14.2	26.1	11.0	21.7	5.4	15.8

1. The relationship of elevation to yearly rainfall for these U.S. cities:

____

Average Temperature (°F)	81	51	42	60	58	32	98	73	90	29	36
Number of Pizzas Sold	125	210	254	180	189	310	112	146	121	299	304

2. The trend in the sales at Joe's Pizza as the temperature increased.

____

Month	Feb.	July	Dec.	Sep.	March	Nov.	May	Jan.	April	Aug.	June	Oct.
Profits	$314	$396	$503	$469	$286	$608	$462	$106	$312	$472	$384	$538

3. The trend in profits at Dan's Bike Shop in its first year of business.

____

Age	12	62	53	15	27	48	59	41	31	24	63	55	46	22
Score	206	143	213	235	157	179	292	128	211	288	300	16	246	124

4. The relationship between age and bowling score.

____

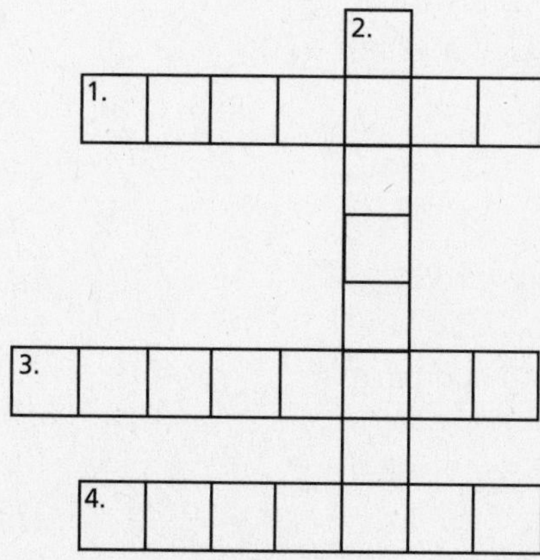

Name ______________________ Class ______________ Date ______________

Chapter 11 Project: Too Many to Count

Estimate the Size of a Crowd and Take a Survey

Beginning the Chapter Project

Chances are there's at least one person in a crowd that has the same birthday as you! How many people do you think have the same favorite food? How many like the same television show? What kinds of cars do the people in the crowd have? Pollsters face questions like these all of the time, and they take surveys to help answer them.

In this chapter project, you will take a survey and present your results in a graph.

Activities

Activity 1: Collecting Data

In a magazine or newspaper, find a picture of a large crowd. Use a sporting event or concert. Guess how many people are in the picture. Save the picture to use later in your project.

Activity 2: Analyzing

Use the picture you found for Activity 1. To estimate the number of people in the crowd, first divide the picture into equal rectangular sections. Count the number of people in several sections. Be careful! The people in the front of the picture appear larger than those in the back. Find the average number of people in a rectangle. Use your average to estimate the number of people in the picture.

Activity 3: Surveying

Suppose you want to know what kinds of foods people might buy during a sporting event or a concert. Write a fair survey question. Survey a random sample of the students in your grade. Use a graph to display your results.

Activity 4: Calculating

Use Activities 2 and 3. Suppose the students you surveyed are a representative sample of the people in the crowd picture. Use your results to make predictions about the food preferences of the people in your crowd picture.

Name ______________________ Class ______________ Date ______________

Chapter 11 Project: Too Many to Count (continued)

Finishing the Project

Use your estimate of the crowd size and your survey results to plan what type of concessions you would have at a new stadium or arena.

Be sure all of your work is neat and clear. You want to impress the city planners!

Reflect and Revise

Ask a classmate to review your project with you. Is your method for finding the estimate of the size of the crowd clear? Do you explain how you chose your random sample? If necessary, make changes to improve your project.

Extending the Project

Write more survey questions about the food at your school. Perhaps if you show your principle the results, he can help get different types of food at your school for lunch.

Visit PHSchool.com for information and links you might find helpful as you complete your project.

Name ______________________ Class ______________ Date ____________

Chapter Project Manager

Getting Started

Read about the project. As you work on it, you will need several sheets of paper. If available, a spreadsheet program also can be used. Keep all your work for the project in a folder, along with this Project Manager.

Checklist	Suggestions
❑ Activity 1: collecting	❑ Look at sports magazines where they might have a picture of a crowded stadium.
❑ Activity 2: analyzing	❑ Use a magnifying glass to help see the people in the picture.
❑ Activity 3: surveying	❑ Make sure your questions are not biased. Stay away from words that insinuate any opinions.
❑ Activity 4: calculating	❑ Your prediction should be true to your survey questions.
❑ Recommendations	❑ Be sure not to ask only your friends because it would not be random. Perhaps, ask a few students in each of your classes.

Scoring Rubric

3 Your calculations and estimations are correct. Your survey question is fair and you selected a random sample of students to survey. Your data display is complete and neat and your predictions are appropriate.

2 Your calculations and estimations are correct. Your survey was appropriate but your predictions were not. Your data display was complete and accurate.

1 Your calculations or estimations have minor errors. Your survey data is complete, but your data display is not.

0 Your calculations were incomplete. Either your survey was not thorough or complete, or you left out important parts of your display.

Your Evaluation of Project Evaluate your work, based on the Scoring Rubric.

Teacher's Evaluation of Project

Name ______________________ Class ______________ Date ______________

Chapter Project Teacher Notes

About the Project Students will explore the connection between math and marketing. The activities help students take a survey, display the results in a graph, and use the results to plan a market strategy.

Introducing the Project

Have students estimate the student attendance at their school. Ask students:

- *About how many students are in each classroom?*
- *About how many classrooms are there in the school?*
- *What important characteristics make a graph accurate and easy to read?*

Activity 1: Collecting Data

Have magazines available for the students to use.

Activity 2: Analyzing

Review the definition of mean, or average, with students.

Activity 3: Surveying

Students survey questions should be interesting and unbiased.

Activity 4: Calculating

Ask students to justify their predictions.

Finishing the Project

You may wish to plan a project day on which students share their completed projects. Encourage students to explain their process as well as their products.

Have students review their methods for conducting market research, making graphs, and calculating summary statistics for the project.

Visit PHSchool.com for information and links you might find helpful as you complete your project.

Name ______________________ Class ______________ Date ______________

✔ Checkpoint Quiz 1

Use with Lessons 11-1 through 11-3.

Give the content or value (°F) of each cell in the spreadsheet below.

1. B3 ____________ 2. C4 ____________ 3. A5 ____________

4. Which rows of the spreadsheet below most likely generated the double bar graph shown? ____________

Normal Maximum/Minimum Temperatures (°F) in January

	A	B	C
1	State	Max	Min
2	CO	43	16
3	CA	55	42
4	AK	50	30
5	NY	37	26

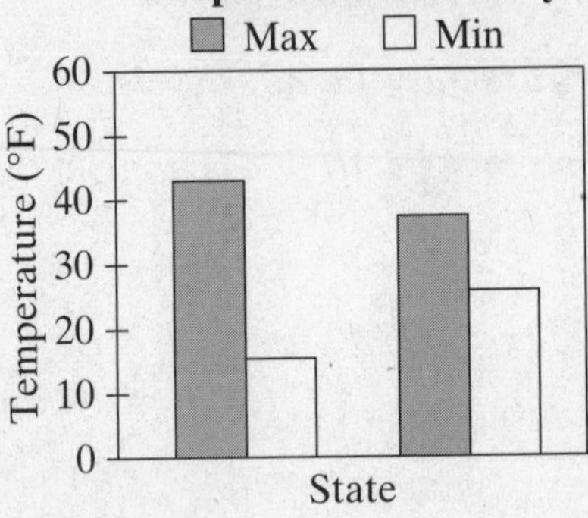

5. Make a frequency table and a line plot of the data.

10 7 7 9 10 8 11 12 10 8 10

6. Create a stem-and-leaf plot for this set of data.

Daily low temperatures (°F)

23 35 25 32 23 18 26 16 21 31 17 18 22

- - - - ✂ -

Name ______________________ Class ______________ Date ______________

✔ Checkpoint Quiz 2

Use with Lessons 11-4 through 11-6.

1. The graph shows a book store's profits. Explain why the graph is misleading. Redraw the graph so it does not mislead.

____

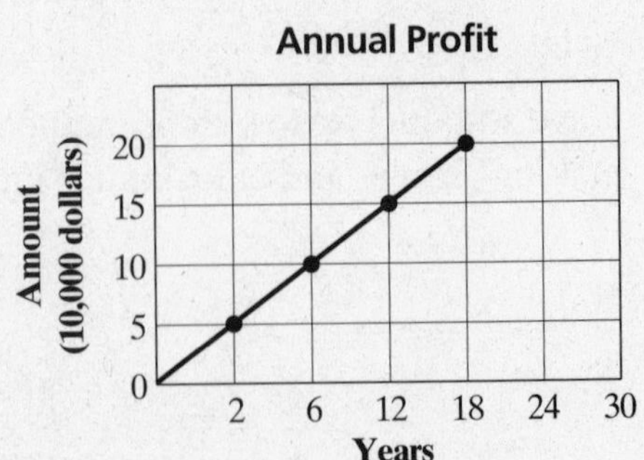

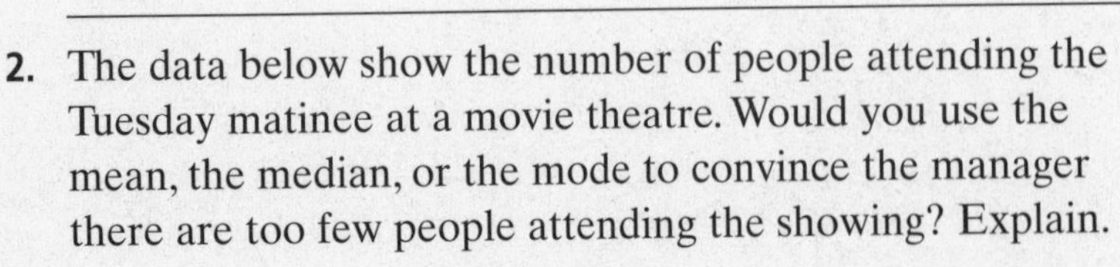

2. The data below show the number of people attending the Tuesday matinee at a movie theatre. Would you use the mean, the median, or the mode to convince the manager there are too few people attending the showing? Explain.

15 16 21 14 19 14 20

3. Choose a survey topic. Write a survey question. How could you get a random sample?

____

4. A marine biologist tags 100 whales. Later, a sample of 115 whales was gathered and 5 were tagged. Estimate the total whale population.

____

Name ______________________ Class ______________ Date ______________

Chapter Test

Form A

Chapter 11

Fifteen students were asked, "How many hours of TV did you watch last night?" Use the responses below to make each data display.

1 0 1 4 6 3.5 2.5 2 1 1.5 2.5 3.5 3.5 4 5.5

1. frequency table

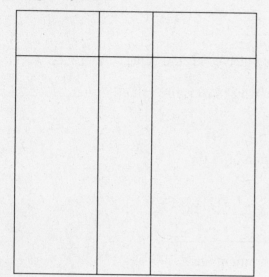

2. line plot

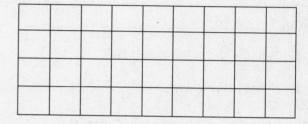

3. histogram

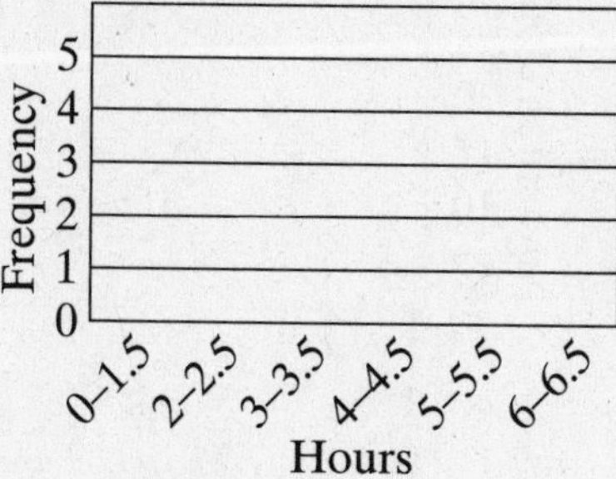

4. stem-and-leaf plot

5. The following are your scores on science tests.

86 80 91 86 95 100

a. Which is the most impressive representation of how well you are doing in class: the mean, the mode, or the median of your scores? Explain.

____

____

b. Which is the most accurate? Explain.

____

Name ______________________ Class ______________ Date ______________

Chapter Test (continued) **Form A**

Chapter 11

Use the spreadsheet below for Exercises 6–9.

	A	B	C	D
1	Type of Store	Pens Sold	Pencils Sold	Markers Sold
2	Supermarket	14	11	3
3	Book Store	27	22	9

6. What is the value in cell B3? ____________

7. In which cell is the value 3? ____________

8. What is the value in cell C2? ____________

9. In which cell is the value 14? ____________

Is each question *biased* or *fair*? Explain.

10. Would you prefer a vacation in pleasant, sunny Florida or in the barren wasteland of the Arctic?

____

____

11. Would you prefer going to the beach or going to the mountains?

____

The double line graph at right shows how much money Andreas and John spent for lunch each week during the month of October. Use the graph to answer Exercises 12 and 13.

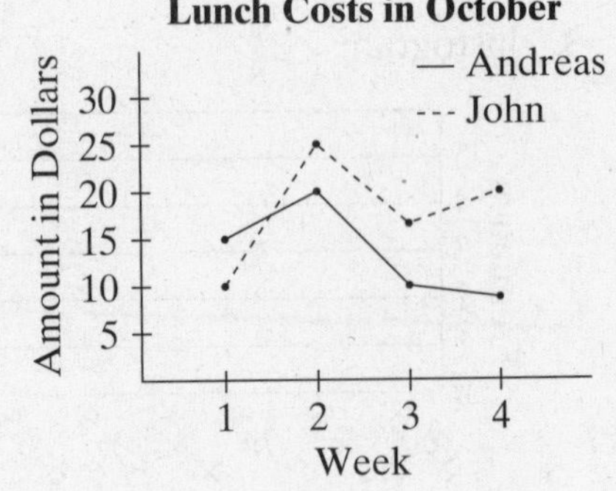

12. During which week did Andreas spend more than John?

____

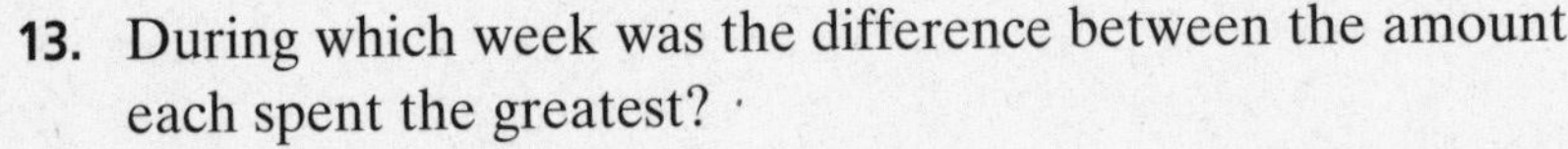

13. During which week was the difference between the amount each spent the greatest?

____

Use a proportion to estimate each population.

14. total deer counted: 64
tagged deer counted: 24
total deer tagged: 46

____

15. total birds counted: 146
tagged birds counted: 48
total birds tagged: 250

____

Name ______________________ Class ______________ Date ______________

Chapter Test

Form B

Chapter 11

Fifteen students were asked, "How many hours of TV did you watch last night?" Use the responses below to make each data display.

1 0 1 4 6 3.5 2.5 2 1 1.5 2.5 3.5 3.5 4 5.5

1. frequency table

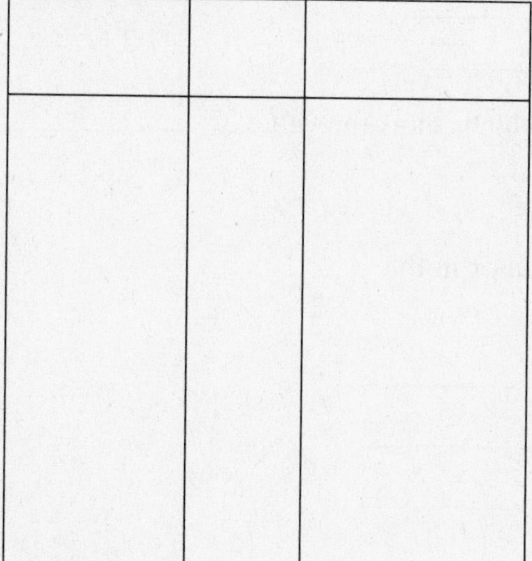

2. line plot

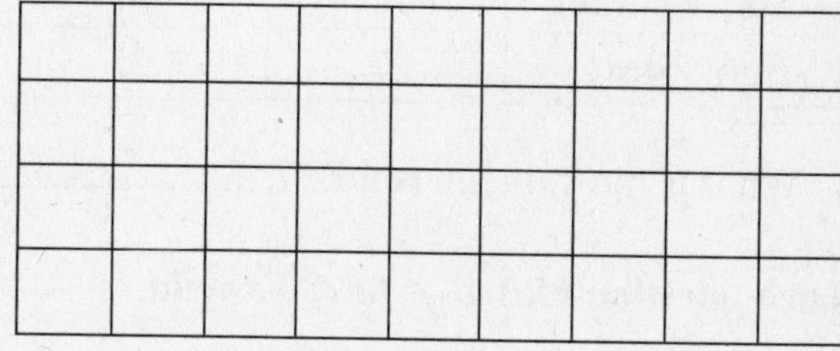

3. histogram

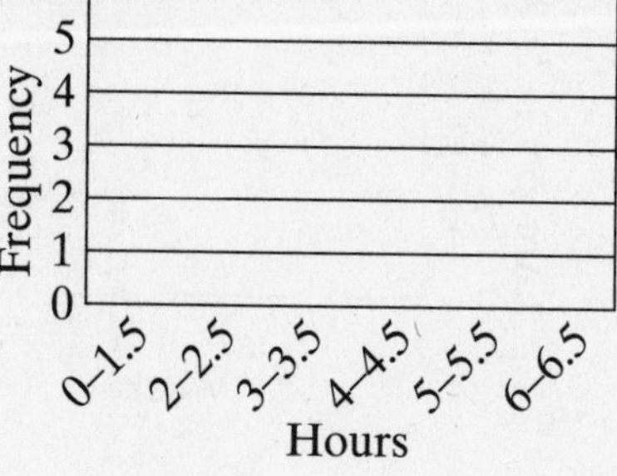

4. stem-and-leaf plot

5. The following are your scores on science tests.

86 80 91 86 95 100

Which is the most impressive representation of how well you are doing in class: the mean, the mode, or the median of your scores? Explain.

____

____

Name ________________ Class ________________ Date ________________

Chapter Test (continued) Form B

Chapter 11

Use the spreadsheet below for Exercises 6 and 7.

	A	B	C	D
1	Type of Store	Pens Sold	Pencils Sold	Markers Sold
2	Supermarket	14	11	3
3	Book Store	27	22	9

6. What is the value in cell B3? ____________ 7. In which cell is the value 3? ____________

Is each question *biased* or *fair*? Explain.

8. Would you prefer a vacation in pleasant, sunny Florida or in the barren wasteland of the Arctic?

____

____

____

The double line graph at right shows how much money Andreas and John spent for lunch each week during the month of October. Use the graph to answer Exercises 12 and 13.

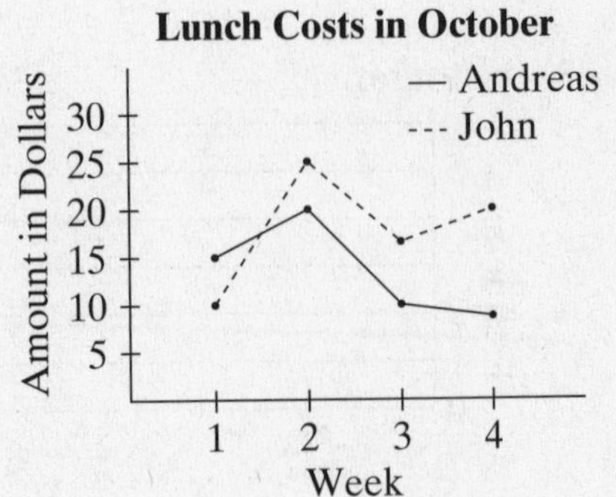

9. During which week did Andreas spend more than John?

____

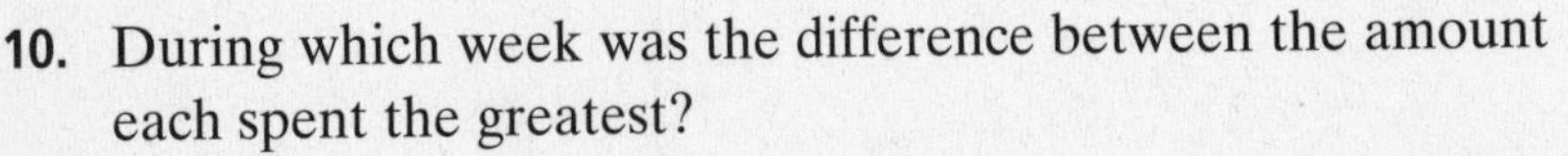

10. During which week was the difference between the amount each spent the greatest?

____

Use a proportion to estimate each population.

11. Use a proportion to estimate the population.

total deer counted: 64
tagged deer counted: 24
total deer tagged: 46

____

____

Name ______________________ Class ______________ Date ______________

Alternative Assessment

Form C

Chapter 11

AT YOUR SERVICE

Jill owns an ice cream parlor. She needs your help in making a schedule to show which employees will work on which Saturdays. First she studied her cash register receipts from last Saturday. Then she made the following chart to show the number of customers she had each hour.

CUSTOMERS AT JILL'S ICE CREAM PARLOR		
From	**Until**	**Number of Customers**
11:00 A.M.	12:00 Noon	63
12:00 Noon	1:00 P.M.	120
1:00 P.M.	2:00 P.M.	102
2:00 P.M.	3:00 P.M.	86
3:00 P.M.	4:00 P.M.	50
4:00 P.M.	5:00 P.M.	29
5:00 P.M.	6:00 P.M.	56
6:00 P.M.	7:00 P.M.	87
7:00 P.M.	8:00 P.M.	143
8:00 P.M.	9:00 P.M.	119
9:00 P.M.	10:00 P.M.	86
10:00 P.M.	11:00 P.M.	58

Show all of your work on a separate sheet of paper.

1. Make a graph to illustrate the data above.
2. When planning each Saturday's schedule, Jill likes to follow certain guidelines. Using the guidelines listed below, make up a time schedule for this Saturday, based on the number of customers Jill had last Saturday.
   - No person works more than 4 hours in a day.
   - No person works fewer than 2 hours in a day.
   - In addition to the servers, there is always 1 person working the cash register each hour.
   - There is always 1 server working for every 30 customers in the store. Jill always rounds up the number of servers needed to the nearest whole number. So, if there are 31 customers in an hour, 2 servers should be working, and so on.

Name ______________________ Class ______________ Date ______________

Alternative Assessment (continued) Form C

Chapter 11

Use fictional names or variables for the employees (for example, Server A, Server B, and so on). Make the schedule easy to read. Show who will be the cashier each hour.

3. Do you think using the cash register receipts for last Saturday was a good way to plan the schedule for this Saturday? Explain.

4. Explain the information shown in this scatter plot. Based on this data, estimate the average amount each customer spends. If every customer spent exactly the same amount, how would this scatter plot change?

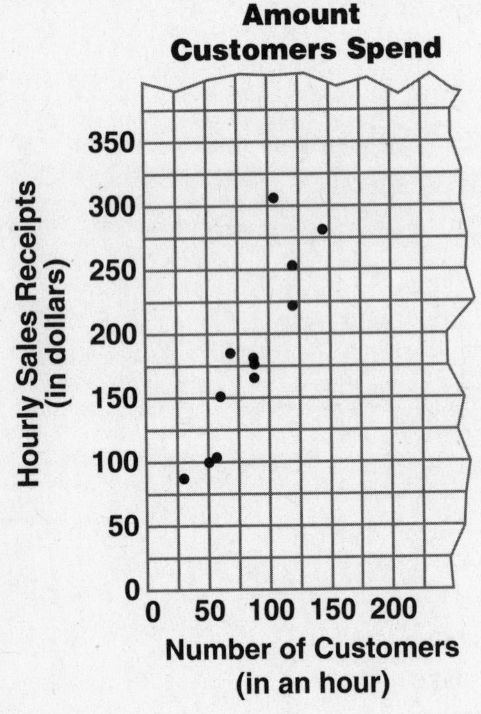

Excursion

Name an after-school job for which you are qualified. Describe where you would work, what you would do, what your schedule would be, and how much you would earn each hour. Make a weekly work schedule for this job. Based on this schedule, determine how much you would earn in a week. If you kept this schedule, how much would you earn in a month?

Name ______________________ Class ______________ Date ______________

Cumulative Review

Chapters 1–11

1. Write 82,700 in scientific notation.

   A. 8.27×10^5　B. 8.27×10^4
   C. 8.27×10^3　D. 8.27×10^2

2. Which of the following is in order from least to greatest?

   F. 0.25, 0.52, 0.5　G. 5.0, 5.05, 5.5
   H. 2.16, 2.1, 2.165　J. 0.03, 0.3, 0.003

3. Estimate the area of the figure.

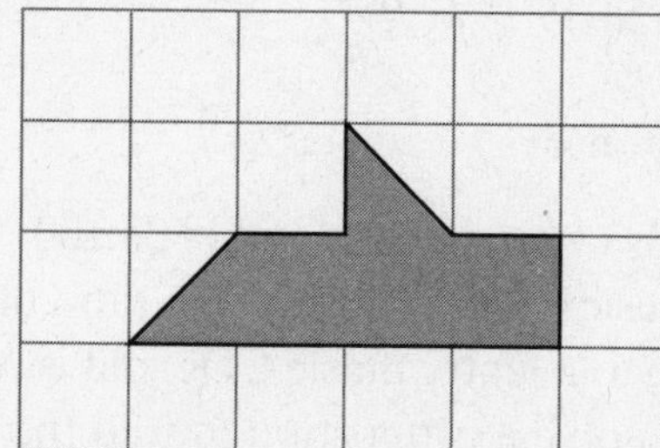

   A. 5 units^2　B. 4 units^2
   C. 3 units^2　D. 2 units^2

4. Solve the inequality $-8x \leq 40$

   F. $x \leq 5$　G. $x \geq 5$
   H. $x \leq -5$　J. $x \geq -5$

5. Evaluate $s(72 + r)$ for $s = 0.1$ and $r = 32$.

   A. 10.4　B. 39.2
   C. 40　D. 104

6. Which of the following is true?

   F. A line plot shows the mean of a set of data.
   G. A stem-and-leaf plot lists each piece of data.
   H. A histogram shows either a positive or negative trend between two sets of data.
   J. A double bar graph compares changes over time of two sets of data.

7. Which is the median of the given data?
   6, 7, 5, 4, 8, 9, 5, 3, 1, 10

   A. 5　B. 5.5
   C. 6　D. 9

8. For the data in Exercise 7, which is largest?

   F. mean　G. median
   H. mode　J. range

9. What does the scatter plot show?

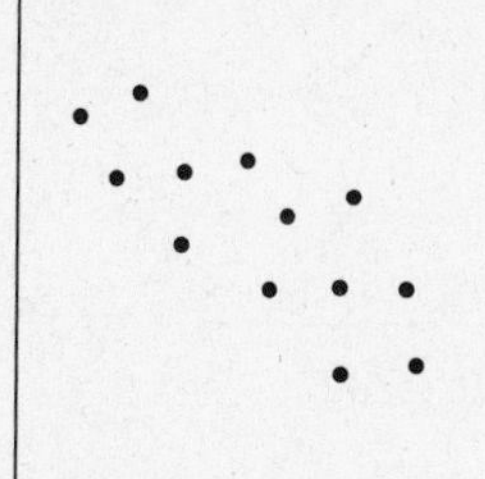

   A. no trend　B. positive trend
   C. negative trend　D. extreme trend

10. 60 is 24% of what number?

   F. 250　G. 240
   H. 144　J. 40

11. Write a function rule for the table.

x	y
1	3
2	4
3	5
4	6

   A. $y = 3x$　B. $y = 2x$
   C. $y = x + 2$　D. $y = x + 3$

12. $10 \cdot |z| = y$ Which statement is true?

   F. z will always be negative
   G. z and y will always be positive
   H. y will always be positive
   J. z will always be positive

Cumulative Review (continued)

Chapters 1–11

Bob and Karen each planted a tree and recorded the number of inches each tree grew over the first four years. They made a double line graph of the data. Use the graph to answer Exercises 13–16.

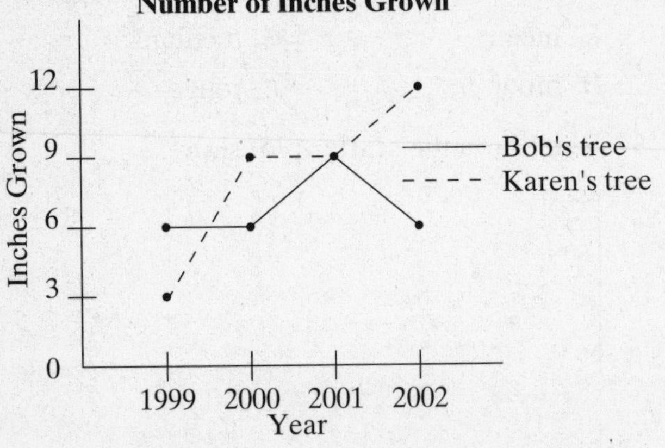

13. During which year did Bob's tree grow more than Karen's tree?

A. 1999 **B.** 2000
C. 2001 **D.** 2002

14. During which year was the difference in the amounts each tree grew the greatest?

F. 1999 **G.** 2000
H. 2001 **J.** 2002

15. What was the average growth of Bob's tree over the four years?

A. 4.0 in. **B.** 5.0 in.
C. 6.75 in. **D.** 7.1 in.

16. About how many inches in all did Karen's tree grow over the four years?

F. 30 in. **G.** 33 in.
H. 35 in. **J.** 39 in.

17. Solve. $\frac{y}{5} - 10 = 4$

A. 70 **B.** -30
C. 30 **D.** 200

18. Mrs. Baker purchased a number of juice packs at a cost of \$.30 each and a loaf of bread that cost \$1.19. The total cost of her purchases was \$2.99. Which equation would you use to determine how many juice packs Mrs. Baker purchased?

F. $\$1.19j + \$.30j = \$2.99$
G. $\$.30j + \$2.99 = \$1.19$
H. $\$2.99 - \$1.19j = \$.30$
J. $\$.30j + \$1.19 = \$2.99$

Extended Response

19. A local music shop sells a total of 35,100 country music CDs each year. The ratio of rock music to country music CDs sold is 5 : 3. Write and solve a proportion to find the number of rock music CDs sold each year. Show your work.

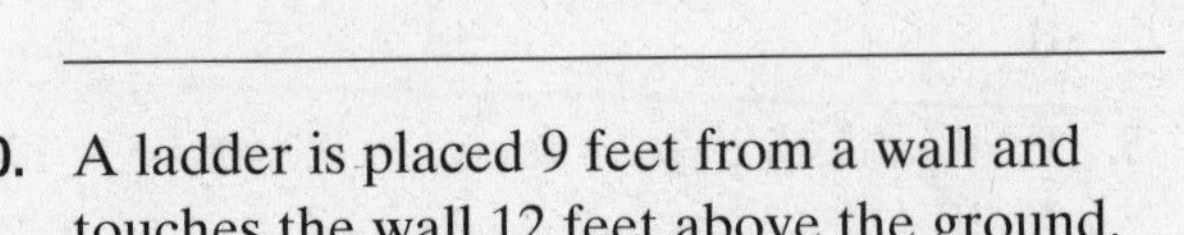

20. A ladder is placed 9 feet from a wall and touches the wall 12 feet above the ground. What is the length of the ladder? Show your work.

Name ______________________ Class ______________ Date ______________

Practice 12-1

Probability

You spin a spinner numbered 1 through 10. Each outcome is equally likely. Find the probabilities below as a fraction, decimal, and percent.

1. *P*(9) ____________
2. *P*(even) ____________
3. *P*(number greater than 0) ____________
4. *P*(multiple of 4) ____________

There are eight blue marbles, nine orange marbles, and six yellow marbles in a bag. You draw one marble at random. Find each probability.

5. *P*(blue marble) ____________
6. *P*(yellow marble) ____________
7. What marble could you add or remove so that the probability of drawing a blue marble is $\frac{1}{3}$?

____

A box contains 12 slips of paper as shown. Each slip of paper is equally likely to be drawn. Find each probability.

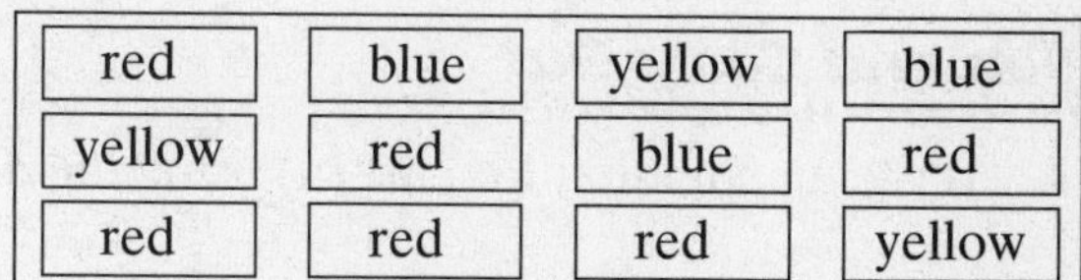

red	blue	yellow	blue
yellow	red	blue	red
red	red	red	yellow

8. *P*(red) ____________
9. *P*(blue) ____________
10. *P*(yellow) ____________
11. *P*(red or blue) ____________
12. *P*(red or yellow) ____________
13. *P*(blue or yellow) ____________
14. *P*(not red) ____________
15. *P*(not blue) ____________
16. *P*(not yellow) ____________

You select a letter randomly from a bag containing the letters S, P, I, N, N, E, and R. Find the odds in favor of each outcome.

17. selecting an N ____________
18. selecting an S ____________

Name ______________________ Class ______________ Date ______________

12-1 • Guided Problem Solving

GPS Student Page 583, Exercise 32:

a. Suppose $P(E) = 0.3$. Find $P(\text{not } E)$.

b. Suppose $P(\text{not } E) = 65\%$. Find $P(E)$.

Understand

1. What is the relationship between E and not E?

____

2. What is the sum of the probability of an event and the probability of the event's complement?

____

3. What is the difference between part a and part b?

____

____

Plan and Carry Out

4. Write an equation for part (a) using the definition of a complement.

____

5. Solve the equation for $P(\text{not } E)$. ______________

6. Write 65% as a decimal. ______________

7. Write an equation for part (b) using the definition of a complement.

____

8. Solve the equation for $P(E)$. ______________

Check

9. How could you use a sum to check your answers?

____

____

Solve Another Problem

10. Suppose $P(E) = \frac{4}{5}$. Find $P(\text{not } E)$.

____

Name ______________________ Class ______________ Date ____________

Practice 12-1

Probability

You spin a spinner numbered 1 through 10. Each outcome is equally likely. Find the probabilities below as a fraction, decimal, and percent.

1. *P*(9) ______________
2. *P*(even) ______________
3. *P*(number greater than 0) ______________

There are eight blue marbles, nine orange marbles, and six yellow marbles in a bag. You draw one marble at random. Find each probability.

4. *P*(blue marble) ______________
5. *P*(yellow marble) ______________

A box contains 12 slips of paper as shown. Each slip of paper is equally likely to be drawn. Find each probability.

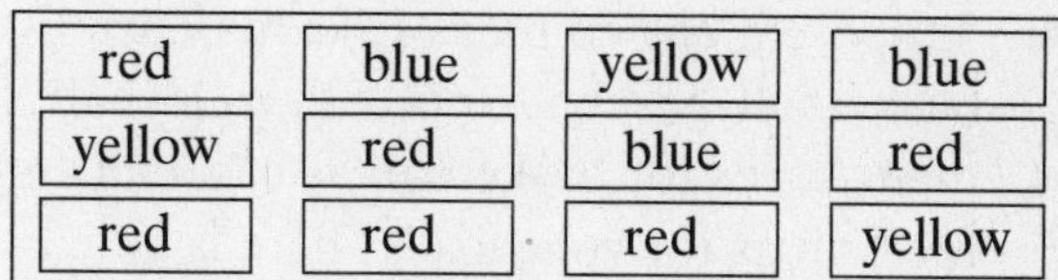

red	blue	yellow	blue
yellow	red	blue	red
red	red	red	yellow

6. *P*(red) ______________
7. *P*(blue) ______________
8. *P*(yellow) ______________
9. *P*(red or blue) ______________
10. *P*(red or yellow) ______________
11. *P*(blue or yellow) ______________

You select a letter randomly from a bag containing the letters S, P, I, N, N, E, and R. Find the odds in favor of each outcome.

12. selecting an N ______________
13. selecting an S ______________

Name ______________________ Class ______________ Date ____________

Activity Lab 12-1

Probability

Suppose a bag contains ten cards with number puzzles. A puzzle involves a problem related to probability, geometry, or algebra. The number of puzzles related to probability is twice the number of puzzles related to algebra. There is at least one puzzle devoted to each type of problem.

1. If the odds of choosing an algebra puzzle are 1 : 9, how many cards for each type of puzzle will there be?

____

2. If the odds of choosing an algebra puzzle are 1 : 4, how many cards for each type of puzzle will there be?

____

3. If the odds of choosing a probability puzzle are 3 : 2, how many cards for each type of puzzle will there be?

____

4. Suppose a bag contains 15 cards, each listing one of these sports: basketball, baseball, football, volleyball. There are three times as many cards for basketball as baseball and twice as many cards for football as for volleyball. There is at least one card for each sport.

a. What are the odds for drawing a card that shows each of the following sports?

basketball ____________ baseball ____________

football ____________ volleyball ____________

b. Which sport is more likely to be picked in a random drawing? Explain.

____

____

5. Record several school subjects on the chalkboard. Have each person in the room write his or her favorite subject on a card and put the cards in a bag. What are the odds of drawing a card at random that shows your favorite subject? What are the odds of drawing a card that shows each of the other subjects?

____

Name ______________________ Class ______________ Date ______________

Reteaching 12-1

Probability

To find a **theoretical probability,** first list all possible **outcomes.** Then use the formula:

$$P(\text{event}) = \frac{\text{number of favorable outcomes}}{\text{total number of possible outcomes}}$$

A letter is selected at random from the letters of the word FLORIDA. What is the probability that the letter is an A?

- There are 7 letters (possible outcomes).
- There is one A, which represents a favorable outcome.

$$P(\text{A}) = \frac{\text{number of favorable outcomes}}{\text{total number of outcomes}} = \frac{1}{7}$$

The probability that the letter is an A is $\frac{1}{7}$.

Selecting a letter other than A is called *not* A and is the **complement** of the event A. The sum of the probabilities of an event and its complement equals 1, or 100%.

What is the probability of the event "*not* A"?

$$P(\text{A}) + P(\textit{not}\ \text{A}) = 1$$

$$\tfrac{1}{7} + P(\textit{not}\ \text{A}) = 1$$

$$P(\textit{not}\ \text{A}) = 1 - \tfrac{1}{7} = \tfrac{6}{7}$$

The probability of the event "*not* A" (selecting F, L, O, R, I, or D) is $\frac{6}{7}$.

Spin the spinner shown once. Find each probability as a fraction, a decimal, and a percent.

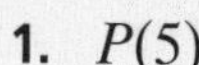

1. $P(5)$

$\frac{\text{number of favorable outcomes}}{\text{total number of outcomes}}$

$= \frac{\square}{5}$ ______________

2. $P(\text{odd number})$

$\frac{\text{number of favorable outcomes}}{\text{total number of outcomes}}$

$= \frac{2}{\square}$ ______________

You select a card at random from a box that contains cards numbered from 1 to 10. Find each probability as a fraction, a decimal, and a percent.

3. $P(\text{even number})$ ______________

4. $P(\text{number less than 4})$ ______________

5. $P(\text{not } 5)$ ______________

The letters H, A, P, P, I, N, E, S, and S are written on pieces of paper. Select one piece of paper. Find each probability.

6. $P(\text{not vowel})$ ______________

7. $P(\text{not E})$ ______________

A number is selected at random from the numbers 1 to 50. Find the odds in favor of each outcome.

8. selecting a multiple of 5

____

9. selecting a factor of 50

____

Name ______________________ Class ______________ Date ______________

Enrichment 12-1

Probability

Critical Thinking

Odds The probability ratio compares favorable outcomes to total outcomes. When outcomes are equally likely, you can write ratios, called *odds,* that compare favorable outcomes to unfavorable outcomes.

Odds in favor of an event = the ratio of the number of favorable outcomes to the number of unfavorable outcomes

Odds against an event = the ratio of the number of unfavorable outcomes to the number of favorable outcomes

Suppose a bag contains ten slips with classroom math challenge tasks you can do for extra credit. The tasks include problems related to probability, geometry, and algebra. The number of tasks related to probability is twice the number of tasks related to algebra. There is at least one task devoted to each type of problem.

1. If the odds of choosing an algebra task are 1 : 9, how many slips for each task will there be?

   ____

2. If the odds of choosing an algebra task are 1 : 4, how many slips for each task will there be?

   ____

3. If the odds of choosing a probability task are 3 : 2, how many slips for each task will there be?

   ____

Suppose a bag contains 15 slips, each listing one of these sports: basketball, baseball, football, volleyball. There are three times as many slips for basketball as baseball and twice as many slips for football as for volleyball. There is at least one slip for each sport.

4. What are the odds of drawing a slip that shows each of the following sports?

   basketball ____________ baseball ____________

   football ____________ volleyball ____________

5. Which sport is most likely to be picked in a random drawing? Explain.

   ____

   ____

Name ______________________ Class ______________ Date ______________

12A: Graphic Organizer

For use before Lesson 12-1

Study Skill Try to read new lessons before your teacher presents them in class. Important information is sometimes printed in **boldface** type or highlighted inside a box or with color. Pay special attention to this information.

Write your answers.

1. What is the chapter title?

 ____

2. How many lessons are there in this chapter?

 ____

3. What is the topic of the Test-Taking Strategies page?

 ____

4. Complete the graphic organizer below as you work through the chapter.
   - In the center, write the title of the chapter.
   - When you begin a lesson, write the lesson name in a rectangle.
   - When you complete a lesson, write a skill or key concept in a circle linked to that lesson block.
   - When you complete the chapter, use this graphic organizer to help you review.

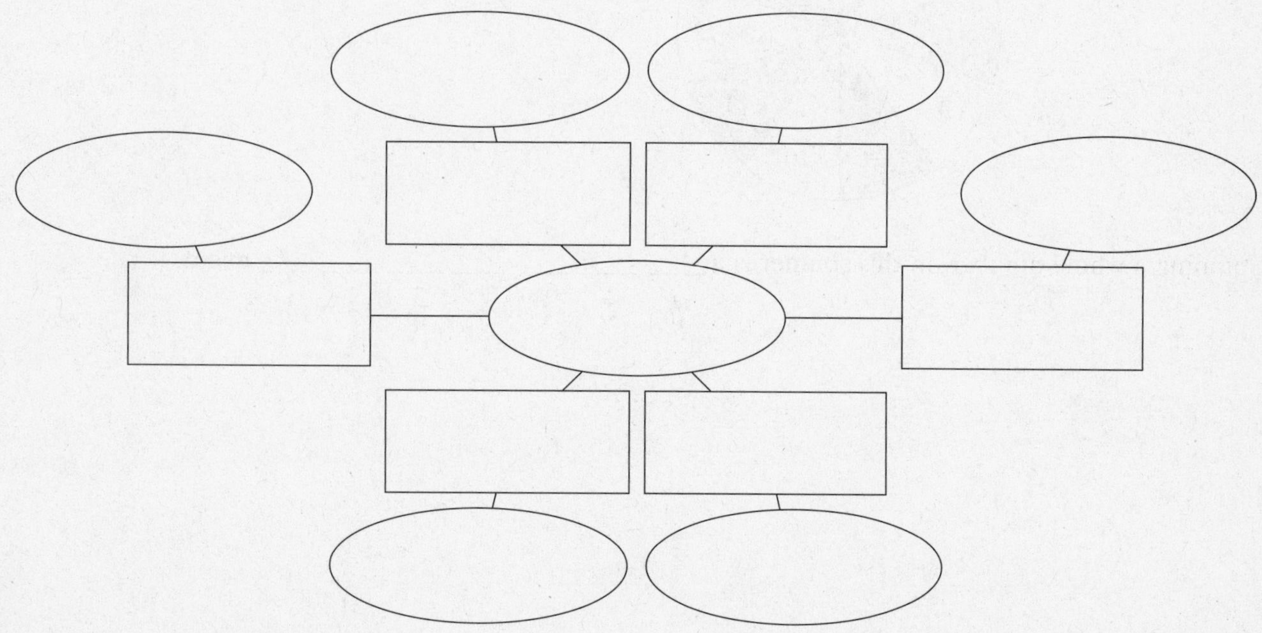

Name ______________________ Class ______________ Date ______________

Puzzle 12-1

Probability

Read each description and use the spinner below to determine each probability.

I. I am the probability of spinning a number with a dark background.

____

T. I am the probability of landing on a double-digit number.

____

A. I am the probability of landing on a perfect square.

____

C. I am the probability of landing on an odd number.

____

E. I am the probability of landing on a multiple of three.

____

N. I am the probability of landing on a factor of seven.

____

R. I am the probability of landing on a multiple of 4.

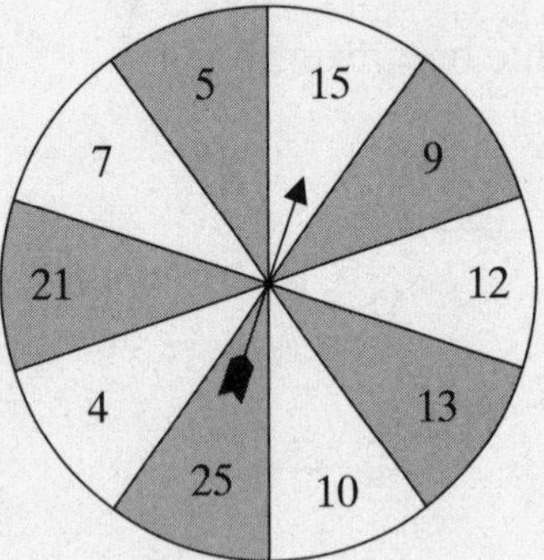

Spinning a whole number on this spinner is a ___ ___ ___ ___ ___ ___ ___ event.

$\frac{7}{10}$ $\frac{2}{5}$ $\frac{1}{5}$ $\frac{3}{5}$ $\frac{3}{10}$ $\frac{1}{2}$ $\frac{1}{10}$

Name ____________ Class ____________ Date ____________

Practice 12-2

Experimental Probability

Suppose you observe the color of socks worn by students in your class: 12 have white, 4 have black, 3 have blue, and 1 has red. Find each experimental probability as a fraction in simplest form.

1. P(white) ____________
2. P(red) ____________
3. P(blue) ____________
4. P(black) ____________
5. P(yellow) ____________
6. P(black or red) ____________

Use the data in the table at the right for Exercises 7–12. Find each experimental probability as a percent.

Favorite Snack Survey Results

Snack	Number of Students
Fruit	8
Granola	2
Pretzels	3
Chips	7
Carrots	5

7. P(fruit) ____________
8. P(granola) ____________
9. P(pretzels) ____________
10. P(carrots) ____________
11. P(not fruit) ____________
12. P(granola or chips) ____________

13. Do an experiment to find the probability that a word chosen randomly in a book is the word *the.* How many words did you look at to find P(the)? What is P(the)?

____

14. Suppose the following is the result of tossing a coin 5 times:

heads, tails, heads, tails, heads

What is the experimental probability for heads?

____

Solve.

15. The probability that a twelve-year-old has a brother or sister is 25%. Suppose you survey 300 twelve-year-olds. About how many do you think will have a brother or sister? ____________

16. a. A quality control inspector found flaws in 13 out of 150 sweaters. Find the probability that a sweater has a flaw. Round to the nearest tenth of a percent. ____________

b. Suppose the company produces 500 sweaters a day. How many will not have flaws? ____________

c. Suppose the company produces 600 sweaters a day. How many will have flaws? ____________

Name ______________________ Class ______________ Date ______________

12-2 • Guided Problem Solving

GPS Student Page 588, Exercise 14:

a. **Science** The probability that a male human is colorblind is 8%. Suppose you interview 1,000 males. About how many would you expect to be colorblind?

b. **Reasoning** Will you always get the same number? Explain.

Understand

1. What does it mean to be colorblind?

____

2. What are you being asked to do in part (a)?

____

____

Plan and Carry Out

3. Find 8% of 1,000. ______________

4. How many males out of 1,000 would you expect to be colorblind?

____

5. Will you always get exactly this number? Explain.

____

____

____

Check

6. How could you find the answer another way?

____

Solve Another Problem

7. The probability of a person being left-handed is about 11%. Suppose you interview 500 people. About how many would you expect to be left-handed?

____

Name ____________ Class ____________ Date ____________

Practice 12-2

Experimental Probability

Suppose you observe the color of socks worn by students in your class: 12 have white, 4 have black, 3 have blue, and 1 has red. Find each experimental probability as a fraction in simplest form.

1. *P*(white) ____________ **2.** *P*(red) ____________

3. *P*(blue) ____________ **4.** *P*(black) ____________

5. *P*(yellow) ____________ **6.** *P*(black or red) ____________

Use the data in the table at the right for Exercises 7–10. Find each experimental probability as a percent.

Favorite Snack Survey Results

Snack	Number of Students
Fruit	8
Granola	2
Pretzels	3
Chips	7

7. *P*(fruit) ____________ **8.** *P*(granola) ____________

9. *P*(pretzels) ____________ **10.** *P*(not fruit) ____________

11. Do an experiment to find the probability that a word chosen randomly in a book is the word *the.* How many words did you look at to find *P*(the)? What is *P*(the)?

____

12. Suppose the following is the result of tossing a coin 5 times:

heads, tails, heads, tails, heads

What is the experimental probability for heads?

____

Solve.

13. The probability that a twelve-year-old has a brother or sister is 25%. Suppose you survey 300 twelve-year-olds. About how many do you think will have a brother or sister? ____________

14. a. A quality control inspector found flaws in 13 out of 150 sweaters. Find the probability that a sweater has a flaw. Round to the nearest tenth of a percent. ____________

b. Suppose the company produces 500 sweaters a day. How many will not have flaws? ____________

Name ______________________ Class ______________ Date ____________

Activity Lab 12-2

Experimental Probability

Materials needed: standard number cube.

Work in pairs.

1. Copy the table below.

Outcome	1	2	3	4	5	6
Tally						
Percent						

2. Roll the number cube 120 times. Use the table to keep a tally of how many times you roll a 1, 2, 3, 4, 5, or 6.
3. Write the tallies as percents of 120 rolls in the third row of the table. These percents represent the experimental probability of each outcome for your group.
4. Share your tallies with the other groups in your class. On a separate sheet of paper, fill in the second row of the table below with the total tallies.

Outcome	1	2	3	4	5	6
Tally						
Percent						

5. Write the class tallies as percents of the total rolls in the third row of the table. These percents represent the experimental probability of each outcome for your class.
6. The theoretical (or expected) probability of rolling a specific number on a standard number cube is $\frac{1}{6}$. Use this information to complete a table of theoretical results for 120 rolls.

Outcome	1	2	3	4	5	6
Tally						
Percent						

7. **a.** How do your theoretical results compare to the experimental results of rolling a number cube 120 times?

   b. How do your theoretical results compare to the experimental results for the class?

8. Based on your observations, which experiment is better for determining the probability of rolling a number on a number cube: rolling a number cube 120 times or pooling the results of the class? Explain.

Name ______________________ Class ______________ Date ______________

Reteaching 12-2

Experimental Probability

Probability measures how likely it is that an event will occur. For an **experimental probability,** you collect data through observations or experiments and use the data to state the probability.

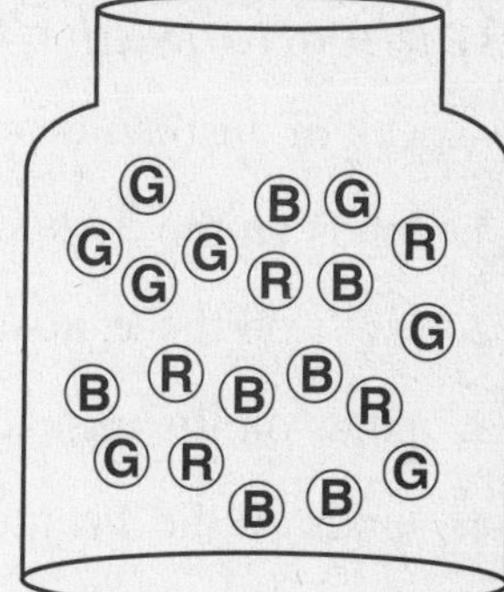

The jar contains red, green, and blue chips. You shake the jar, draw a chip, note its color, and then put it back. You do this 20 times with these results: 7 blue chips, 5 red chips, and 8 green chips. The experimental probability of drawing a green chip is

$$P(\text{green chip}) = \frac{\text{number of times "green chips" occur}}{\text{total number of trials}}$$

$$P(\text{green chip}) = \frac{8}{20} = \frac{2}{5} = 0.4 = 40\%$$

The probability of drawing a green chip is $\frac{2}{5}$, or 0.4, or 40%.

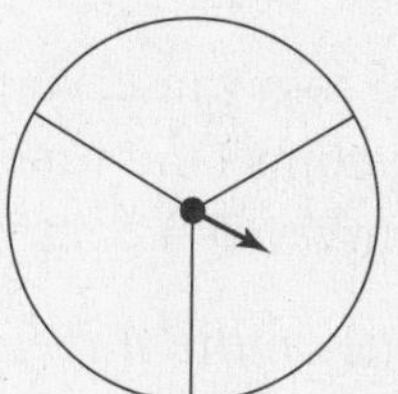

Sometimes a model, or simulation, is used to represent a situation. Then, the simulaton is used to find the experimental probability. For example, spinning this spinner can simulate the probability that 1 of 3 people is chosen for president of the student body.

Use the 20 draws above to complete each exercise.

1. What is the experimental probability of drawing a red chip? Write the probability as a fraction.

   $P(\text{red chip}) = \frac{\square}{20} =$ ______________

2. What is the experimental probability of drawing a blue chip? Write the probability as a percent.

   $P(\text{blue chip}) = \frac{\square}{\square} =$ ______________

Suppose you have a bag with 30 chips: 12 red, 8 white, and 10 blue. You shake the jar, draw a chip, note its color, and then put it back. You do this 30 times with these results: 10 blue chips, 12 red chips, and 8 white chips. Write each probability as fraction in simplest form.

3. $P(\text{red})$ ______________
4. $P(\text{white})$ ______________
5. $P(\text{blue})$ ______________

Describe a probability simulation for each situation.

6. You guess the answers on a true/false test with 20 questions.

   ____

   ____

7. One student out of 6 is randomly chosen to be the homeroom representative.

   ____

   ____

Name ______________________ Class ______________ Date ______________

Enrichment 12-2

Experimental Probability

Applications of Probability

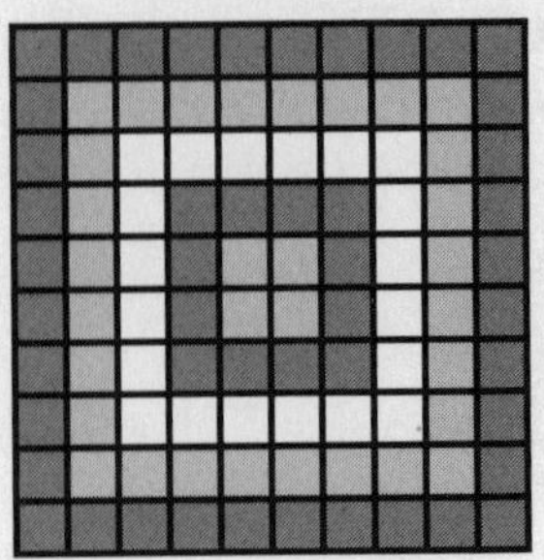

A speck of dust lands on the grid shown. What is the probability that it

1. lands on the dark-shaded area? ____________
2. lands on the light-shaded area? ____________
3. lands on the unshaded area? ____________
4. lands on the 4 center squares? ____________
5. does not land on the unshaded area? ____________
6. does not land on the dark-shaded area? ____________

In a coin toss game, you earn points for landing on the shaded figures. Assume coins land randomly in the large square. What is the probability that a coin

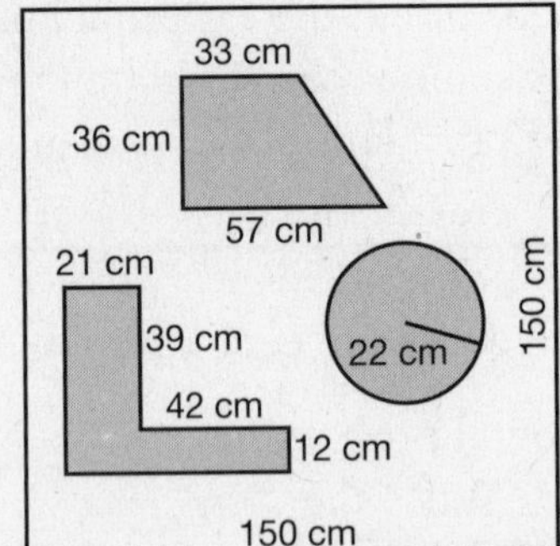

7. lands on the trapezoid? ____________
8. lands on the circle? ____________
9. lands on the L-shape? ____________
10. does not land on the trapezoid? ____________
11. does not land on the circle or the L-shape? ____________
12. lands in the unshaded area? ____________
13. lands in the square? ____________

Name ______________________ Class ______________ Date ______________

12B: Reading Comprehension

For use after Lesson 12-2

Study Skill When you complete a math exercise, always make sure your answer makes sense.

Below is an 8-day forecast of weather conditions. Use the table to answer the questions.

Date	Weather Prediction	High/Low Temp 8F	% Chance of Precipitation
July 26 evening	Isolated T-Storms	67°	30%
July 27	PM T-Storms	87° / 71°	40%
July 28	Partly Cloudy	91° / 71°	20%
July 29	Scattered T-Storms	90° / 64°	40%
July 30	Partly Cloudy	87° / 65°	20%
July 31	Partly Cloudy	87° / 60°	20%
Aug 01	Partly Cloudy	83° / 59°	20%
Aug 02	Partly Cloudy	87° / 60°	0%

1. For what dates does the table give weather forecasts?

____

2. On which date might there be isolated thunderstorms?

____

3. What is the difference between the high and low temperature on August 1?

____

4. What is the probability of precipitation on July 30?

____

5. What day(s) has (have) the greatest chance for rain?

____

6. What are the odds *for* having rain on July 31?

____

7. What are the odds *against* having rain on July 29?

____

8. **High-Use Academic Words** What is an *exercise,* as mentioned in the study skill?

   a. something done to develop a skill
   b. a group or set alike in some way

Puzzle 12-2

Experimental Probability

A writer for a consumer magazine did research to find the best brand of denim jeans. To learn about the different brands, he interviewed the quality control engineer at each company. He compiled his research in the table below. Find *P*(defective) for each company, then place the name of the company under the proper ranking in the puzzle below.

Manufacturer	Number of Jeans Produced	Defective Jeans	*P* (defective)
Blue Jeans Plus	16,066	482	
Rugged Jeans, Inc.	7,920	198	
Denim Deluxe Co.	15,800	316	
Durable Denim, Co.	6,514	228	

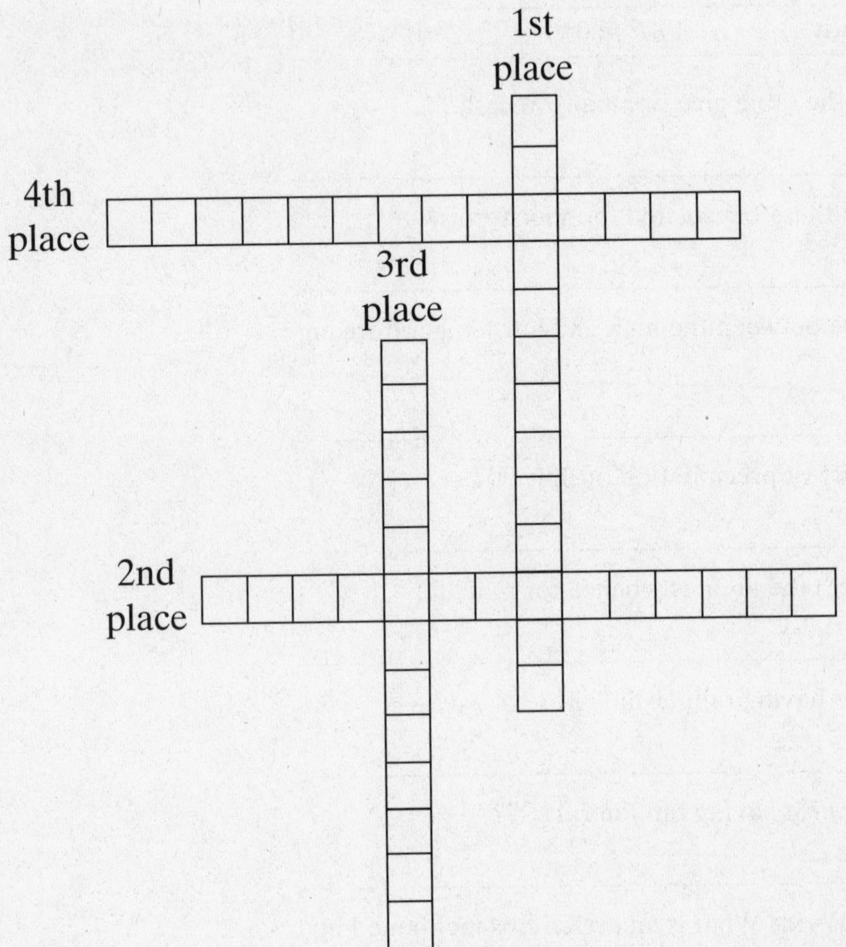

Name ______________________ Class ______________ Date ______________

Practice 12-3

Sample Spaces

Make a table to show the sample space and find the number of outcomes. Then find the probability.

1. A theater uses a letter to show which row a seat is in, and a number to show the column. If there are eight rows and ten columns, what is the probability that you select a seat at random that is in column 1? ______________

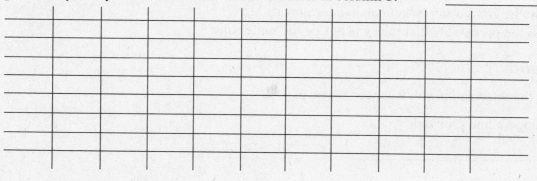

Make a tree diagram. Then find the probability.

2. A coin is tossed three times.
   a. Make a tree diagram that shows all the possible outcomes of how the coin will land.
   b. Find the probability that the coin will land heads up all three times or tails up all three times. ______________

Use the counting principle.

3. A pizza company makes pizza in three different sizes: small, medium, and large. There are four possible toppings: pepperoni, sausage, green pepper, and mushroom. How many different kinds of pizza with one topping are available? ______________

4. You can choose from three types of sandwiches for lunch and three types of juice. How many possible lunch combinations of sandwich and juice can you have? ______________

Susan has red, blue, and yellow sweaters. Joanne has green, red, and white sweaters. Diane's sweaters are red, blue, and mauve. Each girl has only one sweater of each color and will pick a sweater to wear at random. Find each probability.

5. *P*(each girl chooses a different color) ______________

6. *P*(each girl chooses the same color) ______________

7. *P*(two girls choose the same color, and the third chooses a different color) ______________

8. *P*(each girl chooses a red sweater) ______________

Name ______________________ Class ______________ Date ______________

12-3 • Guided Problem Solving

GPS Student Page 595, Exercise 23:

a. **Clothes** Ardell has four suit jackets (white, blue, green, and tan) and four dress shirts in the same colors. How many different jacket/shirt outfits does Ardell have?

b. Suppose he grabs a suit jacket and a dress shirt without looking. What is the probability that they will not be the same color?

Understand

1. Circle the information you will need to solve.

2. How do you find probability?

____

____

Plan and Carry Out

3. How many different suit jackets are there? __________

4. How many different dress shirts are there? __________

5. Using the counting principle, how many different jacket/shirt outfits does Ardell have? __________

6. How many same color jacket/shirt outfits does Ardell have? __________

7. How many different color jacket/shirt outfits does Ardell have? __________

8. What is the probability that they will *not* be the same color? __________

Check

9. How else could you find the total number of jacket/shirt outfits?

____

Solve Another Problem

10. **a.** Joseph has three pairs of shoes (white, brown, and black) and four pairs of socks (white, brown, black, and blue). How many sock/shoe pairs are there?

b. If Joseph selects a pair of shoes and a pair of socks without looking, what is the probability they will be the same color?

____

Name ______________________ Class ____________ Date ____________

Practice 12-3

Sample Spaces

Make a table to show the sample space and find the number of outcomes. Then find the probability.

1. A theater uses a letter to show which row a seat is in, and a number to show the column. If there are eight rows and ten columns, what is the probability that you select a seat at random that is in column 1? ____________

2. A coin is tossed three times. Make a tree diagram that shows all the possible outcomes of how the coin will land.

Use the counting principle.

3. A pizza company makes pizza in three different sizes: small, medium, and large. There are four possible toppings: pepperoni, sausage, green pepper, and mushroom. How many different kinds of pizza with one topping are available? ____________

4. You can choose from three types of sandwiches for lunch and three types of juice. How many possible lunch combinations of sandwich and juice can you have? ____________

Susan has red, blue, and yellow sweaters. Joanne has green, red, and white sweaters. Diane's sweaters are red, blue, and mauve. Each girl has only one sweater of each color and will pick a sweater to wear at random. Find each probability.

5. *P*(each girl chooses a different color) ____________

6. *P*(each girl chooses the same color) ____________

Activity Lab 12-3

Sample Spaces

You are going to print T-shirts to sell at your club's fundraiser. Use the chart below to draw a tree diagram that lists the possible outcomes. Use your tree diagram to answer the questions.

Sizes	Shirt Colors	Ink Colors
Small	Black	Black
Medium	Red	White
Large	Gray	
X-Large		

1. How many different T-shirts can you print? ______________

2. Are all of the possible combinations practical choices or should you eliminate some of the combinations? Why?

   ____

3. How many of the different combinations will you actually print to sell for your fundraiser?

   ____

4. Each T-shirt costs \$5 to make and sells for \$12.50. If you want to raise at least \$900 for your club, how many T-shirts should you print?

   ____

5. To raise the \$900, you are going to print an equal number of each practical combination. Of the T-shirts you print, how many will be medium, black, and have white ink?

   ____

6. How many red T-shirts will you print? ______________

7. You take a survey and discover that the most popular colors are red and black, so you decide not to print the gray T-shirts. How many different combinations will you print? (Take into account your answers from Exercises 2 and 3 above.)

   ____

Name ______________________ Class ______________ Date ______________

Reteaching 12-3

Sample Spaces

The set of all possible outcomes of an experiment is called the **sample space.**

You can use a *tree diagram* or a table to show the sample space for an experiment. The tree diagram below shows the sample space for spinning the spinner and tossing a coin.

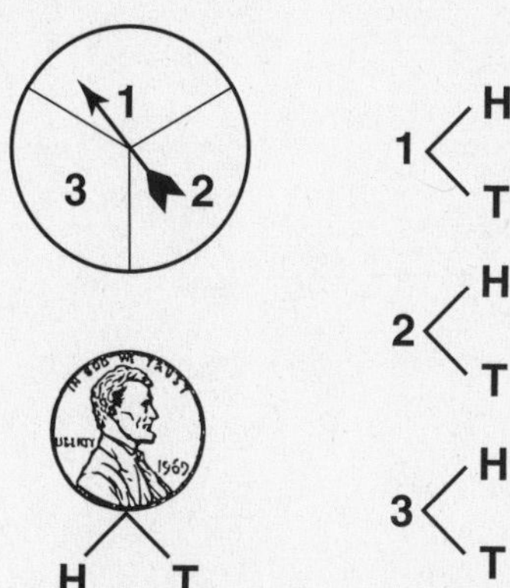

There are 6 possible outcomes: 1H, 1T, 2H, 2T, 3H, 3T. What is the probability of spinning a 3 and tossing heads? There is one favorable outcome (3H) out of 6 possible outcomes. The probabilty is $\frac{1}{6}$.

You can use the *counting principle* to find the number of possible outcomes: If there are *m* ways of making one choice and *n* ways of making a second choice, then there are $m \times n$ ways of making the first choice followed by the second.

Evelyn and Kara are planning to go skating or to a movie. Afterward they want to go out for pizza, tacos, or cheeseburgers. How many possible choices do they have?

- There are *two choices* for an activity and *three choices* for food.
- First choices × Second choices

  $2 \quad \times \quad 3 \quad = 6$

There are 6 possible choices.

Complete the tree diagram to show the sample space.

1. Roll a number cube and toss a coin. What is the probability of getting (4, Heads)?

1 2 3 4 5 6

_ _ _ _ _ _ _ _ _ _ _ _

Number of outcomes ______________

$P(4, \text{heads}) =$ ______________

Use the counting principle to find the number of possible outcomes.

2. 4 kinds of yogurt and 8 toppings

____

3. 6 shirts and 9 pairs of slacks

____

4. 3 types of sandwiches and 3 flavors of juice

____

5. 4 types of bread and 6 different sandwich spreads

____

Name ______________________ Class ______________ Date ______________

Enrichment 12-3

Sample Spaces

Decision Making

Suppose you need to wash your car, meet a friend for lunch, and go to the bank between 10:00 A.M. and 2:00 P.M. on Saturday. The bank closes at 11:30 A.M. You need to decide in which order you will complete these tasks.

1. Make a tree diagram to show the possible orders.

2. How many possible orders does the diagram show?

____

3. Can you eliminate any of the activities as a first choice? Explain.

____

4. Can you eliminate any of the activities as a last choice? Explain.

____

5. In what order will you perform the tasks on Saturday?

____

6. Suppose you also want to go to the library.

a. How many possible orders are there now?

____

b. How will this affect the order in which you perform the tasks? Explain.

____

____

____

Name ______________________ Class ______________ Date ______________

Puzzle 12-3

Sample Spaces

The table below represents a sample space for rolling two number cubes. Study the ordered pairs to find the value of each variable.

	g	a	c	3	y	7
6	$(g, 6)$	$(a, 6)$	$(c, 6)$	$(3, 6)$	$(5, 6)$	$(7, 6)$
d	(g, d)	(a, d)	$(1, d)$	$(3, 12)$	(y, d)	$(7, d)$
x	(g, x)	(a, x)	(c, x)	$(3, x)$	(y, x)	$(7, 4)$
f	$(11, f)$	$(a, 10)$	(c, f)	$(3, f)$	(y, f)	$(7, f)$
2	$(g, 2)$	$(a, 2)$	$(c, 2)$	$(3, 2)$	$(y, 2)$	$(7, 2)$
b	(g, b)	$(9, b)$	$(c, 8)$	$(3, b)$	(y, b)	$(7, b)$

$g =$ ____ $a =$ ____ $c =$ ____ $y =$ ____

$d =$ ____ $x =$ ____ $f =$ ____ $b =$ ____

Check your answers by substituting them in the equations below.

$g + a = 20$ $c + y = 6$

$d - x = 8$ $f - b = 2$

Name ______________________ Class ______________ Date ______________

Practice 12-4

Compound Events

Each letter in the word MASSACHUSETTS is written on a card. The cards are placed in a basket. Find each probability.

1. What is the probability of selecting two S's if the first card is replaced before selecting the second card?

2. What is the probability of selecting two S's if the first card is not replaced before selecting the second card?

You roll a fair number cube. Find each probability.

3. *P*(3, then 5)

4. *P*(2, then 2)

5. *P*(5, then 4, then 6)

6. *P*(6, then 0)

Four girls and eight boys are running for president or vice president of the Student Council. Find each probability.

7. Find the probability that two boys are elected.

8. Find the probability that two girls are elected.

9. Find the probability that the president is a boy and the vice president is a girl.

10. Find the probability that the president is a girl and the vice president is a boy.

A box contains ten balls, numbered 1 through 10. Marisha draws a ball. She records its number and then returns it to the bag. Then Penney draws a ball. Find each probability.

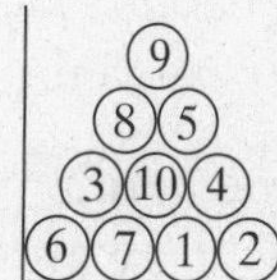

11. *P*(9, then 3)

12. *P*(even, then odd)

13. *P*(odd, then 2)

14. *P*(the sum of the numbers is 25)

15. *P*(prime, then composite)

16. *P*(a factor of 8, then a multiple of 2)

Name ______________________ Class ______________ Date ______________

12-4 • Guided Problem Solving

GPS Student Page 602, Exercise 26:

Events with no outcomes in common are called *disjoint events* or *mutually exclusive events*. To find the probability of mutually exclusive events, add the probabilities of the individual events. Suppose you select a number from 21 to 30 at random. What is the probability of selecting a number that is even or prime?

Understand

1. What are disjoint or mutually exclusive events?

____

2. What are you being asked to do?

____

____

3. Why are selecting an even and selecting a prime number between 21 and 30 disjoint events?

____

Plan and Carry Out

4. How many numbers are there from 21 to 30? (Remember to include 21 and 30.) ______________
5. List all the even numbers between 21 and 30. How many are there? ______________
6. What is the probability of choosing an even number between 21 and 30? ______________
7. List all the prime numbers between 21 and 30. How many are there? ______________
8. What is the probability of choosing a prime number between 21 and 30? ______________
9. What is the probability of choosing an even or prime number between 21 and 30? ______________

Check

10. Write your answer as a fraction, decimal, and percent. ______________

Solve Another Problem

11. Suppose you roll a number cube. What is the probability that you roll a number less than 3 or a number greater than or equal to 5?

____

Name ______________________ Class ______________ Date ______________

Practice 12-4

Compound Events

Each letter in the word MASSACHUSETTS is written on a card. The cards are placed in a basket. Find each probability.

1. What is the probability of selecting two S's if the first card is replaced before selecting the second card?

____

2. What is the probability of selecting two S's if the first card is not replaced before selecting the second card?

____

You roll a fair number cube. Find each probability.

3. *P*(3, then 5)

____

4. *P*(2, then 2)

____

5. *P*(5, then 4, then 6)

____

6. *P*(6, then 0)

____

Four girls and eight boys are running for president or vice president of the Student Council. Find each probability.

7. Find the probability that two boys are elected.

____

8. Find the probability that two girls are elected.

____

A box contains ten balls, numbered 1 through 10. Marisha draws a ball. She records its number and then returns it to the bag. Then Penney draws a ball. Find each probability.

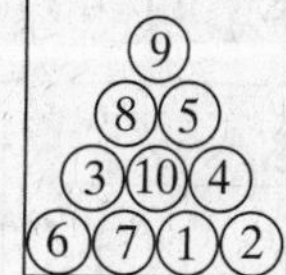

9. *P*(9, then 3)

____

10. *P*(even, then odd)

____

11. *P*(odd, then 2)

____

12. *P*(the sum of the numbers is 25)

____

Name _______________ Class _______________ Date _______________

Activity Lab 12-4

Compound Events

Materials needed: four blue cubes, six red cubes, and a bag

1. A bag contains six red cubes and four blue cubes. You remove one cube at random. What is the probability that it is red? What is the probability that it is blue?

____

2. Suppose you remove one cube, replace it, and then remove a second cube. Are these events dependent or independent? What is the probability of you removing two red cubes?

____

3. Suppose you remove one cube, then, without replacing the first, you remove a second cube. Are these events dependent or independent? What is the probability of removing two red cubes?

____

4. Work in small groups. Place the ten colored cubes into the bag, and take turns removing one cube, replacing it, and then removing a second cube. Record your results in the table below, for example, if you remove a blue cube and then a red cube, write "Blue Red" in one of the squares of the table. Take turns drawing cubes from the bag until the table is complete.

5. Using the information from the table, find the experimental probability of removing two red cubes from the bag. How does this compare to your answer from Exercise 2?

____

6. Repeat the exercise, but **do not** replace the first cube before drawing the second. Once again, take turns drawing cubes from the bag and recording your group's results in the table.

7. Find the experimental probability of drawing two red cubes from the bag. Compare your answer to the answers from Exercises 3 and 5. Explain any similarities or differences.

____

Name ______________________ Class ______________ Date ______________

Reteaching 12-4

Compound Events

If you toss a coin and roll a number cube, the events are **independent.** The outcome of one event does not affect the outcome of the second event.

Find the probability of tossing a heads (H) and rolling an even number (E).

Find $P(\text{H and E})$. H and E are independent.

① Find $P(\text{H})$:

$$P(\text{H}) = \frac{1 \text{ heads}}{2 \text{ sides}} = \frac{1}{2}$$

② Find $P(\text{E})$:

$$P(\text{E}) = \frac{3 \text{ evens}}{6 \text{ faces}} = \frac{1}{2}$$

③ $P(\text{H and E}) = P(\text{H}) \times P(\text{E}) = \frac{1}{2} \times \frac{1}{2} = \frac{1}{4}$

If the outcome of the first event affects the outcome of the second event, the events are **dependent.**

A bag contains 3 blue and 3 red marbles. Draw a marble, then draw a second marble without replacing the first marble. Find the probability of drawing 2 blue marbles.

① Find $P(\text{blue})$.

$$P(\text{blue}) = \frac{3 \text{ blue}}{6 \text{ marbles}} = \frac{1}{2}$$

② Find $P(\text{blue after blue})$.

$$P(\text{blue after blue}) = \frac{2 \text{ blue}}{5 \text{ marbles}} = \frac{2}{5}$$

③ Find $P(\text{blue, then blue})$

$P(\text{blue, then blue})$
$= P(\text{blue}) \times P(\text{blue after blue})$

$= \frac{1}{2} \times \frac{2}{5} = \frac{1}{5}$

In Exercises 1–3, you draw a marble at random from the bag of marbles shown. Then, you replace it and draw again. Find each probability.

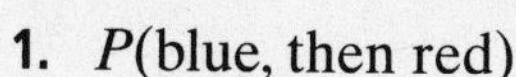

1. $P(\text{blue, then red})$ ________
2. $P(\text{2 reds})$ ________
3. $P(\text{2 blues})$ ________

Next, you draw two marbles randomly *without* replacing the first marble. Find each probability.

4. $P(\text{blue, then red})$ ________
5. $P(\text{2 reds})$ ________
6. $P(\text{2 blues})$ ________

You draw two letters randomly from a box containing the letters M, I, S, S, O, U, R, and I.

7. Suppose you do not replace the first letter before drawing the second. What is $P(\text{M, then I})$?

____

8. Suppose you replace the first letter before drawing the second. What is $P(\text{M, then I})$?

____

Name ______________________ Class ______________ Date ______________

Enrichment 12-4

Compound Events

Critical Thinking

A spinning top has four sides with one letter on each side: A, B, C, D. When a child spins the top, any one of the four letters is equally likely to come up.

1. How many sides does the top have?

____

2. Will the result of the first spin change the possible outcome for the second spin?

____

3. How many possible outcomes are there for one spin?

____

4. How many ways can you spin a B?

____

5. What is the probability of spinning a B on the

   a. first spin? ______________ b. second spin? ______________

6. How can you find the probability of two events?

____

7. Are the spins of the top dependent or independent events?

____

8. What is the probability of spinning 2 Bs in a row?

____

9. How did you decide whether or not the events were dependent or independent?

____

____

10. What is the probability of spinning an A, then spinning a B, on the top?

____

Name ______________________ Class ______________ Date ______________

Puzzle 12-4

Compound Events

Decide whether each set of events is independent or dependent, then calculate each probability. Order the sets of events from most probable to least probable and write the corresponding letters in the blanks to solve the puzzle at the bottom of the page.

I. You roll a number cube twice.

Independent Dependent *P*(odd, then 5) = __________

D. There are 15 girls and 10 boys in Ms. Geller's science class. Ms. Geller selects a student at random and the student selects a partner at random.

Independent Dependent *P*(both girls) = __________

T. You select a marble from a bag containing 3 red and 4 blue marbles. You put the marble in your pocket and select another marble.

Independent Dependent *P*(red, then green) = __________

E. You flip a coin once, take a break for lunch, then flip the coin three more times.

Independent Dependent *P*(four tails) = __________

N. A bag of 9 coins contains 6 dimes. You select a coin, replace it, and select another coin.

Independent Dependent *P*(both dimes) = __________

S. A bag contains 4 purple, 3 blue, and 2 red cubes. You select 3 cubes and stack them on the table next to the bag.

Independent Dependent *P*(red, purple, then blue) = __________

I. You select a book from a shelf containing 16 paperbacks and 4 hardcover books. You put the book back and select a second book. You keep it and select a third book.

Independent Dependent *P*(all three paperbacks) = __________

W. There is a 20% chance that you will burn a batch of cookies. There is a 10% chance that you will burn a cake. You bake one batch of cookies and one cake.

Independent Dependent *P*(neither is burnt) = __________

Dodge City, Kansas, is the __ __ __ __ __ __ __ __ city in the United States.

↑ Most probable ... ↑ ... Least probable

Name ______________________ Class ______________ Date ______________

Practice 12-5

Permutations

Find the number of permutations of each group of letters.

1. C, H, A, I, R ____________
2. L, I, G, H, T, S ____________
3. C, O, M, P, U, T, E, R ____________

Write the number of permutations in factorial form. Then simplify.

4. S, P, A, C, E ____________
5. P, L, A, N ____________
6. S, A, M, P, L, E ____________

Find the number of three-letter permutations of the letters.

7. A, P, Q, M ____________
8. L, S, U, V, R ____________
9. M, B, T, O, D, K ____________

Find the value of each factorial expression.

10. 9! ____________
11. 7! ____________
12. 6! ____________

Solve.

13. Suppose that first-, second-, and third-place winners of a contest are to be selected from eight students who entered. In how many ways can the winners be chosen? ____________
14. Antonio has nine different sweat shirts that he can wear for his job doing yardwork. He has three pairs of jeans and two pairs of sweat pants. How many different outfits can Antonio wear for the yardwork? ____________
15. Ramona has a combination lock for her bicycle. She knows the numbers are 20, 41, and 6, but she can't remember the order. How many different arrangements are possible? ____________
16. Travis is planting 5 rosebushes along a fence. Each rosebush has a different flower color: red, yellow, pink, peach, and white. If he wants to plant 3 rosebushes in between white and yellow rosebushes, in how many ways can he plant the 5 rosebushes? ____________

Name ______________________ Class ______________ Date ______________

12-5 • Guided Problem Solving

GPS Student Page 609, Exercise 34:

Tourism The owner of a tour boat business has 15 employees. There are three different jobs—driving the boat, checking the boat for safety, and managing the money. In how many different ways can the jobs be assigned to three different people?

Understand

1. Circle the information you will need to solve.
2. What are you being asked to do?

   ____

   ____

3. What is a permutation?

   ____

   ____

Plan and Carry Out

4. How many people can be assigned to do the first job, driving the boat? ______________
5. After the driver has been chosen, how many people can be assigned to do the second job, checking the boat for safety?

   ____

6. After the manager has been chosen, how many people can be assigned to do the third job, managing the money?

   ____

7. Using the counting principle, in how many different ways can the jobs be assigned? ______________

Check

8. Explain why you do not use 15! in this exercise.

   ____

   ____

Solve Another Problem

9. There are four offices open in the student government: president, vice-president, treasurer, and secretary. If 18 students run in the election, how many ways can the offices be filled?

   ____

Name ______________________ Class ______________ Date ______________

Practice 12-5

Permutations

Find the number of permutations of each group of letters.

1. C, H, A, I, R
2. L, I, G, H, T, S
3. C, O, M, P, U, T, E, R

Write the number of permutations in factorial form. Then simplify.

4. S, P, A, C, E

5. P, L, A, N

Find the number of three-letter permutations of the letters.

6. A, P, Q, M
7. L, S, U, V, R

Find the value of each factorial expression.

8. 7!
9. 6!

Solve.

10. Suppose that first-, second-, and third-place winners of a contest are to be selected from eight students who entered. In how many ways can the winners be chosen?

11. Antonio has nine different sweat shirts that he can wear for his job doing yardwork. He has three pairs of jeans and two pairs of sweat pants. How many different outfits can Antonio wear for the yardwork?

12. Ramona has a combination lock for her bicycle. She knows the numbers are 20, 41, and 6, but she can't remember the order. How many different arrangements are possible?

Name ______________________ Class ______________ Date ______________

Activity Lab 12-5

Permutations

Materials needed: four index cards

1. Write each of the first four letters of your first name on the index cards, one letter per card. If you have a letter in your name that repeats, use the next letter in your name. For example, if your name is Matthew, don't use M-A-T-T, use M-A-T-H. If your first name does not have enough letters, use letters from your last name. For example, Sara Smith would use S-A-R-M.
2. Copy the table below.

Number of Letters	Number of Ways to Arrange the Letters
1	1
2	
3	
4	
5	
6	

3. **a.** Choose two of the cards and put the other two aside. On a sheet of paper, write all of the different orders in which you can arrange the letters.

   b. Count the number of different ways you can arrange the letters and record your answer in the table.
4. Next, choose three of the cards and list the different ways you can arrange the letters. Use your cards to help you find all of the arrangements by scrambling the letters. Compare each new arrangement to the arrangements already on your list. When you have found all of the arrangements, record the number in your table.
5. **a.** Make a list of arrangements for four cards. Record the number of arrangements in your table.

   b. Look at your results. Use multiplication to find a pattern relating the number of letters to the number of arrangements. Write an expression for your pattern using n letters.
6. Use the pattern you found in Step 7 to calculate how many ways you can arrange five letters and six letters. Write your answers in the table.

Name ______________________ Class ______________ Date ______________

Reteaching 12-5

Permutations

You can arrange the letters A, B, and C in different ways: ABC, ACB, and so on. An arrangement in which order is important is a **permutation.**

How many ways can the three blocks be arranged in a line?

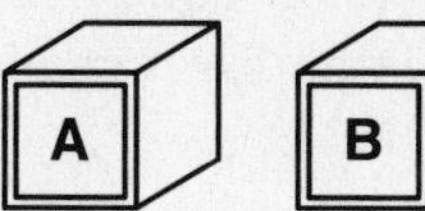

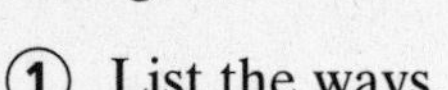

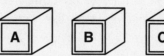

① List the ways.

② Count the number of arrangements.

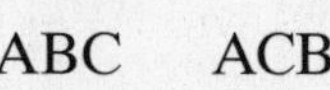

ABC ACB
BAC BCA
CAB CBA

There are 6 possible arrangements.

You can use the counting principle as a shortcut.

choices for 1st block		choices for 2nd block		choice for 3rd block	
3	×	2	×	1	= 6

A factorial can be used to show the product of all integers less than or equal to a number.

$3! = 3 \times 2 \times 1 = 6$

Complete to find the number of permutations for each.

1. In how many ways can you arrange 4 different books on a shelf?

4 × ______ × ______ × 1 = ______

2. In how many ways can the first, second, and third prizes be awarded to 10 contestants?

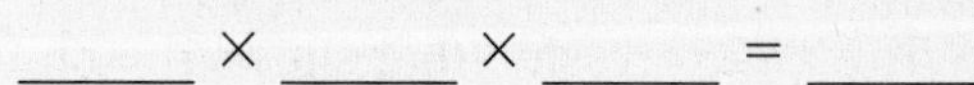

______ × ______ × ______ = ______

Find the number of permutations for each.

3. In how many different ways can the four letters in BIRD be arranged?

____

4. How many different ways can you frame two of five pictures in different frames?

____

5. How many different seating arrangements are possible for a row of five chairs, choosing from six people?

____

6. A basket contains five different pieces of fruit. If three people each choose one piece, in how many different ways can they make their choices?

____

Find the number of two-letter permutations of the letters.

7. R, I, B ______

8. H, E, L, P ______

9. R, A, M, B, L, E ______

10. C, A, N, D, L, E, S ______

Find the number of three-letter permutations of the letters.

11. T, A, B ______

12. R, A, D, I, O ______

13. T, O, P, S ______

14. W, A, L, R, U, S ______

Name ______________________ Class ______________ Date ______________

Enrichment 12-5

Permutations

Critical Thinking

How many ways could you select 3 possible components for a sound system from a tape deck, CD player, laser disk, equalizer, and surround-sound stereo?

1. Circle the number of components that will be in the sound system.
2. Underline the possible components to include in the system.
3. Are you asked for how the system can be assembled or the number of ways it can be assembled?

   ____

4. Write each in factorial notation.

   a. number of ways to select and arrange all components

   ____

   b. number of ways to arrange the selected components

   ____

   c. number of ways to arrange the components that are *not* selected ____________

5. Write an expression that shows the number of ways to assemble the sound system.

   ____

6. How many ways could you select 3 components for the sound system?

   ____

7. Check your answer by making a list of the possible sound-system components. Use T, C, L, E, and S to represent the components.

   ____

8. How many ways could you select 4 possible combinations for a sound system?

   ____

9. How many ways could you select 2 possible combinations for a sound system?

   ____

Name ______________________ Class ______________ Date ______________

12C: Reading/Writing Math Symbols

For use after Lesson 12-5

Study Skill Write assignments down; do not rely only on your memory.

Write the meaning of each mathematical expression.

1. $P(A)$ ______________________

2. $P(\text{not } A)$ ______________________

3. $P(A, \text{ then } B)$ ______________________

____

4. $5!$ ______________________

5. $n!$ ______________________

6. ${}_{n}P_{r}$ ______________________

____

7. ${}_{n}C_{r}$ ______________________

____

8. ${}_{9}C_{4}$ ______________________

____

Write each statement using appropriate mathematical symbols.

9. the probability of event *C* occurring

____

10. the probability of rolling an odd number on a number cube

____

11. the probability of event *D*, and then event *E* occurring

____

12. $7 \cdot 6 \cdot 5 \cdot 4 \cdot 3 \cdot 2 \cdot 1$

____

13. the number of ways 10 items can be chosen 5 at a time where order does not matter

____

14. the number of ways 6 items can be chosen 3 at a time where order matters

____

Name ______________________ Class ______________ Date ______________

Puzzle 12-5

Permutations

Complete the chart. When you are finished, find the sum of all the numbers in the chart and write the sum in the boxes below the puzzle. Use the letter key to fill in the blanks above the sum and solve the puzzle.

Letters	Number permutations of all letters	Number of two-letter permutations	Number of three-letter permutations
F, O, X			
B, E, A, R			
S, N, A, K, E			
M, O, N, K, E, Y			
L, E, O, P, A, R, D			
W, I, L, D, B, O, A, R			

The Sultan of Oman gave Martin Van Buren, the eighth President of the United States, a pair of ___ ___ ___ ___ ___ cubs.

☐☐☐☐☐

Letter Key

A = 17	F = 15	K = 10	P = 13	U = 6
B = 8	G = 1	L = 20	Q = 24	V = 11
C = 24	H = 22	M = 25	R = 2	W = 21
D = 12	I = 7	N = 3	S = 18	X = 9
E = 5	J = 19	O = 16	T = 4	Y = 14

Name ________ Class ________ Date ________

Practice 12-6

Combinations

Find the number of combinations.

1. Choose 3 people from 4.

2. Choose 4 people from 6.

Use the numbers 3, 5, 8, 10, 12, 15, 20. Make a list of all the combinations.

3. 2 even numbers

4. 3 odd numbers

5. 1 even, 1 odd

6. any 2 numbers

7. You just bought five new books to read. You want to take two of them with you on vacation. In how many ways can you choose two books to take?

Charmayne is organizing a track meet. There are 4 runners in her class. Each runner must compete one-on-one against each of the other runners in her class.

8. How many races must Charmayne schedule?

9. Must Charmayne schedule permutations or combinations?

A committee for the end-of-year party is composed of 4 eighth graders and 3 seventh graders. A three-member subcommittee is formed.

10. How many different combinations of eighth graders could there be if there are 3 eighth graders on the subcommittee?

11. How many different combinations of seventh graders could there be if the subcommittee consists of 3 seventh graders?

Name ______________________ Class ______________ Date ______________

12-6 • Guided Problem Solving

GPS Student Page 612, Exercise 22:

Music You have 5 different CDs to play. Your CD player can hold 3 CDs. How many different combinations of 3 CDs can you select?

Understand

1. Circle the information you will need to solve.
2. What are you being asked to do?

   ____

   ____

3. What is a combination?

   ____

   ____

Plan and Carry Out

4. What is the formula you can use to find the number of combinations?

   ____

   ____

5. Find the total number of permutations for the 5 CDs.

   ____

6. Find the total number of permutations for the 3 spaces in your CD player. ______________
7. Find the number of combinations. ______________
8. How many different combinations of 3 CDs can you select?

   ____

Check

9. If you make an organized list of all the possible permutations, how many duplicate groups would you have to eliminate to find the number of combinations? ________

Solve Another Problem

10. You are allowed to take two different elective classes. There are eight different classes you can choose from. How many different combinations of two electives are there?

    ____

Name ______________________ Class ______________ Date ______________

Practice 12-6

Combinations

Find the number of combinations.

1. Choose 3 people from 4.

2. Choose 4 people from 6.

Use the numbers 3, 5, 8, 10, 12, 15, 20. Make a list of all the combinations.

3. 2 even numbers

4. 3 odd numbers

5. 1 even, 1 odd

6. You just bought five new books to read. You want to take two of them with you on vacation. In how many ways can you choose two books to take?

Charmayne is organizing a track meet. There are 4 runners in her class. Each runner must compete one-on-one against each of the other runners in her class.

7. How many races must Charmayne schedule?

8. Must Charmayne schedule permutations or combinations?

9. A committee for the end-of-year party is composed of 4 eighth graders and 3 seventh graders. A three-member subcommittee is formed. How many different combinations of eighth graders could there be if there are 3 eighth graders on the subcommittee?

Name ____________________ Class ____________________ Date ____________________

Activity Lab 12-6

Combinations

An arrangement of items in a particular order is called a *permutation*. You can use this formula to find the number of permutations of n different items, taken r items with no repetitions, when only part of a set is used:

$$_nP_r = \frac{n!}{(n-r)!}$$

For example: How many permutations are there if 5 students are to be selected 3 at a time? To find the number of permutations of 5 students, substitute 5 for n and 3 for r.

$$_5P_3 = \frac{5!}{(5-3)!} = \frac{5!}{2!} = \frac{5 \cdot 4 \cdot 3 \cdot 2 \cdot 1}{2 \cdot 1} = 5 \cdot 4 \cdot 3 = 60$$

There are 60 different ways students can be selected 3 at a time.

A set of items in which order is not important is called a *combination*. You can use this formula to find the number of combinations of n different items, taken r items at a time.

$$_nC_r = \frac{n!}{(n-r)!r!}$$

For example: How many combinations are there if 5 letters are chosen 3 at a time? To find the number of combinations of 5 letters, substitute 5 for n and 3 for r.

$$_5C_3 = \frac{5!}{(5-3)!3!} = \frac{5!}{2!3!} = \frac{5 \cdot 4 \cdot 3 \cdot 2 \cdot 1}{2 \cdot 1 \cdot 3 \cdot 2 \cdot 1} = \frac{5 \cdot 4}{2} = \frac{20}{2} = 10$$

There are 10 different combinations of 5 letters chosen 3 at a time.

Tell which formula you will use to solve each problem. Then find the answer.

1. A random drawing is held to select 2 out 5 students to be sent to a sporting event. How many different pairs of students can be selected?

____

2. How many permutations are there if you have 7 books and need to put four of them on display?

____

3. How many 3-letter "words," real or imaginary, can you make from these letters: T H A N K S? A letter cannot be used twice.

____

____

____

Name ____________________ Class ____________ Date ____________

Reteaching 12-6

Combinations

An arrangement in which order does *not* matter is a **combination.** For example, if you pair Raiz and Carla to play tennis, it is the same as if you pair Carla and Raiz.

How many groups of 2 letters can you form from A, B, C, and D?

① Make an organized list.

② Eliminate any duplicates.

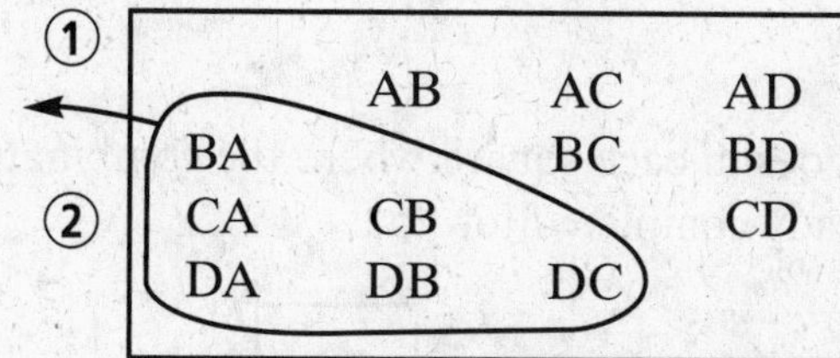

③ List the combinations. AB, AC, AD, BC, BD, CD

There are 6 possible combinations.

You can also get the number of combinations from the number of permutations.

$$\text{combinations} = \frac{\text{total number of permutations}}{\text{number of permutations of smaller group}} = \frac{4 \times 3}{2 \times 1} = 6 \text{ possible combinations}$$

Use the letters C, O, M, P, U, T, E, R for Exercises 1–3

1. How many combinations of 2 vowels are there? Show an organized list with no duplicates.

____

____

____

2. How many combinations of 3 consonants are there? Show an organized list with no duplicates.

____

____

____

3. If you use C, O, M, P, U, T, E, R, S instead of C, O, M, P, U, T, E, R, how many combinations of 3 consonants are there?

____

Find the number of combinations.

4. Sara has 24 different CDs. In how many different ways can she take 2 CDs to school?

____

5 Augusto has purple, green, black, red, and blue T-shirts. In how many ways can he choose 3 for his vacation?

____

6. Abdul selects three light filters from a box of ten different filters. How many different sets could he choose?

____

Name ______________________ Class ______________ Date ______________

Enrichment 12-6

Combinations

Patterns in Numbers

As you know, a set of items in which order is not important is called a *combination.* You can use this formula to find the number of combinations of *n* different items, taken *r* items at a time:

$$_nC_r = \frac{n!}{(n-r)!r!}$$

1. Find the number that goes in each square where the combination is listed. Some are already completed for you.

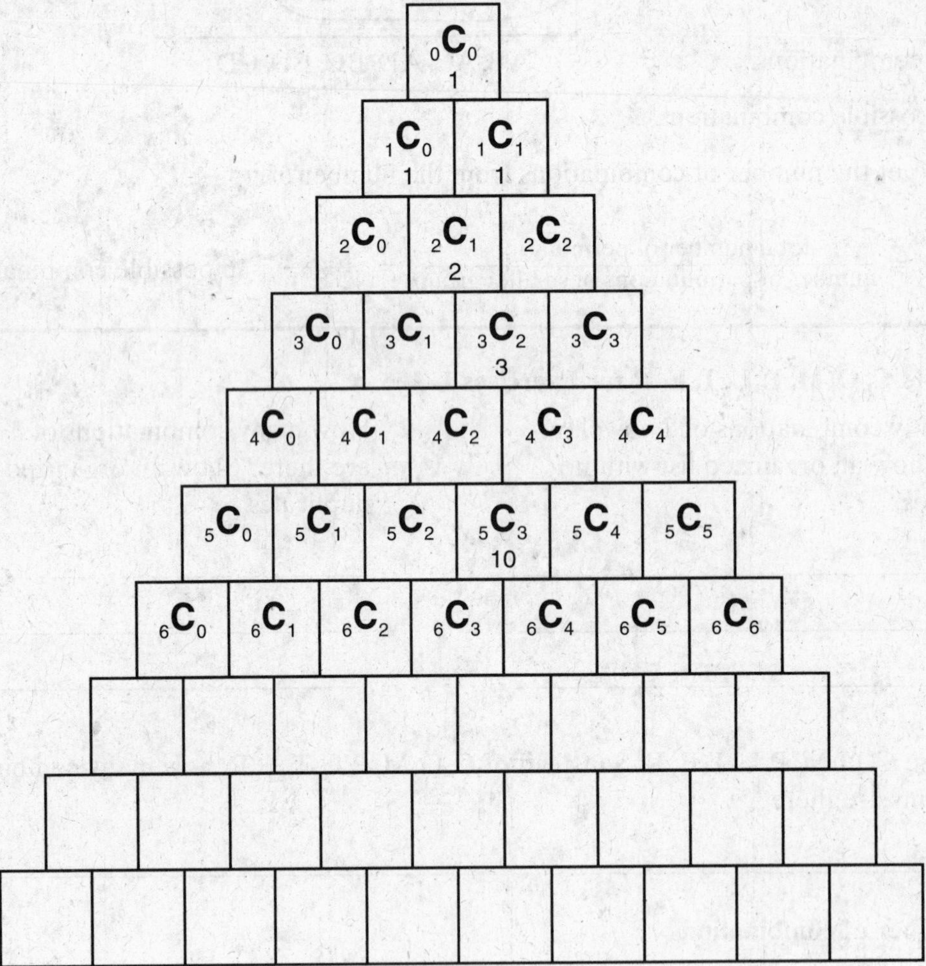

2. Describe any patterns you see. The answers form a pattern known as *Pascal's triangle.*

____

____

____

3. Complete the next three rows of this Pascal's triangle.

12E: Vocabulary Check

For use after Lesson 12-6

Study Skill Strengthen your vocabulary. Use these pages and add cues and summaries by applying the Cornell Notetaking style.

Write the definition for each word or term at the right. To check your work, fold the paper back along the dotted line to see the correct answers.

combination

permutation

event

theoretical probability

experimental probability

12E: Vocabulary Check (continued)

For use after Lesson 12-6

Write the vocabulary word or term for each definition. To check your work, fold the paper forward along the dotted line to see the correct answers.

a grouping of objects in which the order of objects does not matter ______________________

an arrangement of objects in a particular order ______________________

a collection of possible outcomes ______________________

the ratio of the number of favorable outcomes to the number of possible outcomes ______________________

the ratio of the number of times an event occurs to the total number of trials ______________________

Name ______________________ Class ______________ Date ______________

12D: Visual Vocabulary Practice

For use after Lesson 12-6

High-Use Academic Words

Study Skill Mathematics is like learning a foreign language. You have to know the vocabulary before you can speak the language correctly.

Concept List

counting principle	complement	independent events
combinations	permutations	dependent events
outcome	factorial	sample space

Write the concept that best describes each exercise. Choose from the concept list above.

1. $7!$ $= 7 \times 6 \times 5 \times 4 \times 3 \times 2 \times 1$ $= 5{,}040$ ______________	**2.** ABC; AB; AC; BC ______________	**3.** A jar contains 2 red marbles, 1 blue marble, and 1 green marble. You draw one marble and record the color. This is represented by the set {red, blue, and green}. ______________
4. $P(\text{A, then B}) = P(\text{A}) \times \text{P(B)}$ for these events ______________	**5.** If you flip a coin, then flipping heads is an example of this. ______________	**6.** Pedro draws a card from a standard 52-card deck. He then rolls a six-sided number cube. The total number of possible outcomes is $52 \times 6 = 312$. ______________
7. ABC; AB BA; AC CA; BC CB ______________	**8.** $P(\text{A, then B}) = P(\text{A}) \times P(\text{B after A})$ for these events ______________	**9.** Renee rolls a six-sided number cube. If an event represents rolling an even number, then this is represented by the set {1, 3, 5}. ______________

Name ______________________ Class ______________ Date ______________

12F: Vocabulary Review Puzzle

For use with the Chapter Review

Study Skill When using a word bank, read the words first. Then answer the questions.

Complete the crossword puzzle. Use the words from the following list.

parallelogram	conjecture	decagon	equation	mode
combination	symmetry	variable	discount	prime
independent	permutation	dependent	outcome	slope

ACROSS

2. Events are ____________ if the occurrence of one event affects the probability of the occurrence of another event.
4. A figure has __________ if one side of the figure is the mirror image of the other side.
6. four-sided figure with two sets of parallel lines
8. possible result of an action
11. Events are ___________ if the occurrence of one event does not affect the probability of the occurrence of another event.

DOWN

1. prediction that suggests what you expect will happen
2. difference between the original price and the sale price
3. letter that stands for a number
5. ratio that describes the steepness of a line
6. arrangement of objects in a particular order
7. number that occurs most often in a data set
9. grouping of objects in which order does not matter
10. mathematical statement with an equal sign
12. polygon with ten sides
13. whole number with only two factors, itself and the number one

Name ______________________ Class ______________ Date ______________

Puzzle 12-6

Combinations

The local pizza parlor is advertising a special: Buy any three-topping pizza for the price of a single-topping pizza. As a bonus, the management is offering a free pizza to anyone who can tell how many possible combinations there are with the special. Tony guessed 2,730, Jamal guessed 455, and Trey guessed 630. The topping selections are listed below. Each pizza must have three different toppings.

pepperoni	pineapple	tomatoes
sausage	onions	green peppers
Canadian bacon	mushrooms	jalapeños
anchovies	black olives	red peppers
hamburger	green olives	artichoke hearts

Which of the boys won a free pizza? ______________________

Name ______________________ Class ______________ Date ______________

Chapter 12 Project: Everybody Wins

Make Three Number Cubes

Beginning the Chapter Project

Remember the game "Rock, Paper, Scissors"? It is an unusual game because paper wins over rock, rock wins over scissors, and scissors win over paper. You can use mathematics to create and investigate a situation with similar characteristics.

In this chapter project, you design three number cubes A, B, and C, which have a surprising property: A usually beats B, B usually beats C, and C usually beats A. Your final product will be to construct your cubes.

Activities

Activity 1: Analyzing

Suppose you have two number cubes, A and B. Cube A has two 1s and four 4s, and Cube B has six 3s. What is the probability of rolling a 4 on Cube A? What is the probability of rolling a 3 on Cube B? Suppose both number cubes are rolled. Which cube will usually beat the other by having a higher number? Why?

Activity 2: Calculating

Show a sample space of all the possible outcomes for Cubes A and B from Activity 1. What is the probability that A beats B when each cube is rolled?

Activity 3: Designing

Construct three cardboard number cubes A, B, and C. Design your cubes so that A usually beats B, B usually beats C, and C usually beats A. Use sample spaces to support your work.

Name ______________________ Class ______________ Date ______________

Chapter 12 Project: Everybody Wins (continued)

Finishing the Project

Your number cubes should have the property that A usually beats B and B usually beats C, yet C usually beats A. Roll your cubes several times to verify they have this property. How would your use them if you were in charge of a booth at a carnival?

Reflect and Revise

Ask a classmate to review your project with you. Are your sample spaces clear? Are your calculations correct? If necessary, make revisions in the design of your cubes.

Extending the Project

How would your use your number cubes if you were in charge of a booth at a carnival?

Visit PHSchool.com for information and links you might find helpful as you complete your project.

Name ____________________ Class ____________ Date ____________

Chapter Project Manager

Getting Started

Read about the project. As you work on it, you will need several sheets of paper. If available, a spreadsheet program also can be used. Keep all your work for the project in a folder, along with this Project Manager.

Checklist	**Suggestions**
❑ Activity 1: analyzing	❑ Create these two number cubes to help you visualize the problem.
❑ Activity 2: calculating	❑ Remember that a sample space is a list of all possible outcomes.
❑ Activity 3: designing	❑ Draw a net of the cubes on the cardboard first before you start cutting.
❑ Recommendations	❑ Create a rough model of the number cube.

Scoring Rubric

3 You design and construct three cubes (A, B, and C) so that A beats B, B beats C, and C beats A. You provide sample spaces for the cubes in Activity 2 as well as for each of the three pairs of cubes that you designed. Your work also includes either explanations or experimental data showing that your cubes work as predicted.

2 You construct three cubes, and your sample spaces for each pair of cubes show correctly that these cubes satisfy the requirements of the project.

1 You build cubes but either your sample spaces are incorrect or your cubes don't behave as required by the project description.

0 You do not build the cubes, or you fail to use sample spaces or explanations to prove that your cubes behave as they should.

Your Evaluation of Project Evaluate your work, based on the Scoring Rubric.

Teacher's Evaluation of Project

Chapter Project Teacher Notes

About the Project Students will use probability to design a game using three simple number cubes.

Introducing the Project

Ask Students:

- What games have you played that involved chance?
- How did chance affect the outcome of the game?
- How might you use chance to design your own game?

Activity 1: Analyzing

Students will be better able to compare the two cubes if they write their probabilities as decimals or percents.

Activity 2: Calculating

Make sure students count each of the sides on cube A and cube B as a different outcome. There are 36 possible outcomes.

Activity 3: Designing

Students may have a hard time believing this is possible. Suggest that they start with cubes A and B given in Activity 1. Then suggest that they may want to design a cube with four low numbers and two high numbers.

Finishing the Project

You may wish to plan a project day on which students share their completed projects. Encourage students to explain their process as well as their products.

Have students review their methods for designing, making and demonstrating their three number cubes for the project.

Visit PHSchool.com for information and links you might find helpful as you complete your project.

Name ______________________ Class ______________ Date ____________

✔ Checkpoint Quiz 1

Use with Lessons 12-1 through 12-3.

Use the cards at the right for Exercises 1–3. Find the probability of each event as a fraction, a decimal, and a percent.

A P E B E

1. *P*(E) ____________ **2.** *P*(not A) ____________ **3.** *P*(a vowel) ____________

4. Ryan is buying a coat. He must decide if he wants a short coat or a long coat and whether the color should be blue, brown, beige, or black. How many choices does he have? ____________

You flip two coins.

5. Give the sample space. ____________

6. Find *P*(heads, then tails) ____________

7. Find *P*(heads, then heads) ____________

8. The table shows the results of spinning a spinner with four different colored sections. Find the experimental probability of getting "green". ____________

Spin 1	Green
Spin 2	Purple
Spin 3	Green
Spin 4	Blue
Spin 5	Green
Spin 6	Yellow

- - - - ✂ -

Name ______________________ Class ______________ Date ____________

✔ Checkpoint Quiz 2

Use with Lessons 12-4 through 12-6.

A bowl contains 3 red marbles, 4 green marbles, and 5 blue marbles. You select a marble at random, do not replace it, and select a second marble. Find each probability.

1. *P*(red, then red) ________ **2.** *P*(red, then blue) ________ **3.** *P*(green, then blue) ________

Use the letters P, E, A, R, and S. Find the number of permutations and the number of combinations.

4. 2 vowels ____________ **5.** any 3 letters ____________ **6** 1 vowel and 1 consonant ____________

7. Five students get into a line for lunch. How many different arrangements of these students could there be in this line? ____________

Determine whether the situation involves a combination or a permutation. Then answer the question.

8. Fourteen teams are entered in a tournament. Find the number of different ways that teams can place first, second, and third in the rankings. ____________

9. You have ten pizza toppings. How many different 3 topping pizzas can you make? ____________

Name ____________________ Class ____________ Date ____________

Chapter Test — Form A

Chapter 12

Use the data below. Find the experimental probability of each event as a fraction, a decimal, and a percent.

Toss	1	2	3	4	5	6	7	8	9	10	11	12	13	14	15	16	17	18
Heads	✗		✗	✗		✗		✗	✗		✗		✗	✗	✗		✗	✗
Tails		✗			✗		✗			✗		✗				✗		

1. P(heads) ____________ 2. P(tails) ____________

You work at a T-shirt printing business. Of the 4,700 T-shirts shipped, 564 are printed improperly.

3. What is the experimental probability that a T-shirt is printed improperly?

____

4. Predict the number of improperly printed T-shirts in a batch of 2,000.

____

Use the spinner at the right to find the probability of each event.

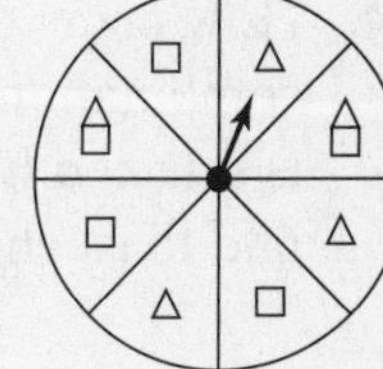

5. $P(\triangle)$ ____________ 6. $P(\square)$ ____________

7. $P(\overset{\triangle}{\square})$ ____________ 8. $P(\triangle \text{ or } \square)$ ____________

9. $P(\triangle \text{or } \overset{\triangle}{\square})$ ____________ 10. $P(\text{neither } \triangle \text{ nor } \square)$ ____________

Suppose you have a bag that contains 4 black, 3 green, 1 red, and 2 orange marbles. Find each probability.

11. P(green) ____________ 12. P(green or red) ____________

13. P(not orange) ____________ 14. P(green or black) ____________

15. P(red, then orange when red is not replaced) ____________ 16. P(black) ____________

The letters G E O M E T R Y are written on a set of cards. You mix the cards thoroughly. Without looking, you draw one letter, replace it, then draw another. Find each probability.

17. P(E, T) ____________ 18. P(M, Y) ____________

Chapter Test (continued) Form A

Chapter 12

A coin is tossed three times. Use this information to solve Exercises 19–21.

19. List the sample space.

____

20. P(tossing heads exactly twice)

____

21. P(tossing tails at least twice)

____

Solve.

22. How many two-letter permutations can be made from the letters L, M, N, O, and P?

____

23. How many three-letter permutations can be made from the letters in the word BLACK?

____

A restaurant offers the following choices for breakfast:

Eggs: scrambled, fried, or poached
Meat: bacon, sausage, or ham
Toast: wheat, white, rye, or pumpernickel

Use this information for Exercises 24 and 25.

24. How many different breakfast combinations are possible if one item is selected from each list of eggs, meat, and toast choices?

____

25. The Super Breakfast allows you to select two items from the meat list. How many breakfast combinations are possible if you select one each of the eggs and toast choices and two different meat choices?

____

Name ______________________ Class ______________ Date ______________

Chapter Test — Form B

Chapter 12

Use the data below. Find the experimental probability of each event as a fraction, a decimal, and a percent.

Toss	1	2	3	4	5	6	7	8	9	10	11	12	13	14	15	16	17	18
Heads	✗		✗	✗		✗		✗	✗		✗		✗	✗	✗		✗	✗
Tails		✗			✗		✗			✗		✗				✗		

1. *P*(heads) ______________ 2. *P*(tails) ______________

You work at a T-shirt printing business. Of the 4,700 T-shirts shipped, 564 are printed improperly.

3. What is the experimental probability that a T-shirt is printed improperly?

____

4. Predict the number of improperly printed T-shirts in a batch of 2,000.

____

Use the spinner at the right to find the probability of each event.

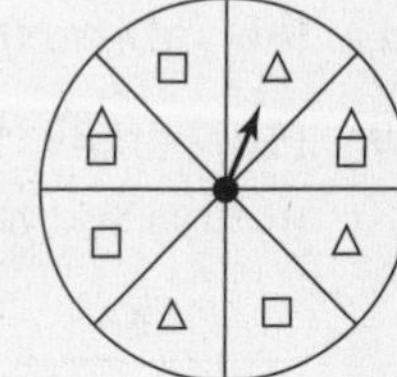

5. *P*(△) ______________ 6. *P*(□) ______________

7. *P*(△ on □) ______________ 8. *P*(△ or □) ______________

Suppose you have a bag that contains 4 black, 3 green, 1 red, and 2 orange marbles. Find each probability.

9. *P*(green) ______________ 10. *P*(green or red) ______________

11. *P*(not orange) ______________ 12. *P*(green or black) ______________

The letters G E O M E T R Y are written on a set of cards. You mix the cards thoroughly. Without looking, you draw one letter, replace it, then draw another. Find each probability.

13. *P*(E, T) ______________ 14. *P*(M, Y) ______________

Chapter Test (continued) Form B

Chapter 12

A coin is tossed three times. Use this information to solve Exercises 15–17.

15. List the sample space.

____

____

16. Find P(tossing heads exactly twice).

____

17. Find P(tossing tails at least twice).

____

Solve.

18. How many two-letter permutations can be made from the letters L, M, N, O, and P?

____

A restaurant offers the following choices for breakfast:

Eggs: scrambled, fried, or poached
Meat: bacon, sausage, or ham
Toast: wheat, white, rye, or pumpernickel

Use this information for Exercises 19 and 20.

19. How many different breakfast combinations are possible if one item is selectedfrom each list of eggs, meat, and toast choices?

____

20. The Super Breakfast allows you to select two items from the meat list. How many breakfast combinations are possible if you select one each of the eggs and toast choices and two different meat choices?

____

Name ______________________ Class ______________ Date ______________

Alternative Assessment Form C

Chapter 12

INITIAL CHANGES

The lists below show the most common names given to girl and boy babies in the United States in the years 1925, 1950, and 1970.

Girls

1925	1950	1970
1. Mary	1. Linda	1. Michelle
2. Barbara	2. Mary	2. Jennifer
3. Dorothy	3. Patricia	3. Kimberly
4. Betty	4. Susan	4. Lisa
5. Ruth	5. Deborah	5. Tracy

Boys

1925	1950	1970
1. Robert	1. Robert	1. Michael
2. John	2. Michael	2. Robert
3. William	3. James	3. David
4. James	4. John	4. James
5. Charles	5. David	5. John

Show all of your work on a separate sheet of paper.

1. Does the popularity of girls' names and boys' names follow the same patterns of change? Explain your thinking with examples.
2. If you wanted to predict a name among the five most common names in 2000, would it be easier to predict a boy's name or a girl's name? Explain.
3. People use their names to identify their possessions, just as you did by putting your name on this paper. Sometimes people just put their initials on their possessions. Initials can also be used on memos, on legal documents, and on forms such as attendance sheets.
   a. How many possibilities are there for the first initial of all the English-language names in the world? Explain.
   b. How many possibilities are there for the last initial? Explain.

Alternative Assessment (continued) Form C

Chapter 12

4. Show how you would set up a tree diagram of the possible combinations of first and last initials. You do not need to make the whole diagram. You do need to show enough to demonstrate fully the pattern of branching.

5. How many possible combinations of first and last initials are there? Show how you found your answer.

6. Some initials may actually be more common than others because names may be more likely to start with some letters than others. Think of a letter that is very common and a letter that is less common as a first initial for the students in your school. Then think of a letter that is very common and a letter that is less common as a last initial.

Make up two sets of initials, a common set and an unusual set. Then explain why you chose these sets of initials.

Excursion

License plates are used to identify motor vehicles. It is important that each vehicle have a unique license plate number. States issue license plates to each vehicle registered in the state. Each state has a somewhat different system of deciding what numbers will be used.

Early license plates used only numbers for identification. But as the number of cars, trucks, and other vehicles grew, many states began adding letters of the alphabet to their license plates.

Look at the license plates of vehicles in your area. See if you can figure out some of the rules used in assigning numbers and letters. List the rules. Then determine how many different plates are available. Decide whether the rules will allow enough plates to be available 20 years from now, or whether the rules will need to be revised.

Name ______________________ Class ______________ Date ______________

Cumulative Review

Chapters 1–12

Multiple Choice. Circle the letter of the best answer.

1. What is the area of the trapezoid below?

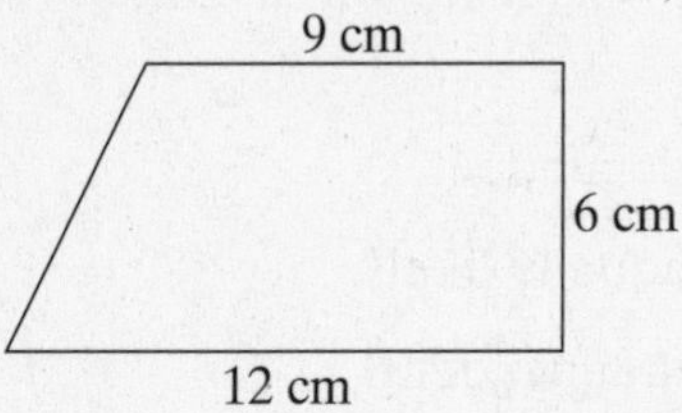

A. 36 cm^2 B. 63 cm^2

C. 64 cm^2 D. 126 cm^2

2. What is the length of the side of a square with area 2.25 m^2?

F. 15 m G. 1.5 m

H. 0.15 m J. 0.015 m

3. A triangle has sides measuring 5 cm, 7 cm, and 13 cm. Which formula could you use to find out whether the triangle is a right triangle?

A. $A = \frac{1}{2}bh$

B. $C = r^2$

C. $a^2 + b^2 = c^2$

D. $P = s_1 + s_2 + s_3$

4. In $\triangle ABC$ below, $\overline{BD}$ is the perpendicular bisector of $\overline{AC}$. The height is 8 in. and the base is 12 in. What are the lengths of $\overline{AB}$ and $\overline{BC}$?

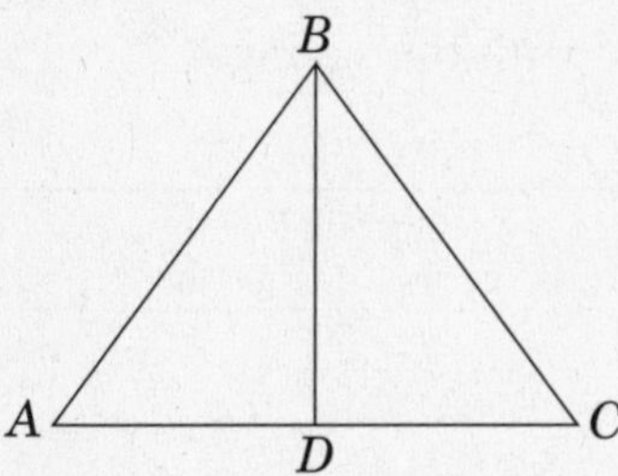

F. 8 in. G. 9 in.

H. 10 in. J. 12 in.

5. Margaret wants to paint a rectangular toy box that is 2 ft wide by 1.5 ft high by 4 ft long. One quart of paint will cover 100 ft^2. How many quarts of paint will she need to buy if she puts two coats on both the inside and outside of the toy box?

A. 1 qt B. 2 qt

C. 3 qt D. 4 qt

6. Which is between 5 and 6?

F. $5\frac{1}{2} + 2\frac{1}{4}$ G. $4\frac{3}{5} + 2\frac{3}{4}$

H. $11\frac{2}{3} - 6\frac{7}{8}$ J. $9\frac{1}{3} - 3\frac{4}{5}$

7. Solve $x - \frac{3}{4} = 9\frac{1}{2}$.

A. $10\frac{1}{4}$ B. 10

C. $9\frac{3}{4}$ D. $8\frac{3}{4}$

8. The length of a room is 12 ft 4 in. The width is 15 ft 6 in. What is the area of the floor of the room in square feet?

F. $17\frac{5}{6}$ ft^2 G. 180 ft^2

H. $180\frac{1}{6}$ ft^2 J. $191\frac{1}{6}$ ft^2

9. Solve $\frac{5}{6}t = 9$.

A. $7\frac{1}{2}$ B. 9

C. 10 D. $10\frac{4}{5}$

10. A bicycle is on sale at $\frac{1}{3}$ off the original price of \$276. What is the sale price of the bike?

F. \$83 G. \$92

H. \$184 J. \$201

11. In this figure, what is the ratio of the shaded area to the unshaded area?

A. $\frac{1}{4}$ B. $\frac{1}{3}$

C. $\frac{3}{4}$ D. $\frac{4}{5}$

Name ______________________ Class ______________ Date ______________

Cumulative Review (continued)

Chapters 1–12

12. Jan earned $125 last week. If she worked 5 hours each day, Monday through Friday, how much did she make per hour?

F. $25 **G.** $5

H. $4.25 **J.** $3.57

13. The trapezoids are similar. What is the length of $\overline{CD}$?

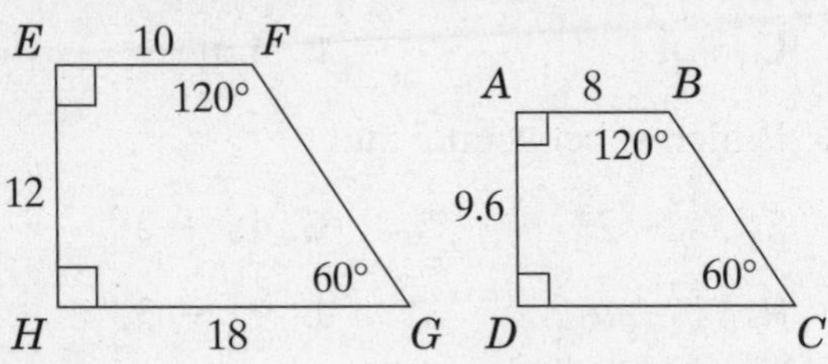

A. 12 **B.** 22

C. 14.4 **D.** 12.4

14. Which proportion will help you find 36% of 290?

F. $\frac{36}{290} = \frac{n}{100}$ **G.** $\frac{290}{36} = \frac{n}{100}$

H. $\frac{n}{290} = \frac{36}{100}$ **J.** $\frac{100}{290} = \frac{n}{36}$

15. Ragan made $5.25 per hour before he received a raise of $.50 per hour. What percent increase is this, rounded to the nearest tenth of a percent?

A. 10.5% **B.** 10%

C. 9.5% **D.** 9%

16. Two angles in a triangle measure 38° and 56°. What type of angle is the third angle?

F. right **G.** straight

H. obtuse **J.** acute

17. A bag contains red, blue, white, and yellow chips. You draw a chip, replace it, and draw another. How many possible outcomes are there?

A. 4 **B.** 10

C. 12 **D.** 16

18. You draw out a second chip from the bag of chips in Exercise 17 above without replacing the first chip. What can you say about the two events?

F. They are dependent.

G. They are equally likely.

H. They are independent.

J. They are unlikely.

19. You know that there are 3 red chips, 4 blue chips, 6 white chips, and 5 yellow chips in a bag. What is the probability that the first two chips you draw are both red if you do not replace the first chip?

A. $\frac{2}{9}$ **B.** $\frac{5}{25}$

C. $\frac{1}{54}$ **D.** $\frac{1}{51}$

Short Response

20.

Week	Savings ($)
4	8
5	10
6	12
7	14

The table above shows Jeffrey's savings between the fourth and seventh weeks. Jeffrey saved at the same rate during this time. Find the slope of the line passing through (7, 14) and (5, 10). How does the slope compare with the savings?

____

____

Chapters 9–12 Answers

Chapter 9

Practice (regular) 9-1

1.

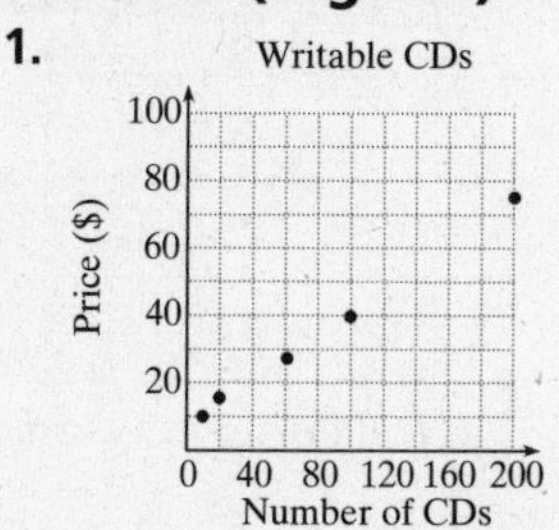

2. about $42,000 **3.** Check students' answers.

4.

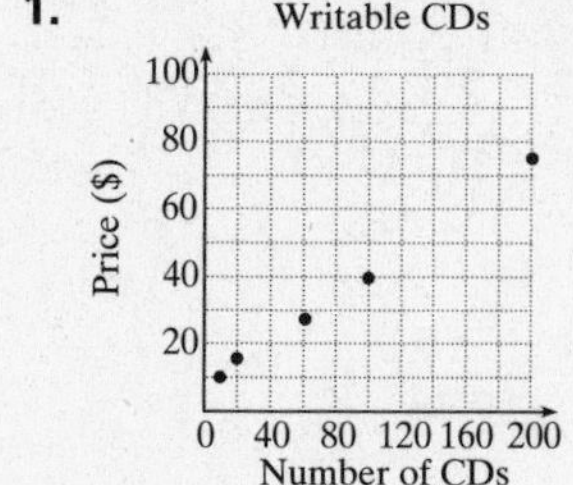

5. About 60°F

Guided Problem Solving 9-1

1. Describe what a graph looks like when both sets of values increase. **2.** the values of the variables shown on the graph's horizontal and vertical axes **3.** farther to the right **4.** farther up **5.** Points farther to the right are located higher up on the coordinate plane. **6.** Sample answer: Distance and time; as time increases, the distance also increases. **7.** Sample answer: Points farther to the right are located lower on the coordinate plane.

Practice (adapted) 9-1

1.

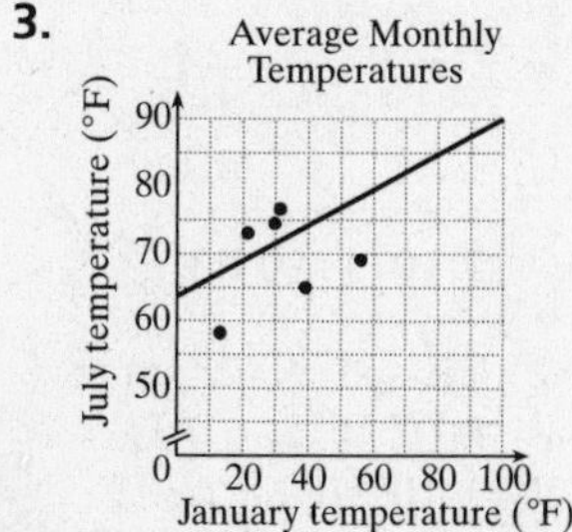

2. Check students' answers.

3.

Average Monthly Temperatures (graph: July temperature (°F) vs. January temperature (°F))

4. About 60°F

Activity Lab 9-1

1. There is an increase in the number of essays. **2.** 1998–1999; shows a significant increase over previous years. **3–4.** Sample answers are given. **3a.** The value will probably increase. **3b.** The number of essays will continue to increase, but at a slower rate. **4.** The number of essays will probably continue to increase, since students will be writing essays in more of their classes.

Reteaching 9-1

1.

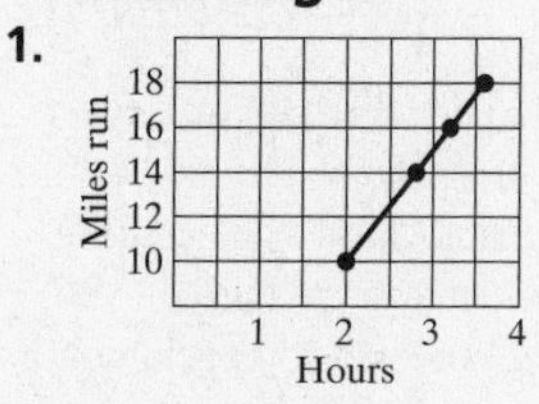

2.

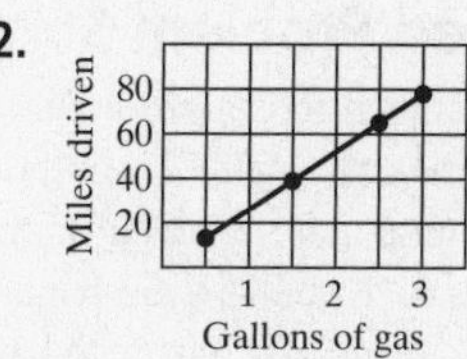

Enrichment 9-1

1.

Sample answer: $30, because the data shows a positive relationship, and the trend line shows a $30 price for July. **2.** Sample answer: Although the stock prices decreased between June and July, the overall trend is an increase in price as time passes. So the stock price will probably continue to increase. **3a.** The stock prices will be half as much but they will continue to increase at about the same rate as in January through June. **3b.** The new trend line is parallel to the old one and shows stock prices increasing at a steady rate.

Puzzle 9-1

△	□	□	□	○	○	⬡	⬡	⬡	⬡	△	□
□	□	○	○	⬡	⬡	⬡	⬡	△	□	□	□
○	○	⬡	⬡	⬡	⬡	△	□	□	□	○	○
⬡	⬡	⬡	⬡	△	□	□	□	○	○	⬡	⬡
⬡	⬡	△	□	**□**	**□**	**○**	**○**	⬡	⬡	⬡	⬡
△	□	□	□	**○**	**○**	**⬡**	**⬡**	⬡	⬡	△	□
□	□	○	○	**⬡**	**⬡**	**⬡**	**⬡**	△	□	□	□
○	○	⬡	⬡	**⬡**	**⬡**	**△**	**□**	□	□	○	○
⬡	⬡	⬡	⬡	△	□	□	□	○	○	⬡	⬡
⬡	⬡	△	□	□	□	○	○	⬡	⬡	⬡	⬡
△	□	□	□	○	○	⬡	⬡	⬡	⬡	△	□
□	□	○	○	⬡	⬡	⬡	⬡	△	□	□	□

Chapters 9–12 Answers (continued)

Practice (regular) 9-2

1. geometric; start with 2 and multiply by 3 repeatedly **2.** geometric; start with 5 and multiply by –2 repeatedly **3.** arithmetic; start with 3 and add 2 repeatedly **4.** neither **5.** neither **6.** arithmetic; start with 17 and add –1 repeatedly **7.** geometric; start with 50 and multiply by –1 repeatedly **8.** neither **9.** 11, −10, 9 **10.** 9, 3, 1 **11.** 54, 110, 222; or 47, 75, 110 **12.** 20, 27, 35 **13.** 2, −6, 18, −54, 162; geometric **14.** 27, 18, 9, 0, −9; arithmetic **15.** 18, 1.8, 0.36, 0.108, 0.0432; neither

Guided Problem Solving 9-2

1. A conjecture is a prediction that suggests what you expect will happen. **2.** After 4 months of training, he will be able to run an 8-minute mile. **3.** Determine whether Mario's conjecture is correct. **4.** 8 min 45 s **5.** 8 min 30 s; 8 min 15 s; 8 min **6.** yes **7.** Sample answer: Start with 8 minutes and add 15 s each month. See if after 4 months the total time is 9 min. **8.** After 6 months Linda can walk a mile in 11 min. Her conjecture is not valid.

Practice (adapted) 9-2

1. geometric; start with 2 and multiply by 3 repeatedly **2.** geometric; start with 5 and multiply by –2 repeatedly **3.** arithmetic; start with 3 and add 2 repeatedly **4.** neither **5.** neither **6.** arithmetic; start with 17 and add –1 repeatedly **7.** 11, −10, 9 **8.** 9, 3, 1 **9.** 2, −6, 18, −54, 162; geometric **10.** 27, 18, 9, 0, −9; arithmetic

Activity Lab 9-2

1. 1, 4, 9, 16; 30 **2.** Sample answer: they are consecutive square numbers. **3.** one 5×5, four 4×4, nine 3×3, sixteen 2×2, twenty-five 1×1; total of 55 squares **4.** one 6×6, four 5×5, nine 4×4, sixteen 3×3, twenty-five 2×2; thirty-six 1×1; total of 91 squares **5.** one 10×10, four 9×9, nine 8×8, sixteen 7×7, twenty-five 6×6, thirty-six 5×5, forty-nine 4×4, sixty-four 3×3, eighty-one 2×2, one hundred 1×1; total of 385 squares

Reteaching 9-2

1. Start with 4 and add 3 repeatedly; 16, 19, 22 **2.** Start with 2 and add 2 repeatedly; 10, 12, 14 **3.** Start with 20 and add 15 repeatedly; 65, 80, 95 **4.** Start with 5 and multiply by 5 repeatedly. 3,125; 15,625; 78,125 **5.** Start with 7 and multiply by 7 repeatedly. 16,807; 117,649; 823,543 **6.** Start with 0.3 and multiply by 3 repeatedly; 24.3, 72.9, 218.7

Enrichment 9-2

1. The third term is equal to the sum of the first two terms. **2.** The fourth term is equal to the sum of the second and third terms **3.** The fifth term is equal to the sum of the third and fourth terms. **4.** Add the last two known terms to find the next term.

5. Sample answers:

Consecutive terms	Product of first and third terms	Square of second term
1, 2, 3	3	4
2, 3, 5	**10**	**9**
3, 5, 8	**24**	**25**
5, 8, 13	**65**	**64**

6. They have a difference of one. **7.** No, it alternates between columns.

Puzzle 9-2

TANZANIA

	Sequence	Pattern	Next three terms	Arithmetic, geometric, both, or neither?
A	3, 8, 13, 18,...	Start with 3 and add 5 repeatedly.	23, 28, 33	arithmetic
N	20, 10, 5, 2.5,...	Start with 20 and multiply by 0.5 repeatedly.	1.25, 0.625, 0.3125	geometric
A	0.1, –1, 10, –100,...	Start with 0.1 and multiply by −10 repeatedly.	1,000; −10,000; 100,000	geometric
N	1, 7, 19, 43,...	Start with 1, add 6, then add 12, then 24, and so on.	91, 187, 379	neither
A	1, 4, 9, 16, 25,...	Square the number of the term (or add consecutive odd integers).	36, 49, 64	neither
T	–8, –8, –8, –8,...	Start with −8 and multiply by 1 (or add 0).	−8, −8, −8	both
I	12, 5, –2, –9,...	Start with 12 and add −7 repeatedly.	−16, −23, −30	arithmetic
Z	1, 0, –2, –6, –14,...	Start with 1 and subtract 1, then 2, then 4, and so on.	−30, −62, −126	neither

Practice (regular) 9-3

1. 40 **2.** 1 **3.** $n + 34$; 134 **4.** $2n + 6$; 206 **5.** $m = 8$; $n = 30$ **6.** $p = 6$; $q = 37$ **7a.**

7b. $3n + 2$

Figure Number	1	2	3	4	5
Number of Squares	5	8	11	14	17

7c. 242 **8.** $6n$; 120 **9.** $3n$; 60

10.

Weight (lb)	1	2	3	4
Cost ($)	2.39	4.78	7.17	9.56

Guided Problem Solving 9-3

Time (h)	0.5	1	1.5	2
Cost ($)	12.50	**25.00**	**37.50**	**50.00**

1. the second row **2.** the cost of a 0.5-h lesson **3.** Determine the cost for 1-h, 1.5-h, and 2-h lessons. **4.** $12.50 **5.** $1 = 0.5 \times 2$ **6.** $25.00 **7.** $12.50 **8.** $37.50 **9.** $50.00 **10.** For the cost for 1 hour, multiply $12.50 by 2. For the cost for 1.5 hours, multiply

Name ______________________ Class ______________ Date ______________

Chapters 9–12 Answers (continued)

\$12.50 by 3. For the cost for 2 hours, multiply \$12.50 by 4.

11.

Time (h)	0.5	1	1.5	2
Cost (\$)	15.75	**31.50**	**47.25**	**63.00**

Practice (adapted) 9-3

1. 40 **2.** 1 **3.** $n + 34$; 134 **4.** $2n + 6$; 206 **5.** $m = 8$; $n = 30$ **6.** $p = 6$; $q = 37$ **7a.**

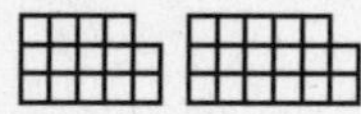

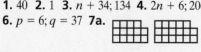

7b. $3n + 2$

Figure Number	1	2	3	4	5
Number of Squares	5	8	11	14	17

8. $6n$; 120 **9.** $3n$; 60

Activity Lab 9-3

Values in table: 3; 5; 8; 13 **1.** The sum is equal to the number of branches for the next year; yes. **2.** 21; 34; 55 **3.** Pattern is 1, 1, 2, 3, 5, 8, 13, 21, 34, 55, 89, 144, 233,...

Reteaching 9-3

1. 4 **2.** $4n$ **3.** Multiply each term by 4. **4.** 24, 28 **5.** $3n - 1$ **6.** n^2 **7.** $5n$

Enrichment 9-3

1–5. Estimates will vary.

Exercise	Length (cm)	Width (cm)	Area (cm²)	Perimeter (cm)
1	8 cm	3 cm	24 cm²	22 cm
2	7 cm	3 cm	21 cm²	20 cm
3	12 cm	2 cm	24 cm²	28 cm
4	5 cm	5 cm	25 cm²	20 cm
5	6 cm	4 cm	24 cm²	20 cm

6. Exercise 4 **7.** Exercise 3 **8.** Exercise 2 **9.** Exercises 2, 4, and 5

Puzzle 9-3

1. 12; 6; 60 **2.** 360; 450; 12 **3.** 12; 1; 17 **4.** −30; 60; 90 **5.** 10; 64; 25 **6.** 81; 270; 101
Sum of solutions: 1601

Practice (regular) 9-4

1. 2; 4; 6; 8 **2.** 5; 6; 7; 8 **3.** 0; 3; 8; 15 **4.** −2; −4; −6; −8 **5.** 4; 7; 10; 13 **6.** 5; 2; −1; −4 **7.** 10; 14; 18; 22 **8.** −4; −3; −2; −1 **9.** 9; 11; 13; 15 **10.** $y = x + 5$ **11.** $y = 4x$ **12.** $y = -3x - 3$ **13.** $y = 2x + 3$ **14.** $y = 3x + 1$ **15.** $y = -2x + 1$ **16a.** $y = 45x$ **16b.** 1,125 words **16c.** 445 minutes

Guided Problem Solving 9-4

1. A function rule tells you what to do to the input in order to get the output. **2.** Write a function rule for the amount of money you put in your piggy bank on any given day of July. **3.** the days in July **4.** the amount of money you put in your piggy bank **5.** n **6.** \$.50 is half of \$1; \$1 is half of \$2 **7.** Multiply by 0.5. **8.** $a = 0.5n$ **9.** 0.50(1) = 0.50, 0.50(2) = 1.00, 0.50(3) = 1.50 **10.** $a = 0.1n$

Practice (adapted) 9-4

1. 2; 4; 6; 8 **2.** 5; 6; 7; 8 **3.** 0; 3; 8; 15 **4.** −2; −4; −6; −8 **5.** 4; 7; 10; 13 **6.** 5; 2; −1; −4 **7.** $y = x + 5$ **8.** $y = 4x$ **9.** $y = 2x + 3$ **10.** $y = 3x + 1$ **11a.** $y = 45x$ **11b.** 1,125 words

Activity Lab 9-4

Table 1: $y = 2x$; 8, 10, 12, 14, 20, 200, 2000 **Table 2:** $y = 2x + 1$; 9, 11, 13, 15, 20, 201, 2001 **2.** Sample Answer: The functon rule is $y = 2x$, and the product of an integer and 2 is always even. **3.** Sample Answer: The function rule is $y = 2x + 1$, and the sum of an even number and 1 is always odd. **4.** Sample answer: $x = 1.5$, $y = 3$ **5.** non-integer values or negative integers **6.** Sample answer: $y = 3x$; 0, 3, 6, 9, 12, 15

Reteaching 9-4

1. output = 2 · input **2.** output = 45 · input

3.

x	y
0	**0**
1	**10**
2	**20**
3	**30**

4.

x	y
0	**−4**
1	**−3**
2	**−2**
3	**−1**

5.

x	y
0	**−1**
1	**2**
2	**5**
3	**8**

6a. $y = 9x$ **6b.** 135 pages **6c.** $8\frac{1}{3}$ minutes

Enrichment 9-4

1.

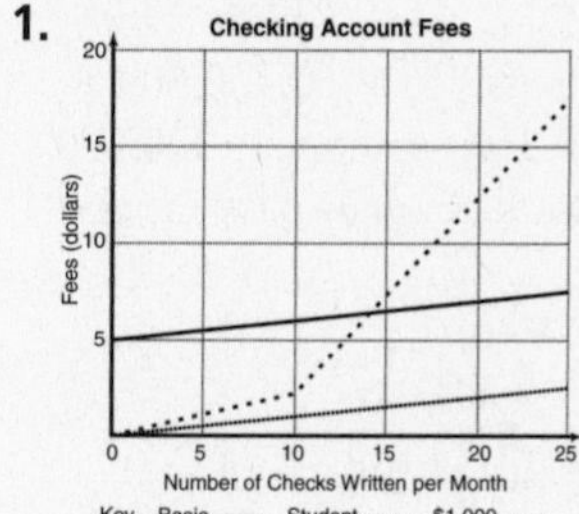

2a. student account **2b.** about \$1 **3a.** Sample answer: Basic Account **3b.** Sample answer: \$7.00 **3c.** Sample answer: Yes; savings in fees by switching from basic to minimum balance are \$5.00. You lose \$4.00/month interest you were earning, bringing the actual savings per month to \$1.00.

Puzzle 9-4

1. O **2.** N **3.** C **4.** K **5.** R **6.** M **7.** B **8.** G **9.** D **10.** I
MOCKINGBIRD

Name ______________________ Class ______________ Date ______________

Chapters 9–12 Answers (continued)

Practice (regular) 9-5

1. 60 mi/h **2.** yes **3.** $d = 60t$
4. Sample answer:

Input	Output
1	60
2	120
3	180
4	240
5	300
6	360

5.

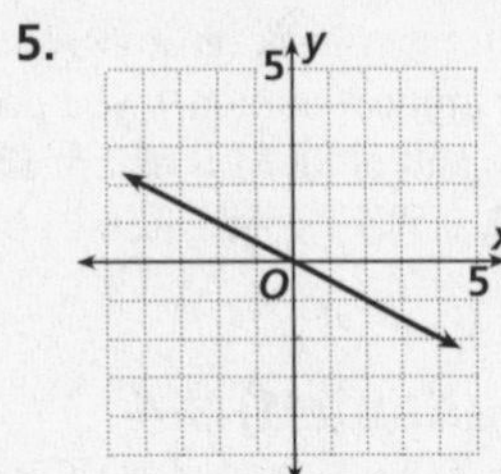

6.

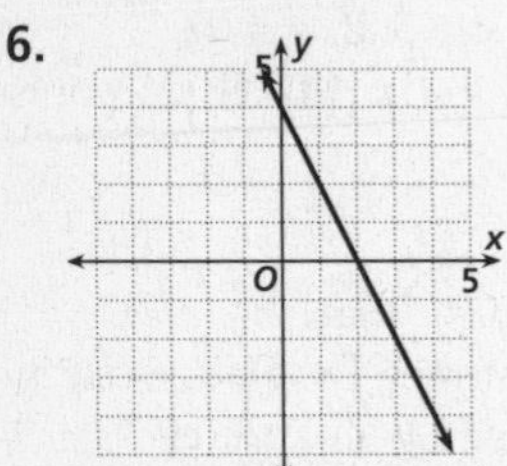

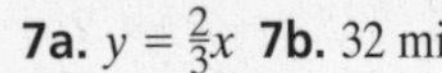

7a. $y = \frac{2}{3}x$ **7b.** 32 mi

Guided Problem Solving 9-5

1. Write a rule for the function represented by the table.
2. 362 mi **3.** 181 mi **4.** hours; distance **5.** $d = 181t$
6. $181(2) = 362, 181(4) = 724, 181(6) = 1{,}086$ **7.** $d = 17{,}500t$

Practice (adapted) 9-5

1. yes **2.** $d = 60t$
3. Sample answer:

Input	Output
1	60
2	120
3	180
4	240
5	300
6	360

4.

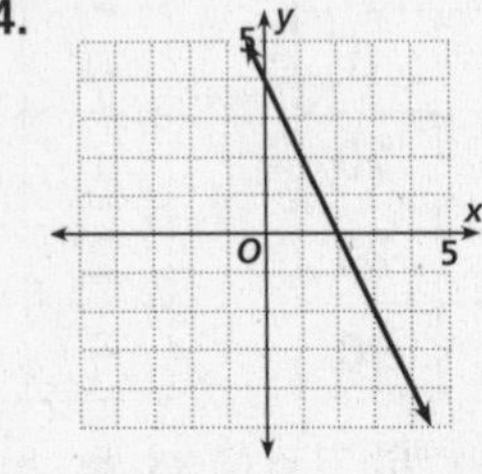

5a. $y = \frac{2}{3}x$ **5b.** 32 mi

Activity Lab 9-5

1. 15v **2.** 5v + 50 **3.** 120 **4.** daily pass: 15, 30, 60, 150, 300; frequent visitor pass: 55, 60, 70, 100, 150; season pass: 120, 120, 120, 120, 120 **5.** Check students' work. **6.** daily pass; the cost is least **7.** $30 **8.** 6 **9.** 15

Reteaching 9-5

1. 4, (−2, 4); 0, (0, 0); −2, (1, −2); −6, (3, −6); −8, (4, −8)
2.

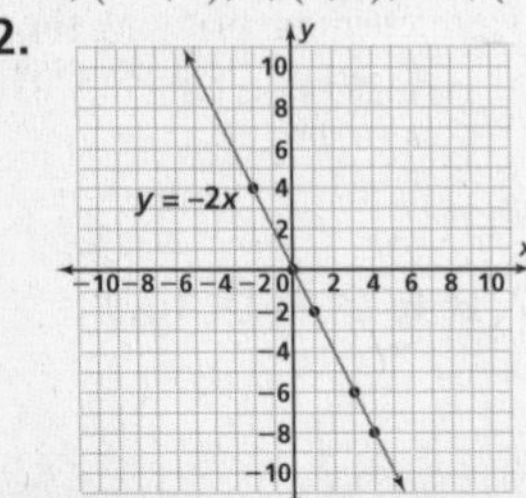

Enrichment 9-5

1. 3 **2.** 5 **3.** 7 **4.** 9 **5.** 2 **6.** 4 **7.** 6 **8.** 8 **9.** 1 **10.** Sample answers: $A + D, F + H, B + C, I + E + D, E + A + C, A + F + B, F + C + I, D - I + F, G \div E + D, A \times E + G, F \times B - H, H \div I + F, D - F + F + A$

Puzzle 9-5

1. $y = \frac{1}{2}x$ **2.** $y = 2$ **3.** $y = -3x + 5$ **4.** $y = -\frac{1}{2}x$
5. $y = 3x + 5$ **6.**

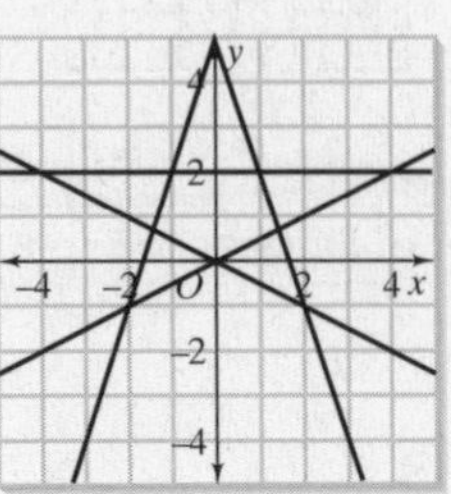

Practice (regular) 9-6

1. II **2.** V **3.** IV **4.** I **5.** III **6.** VI
7–8. Sample graphs are shown.
7.

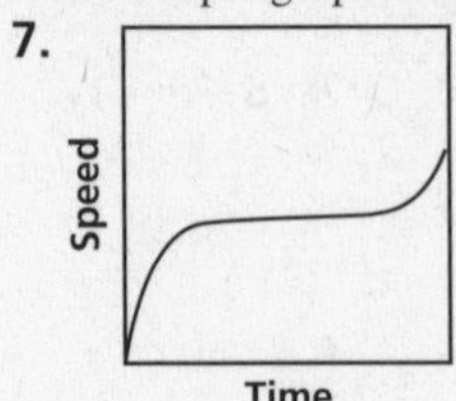

8.

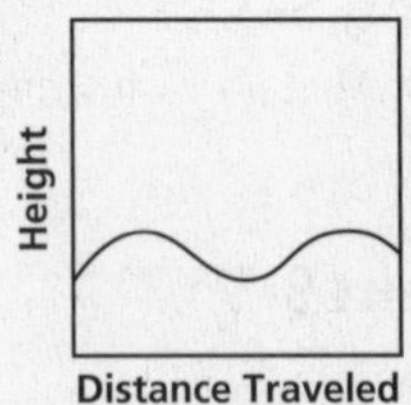

Guided Problem Solving 9-6

1. The rate of pouring sand stays constant. **2.** Determine which graph best represents the relationship between the height of the sand and the amount poured. **3.** The base and the top are smaller than the middle of the bowl. **4.** A cylinder has a constant diameter whereas a bowl does not. **5.** No, the height will rise more slowly at the bowl's widest point. **6.** graph A **7.** Since the height of the sand does not rise at a constant rate, it cannot be graph B. **8.** graph B, because the height rises at a constant rate

Practice (adapted) 9-6

1. II **2.** IV **3.** I **4.** III
5–6. Sample graphs are shown.
5.

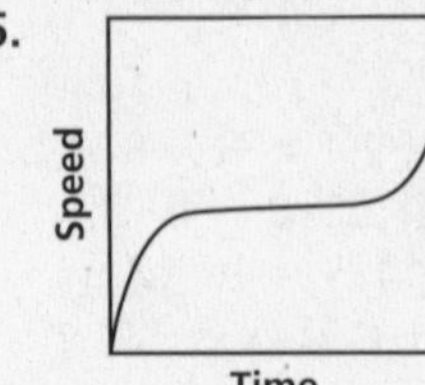

6.

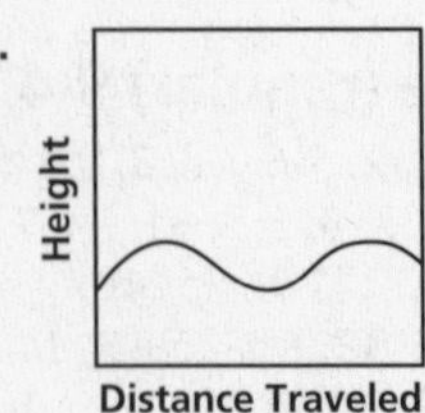

Name ____________ Class ____________ Date ____________

Chapters 9–12 Answers (continued)

Activity Lab 9-6

1–9. Check students' graphs. **1.** red **2.** 2 times **3.** Sample answer: 62.5 to 412.5 by 50 **4.** 3 times **5.** Sample answer: 5 times **6.** the second graph **7.** Sample answer: 0 to 6,500 by 500s **8.** Sample answer: 0 to 1,000 by 200s **9.** the first graph

Reteaching 9-6

1. C **2.** B **3.** A

4.

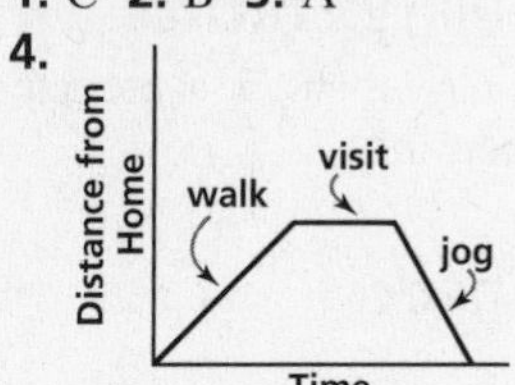

5.

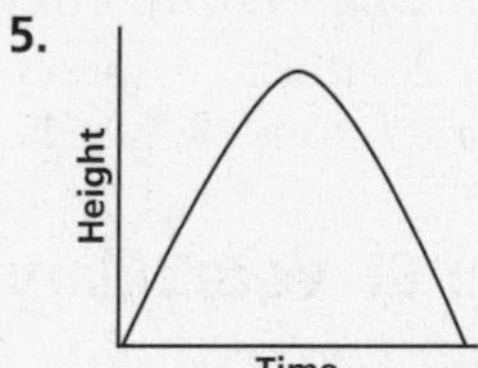

Enrichment 9-6

1. increasing width, same width, and decreasing width
2. 2 times **3.** 3 in., 8 in. **4.** 8 in. to 10 in. **5.** 3 in. to 8 in.
6. 0 in. to 3 in.

7.

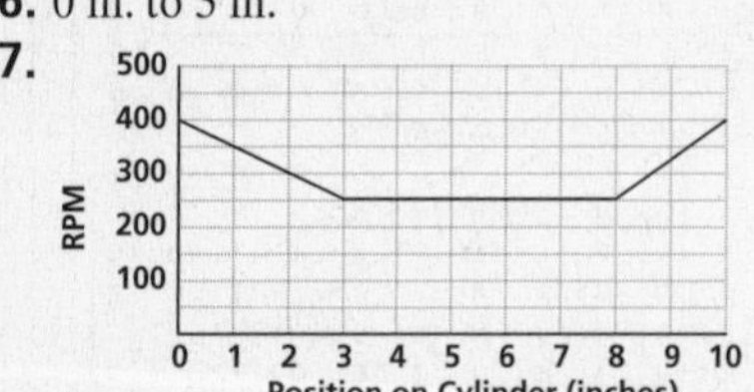

8.

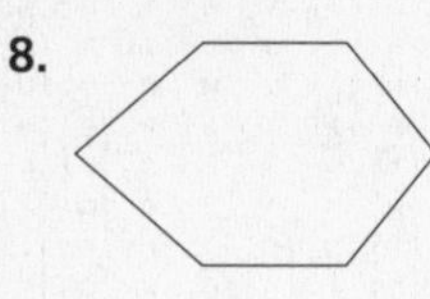

Puzzle 9-6

1. B **2.** M **3.** E **4.** R **5.** T **6.** L
MT. ELBERT

Practice (regular) 9-7

1–3. Sample graphs are shown.

1.

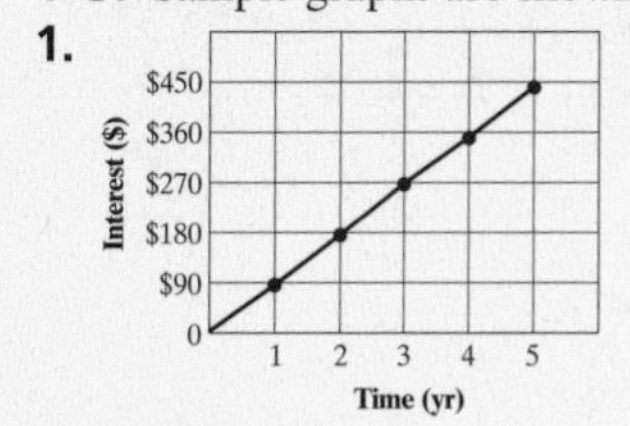

2.

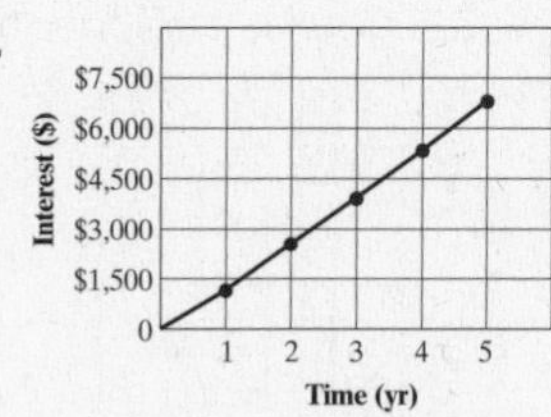

3.

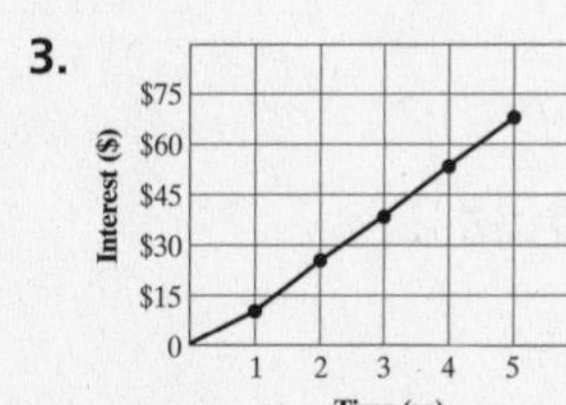

4. \$40 **5.** \$2,000 **6.** \$3.75 **7.** \$5,312.50 **8.** \$1,351.58 **9.** \$6,320.63 **10.** \$5,435.39 **11.** \$729.30 **12.** \$4,024.39 **13.** 4%

Guided Problem Solving 9-7

1. interest that is paid on both the original principal plus any other interest on the principal **2.** Find how much you owe after 6 months. **3.** $B = p(1 + r)^2$ **4.** \$500 **5.** 18% **6.** $\frac{1}{2}$ year **7.** $B = 500(1 + 0.18)^{\frac{1}{2}}$ **8.** \$543.14 **9.** \$45; \$545; This number should be close to the amount owed with compound interest because little time has passed since the principal was borrowed. **10.** \$1,173.63

Practice (adapted) 9-7

1–2. Sample graphs are shown.

1.

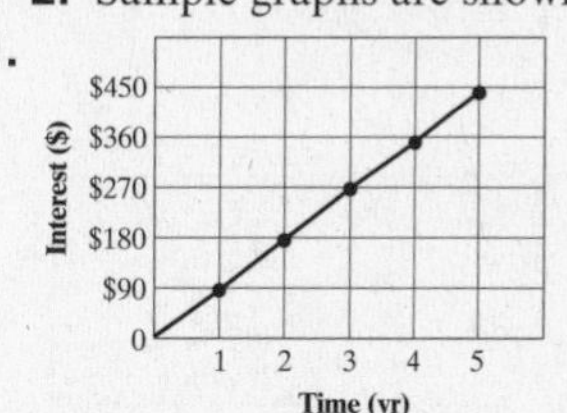

2.

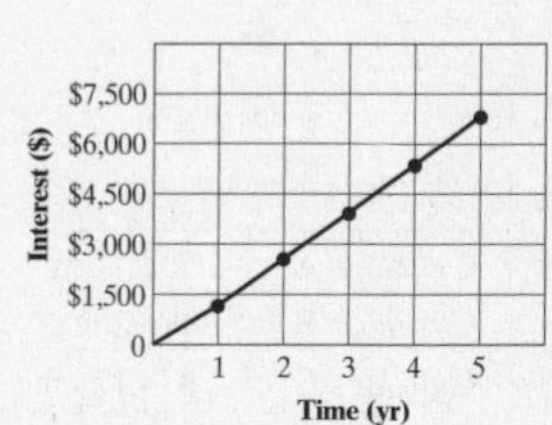

3. \$40 **4.** \$2,000 **5.** \$3.75 **6.** \$5,312.50 **7.** \$1,351.58 **8.** \$6,320.63 **9.** \$729.30 **10.** \$4,024.39

Activity Lab 9-7

1. Check students' answers. **2.** \$255.00 **3.** \$1,755.00 **4.** \$1749.60 **5.** Bank B; Check students' answers. **6.** Bank A: \$1882.50; Bank B: \$1889.57 **7.** Bank A **8.** Check students' answers.

Reteaching 9-7

1. 800; 0.04; 5; \$160 **2.** \$96 **3.** \$1,710 **4.** \$10,500 **5.** 600; 0.06; \$714.61 **6.** 9,000; 0.05; 4; \$10,939.56

Enrichment 9-7

1. \$2,000 at 8% and \$1,200 at 5% **2.** the 2% compound interest account **3.** 6% **4.** 4.5% **5.** $B = 2{,}500(1 + 0.032)^{0.5}$ or $B = 2{,}500(1 + 0.032)^{\frac{1}{2}}$ **6.** to find the square root of the base **7.** \$2,539.69 **8.** \$12,163.88

Puzzle 9-7

1. \$120.00 **2.** \$72.00 **3.** \$288.00 **4.** \$423.20 **5.** \$21.60 **6.** \$1,129.89 **7.** \$455.00 **8.** \$573.76

Practice (regular) 9-8

1. $r = \frac{d}{t}$ **2.** $s = \frac{P}{4}$ **3.** $C = K - 273$ **4.** $n = \frac{S + 360}{180}$ **5.** $a = 3m - b - c$ **6.** $b = \frac{P}{2} - h$ **7.** $B = \frac{3V}{h}$ **8.** $l = 8$ **9.** $F = 77$ **10.** $m = 12$ **11.** $5.7h$ **12.** 1,811 sq. ft

Guided Problem Solving 9-8

1. $N = 7lh$; 980 bricks are used; 20 ft long **2.** Find the height of the wall. **3.** feet **4.** $N = 7lh$ **5.** 980 bricks **6.** 20 feet **7.** $980 = 7(20)h$ **8.** $h = 7$ **9.** 7 feet **10.** $980 = 7(20)(7)$; $980 = 980$; yes **11.** 204 beats per minute

Name ______________________ Class ______________ Date ______________

Chapters 9–12 Answers (continued)

Practice (adapted) 9-8

1. $r = \frac{d}{t}$ **2.** $s = \frac{P}{4}$ **3.** $C = K - 273$ **4.** $B = \frac{3V}{h}$ **5.** $F = 77$ **6.** $m = 12$ **7.** 5.7 h **8.** 1,811 sq. ft

Activity Lab 9-8

1. $h = \frac{V}{\pi \times r^2}$ **2.** $r^2 = \frac{V}{\pi \times h}$ **3.** $V = h \times \pi \times r^2$
4. $h = \frac{V}{\pi \times r^2}$ **5.** $r^2 = \frac{V}{\pi \times h}$

6.

	V	*h*	*r*
Cylinder A	502.4 cm^3	10 cm	4 cm
Cylinder B	87.92 cm^3	7 cm	2 cm
Cylinder C	339.12 cm^3	12 cm	3 cm

Reteaching 9-8

1. $r = \frac{d}{t}$ **1b.** 6 mi/hr **2.** $A = 770$ m^2 **3.** $l = 8$ in. **4.** $l = 4$ ft **5.** $I = \$10$

Enrichment 9-8

1. $d = 55 \times t$

2.

Rate (mph)	40	55	60	65	70
Time (hours)	$12\frac{1}{2}$	9	$8\frac{1}{4}$	$7\frac{3}{4}$	$7\frac{1}{4}$
Distance (miles)	500	500	500	500	500

3. Division: $t = \frac{d}{r}$ **4.** $r = \frac{d}{t}$ Sample answer: To find the rate, divide the distance by the time. **5.** Sample answer: You use inverse operations to isolate the variable. **6.** Sample answer: to find many solutions using the same equation; it would be faster to isolate the variable before doing each calculation. **7.** $s = \frac{P}{n}$

Puzzle 9-8

1. N **2.** E **3.** W, J **4.** E, R **5.** S **6.** E, Y
NEW JERSEY

Chapter 9A Graphic Organizer

1. Patterns and Rules **2.** 8 **3.** Estimating the Answer **4.** Check students' diagrams.

Chapter 9B Reading Comprehension

1. the amount of money earned by the top 5 movies of the weekend **2.** 370.4 million **3.** The movie brought in less money this week than last week. **4.** The movie has only played for one week. **5.** movie E **6.** movie A **7.** \$370.4 million ÷ 6 weeks = \$61.7 million **8.** b

Chapter 9C Reading/Writing Math Symbols

1. *x* is less than or equal to three. **2.** The length of segment *MN* is equal to three. **3.** *y* is equal to three times *x*. **4.** The quantity 4 plus negative 7 is equal to negative 3. **5.** The ratio of four to five is equivalent to the ratio of eight to ten. **6.** Triangle *EFG* is congruent to triangle *KLM*. **7.** *x* is greater than three. **8.** Segments *MN* and *AB* are congruent. **9.** Sixty percent is equal to 60 divided by 100. **10.** Five squared equals twenty-five. **11.** Triangle *EFG* is similar to triangle *KLM*. **12.** The square root of 17 is approximately equal to four. **13.** *y* is equal to four more than *x*. **14.** Three divided by five is not equal to four divided by six.

Chapter 9D Visual Vocabulary Practice

1. property **2.** measure **3.** classify **4.** dimensions **5.** abbreviate **6.** symbolize **7.** name **8.** rule **9.** acronym

Chapter 9E Vocabulary Check

Check students' answers.

Chapter 9F Vocabulary Review Puzzle

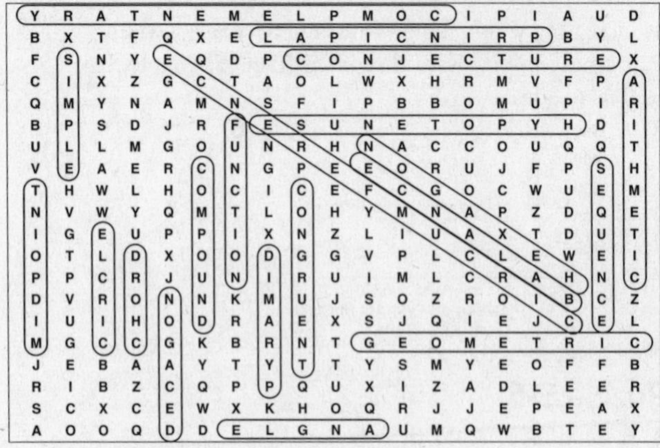

Chapter 9 Checkpoint Quiz 1

1. Start with 0.6 and multiply by 3 repeatedly; 48.6, 145.8, 437.4 **2.** Start with 25 and subtract 7 repeatedly; –3, –10, –17 **3.** Exercise 1 **4.** $m = 5, n = 11$

5.

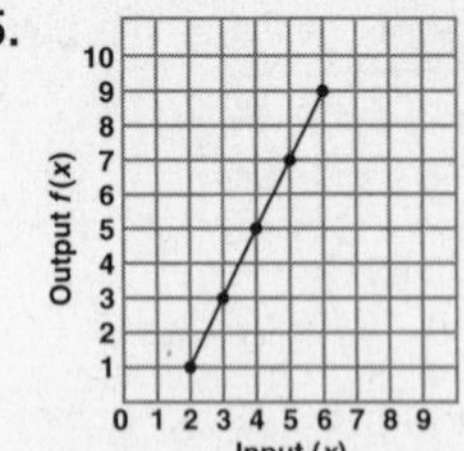

6. about 9 **7.** $y = 27$

Chapter 9 Checkpoint Quiz 2

1.

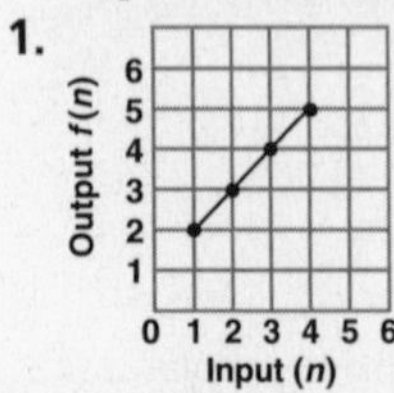

2. $y = 5x$ **3.** $y = x - 4$ **4.** $y = 2x + 1$

Name ______________________ Class ______________ Date ______________

Chapters 9–12 Answers (continued)

Chapter 9 Test (regular)

1. Start with 8 and add 6 repeatedly; 32, 38, 44 **2.** Start with 96 and subtract 12 repeatedly; 48, 36, 24 **3.** Start with 1 and square the number of the term; 25, 36, 49 **4.** Start with 300 and divide by 2 repeatedly; 18.75, 9.375, 4.6875 **5.** Start with 248 and subtract the next even number each time; 228, 218, 206 **6.** Start with 6 and multiply by 2 repeatedly; 96, 192, 384 **7.** arithmetic **8.** arithmetic **9.** neither **10.** geometric **11.** neither **12.** geometric **13.** geometric **14.** the ninth week **15.** −10, −9, −6 **16.** 2, 5, 8 **17.** −3, −2, −1 **18.** $n = 2xp - 3$ **19.** $n = \frac{t}{100} - 3$ **20.** $n = 3b - 4a$ **21.** $y = 4x + 1$ **22.** $y = -2x + 6$ **23.** $5,408 **24.** 8 cm **25.** 15, 17, 19 **26.**

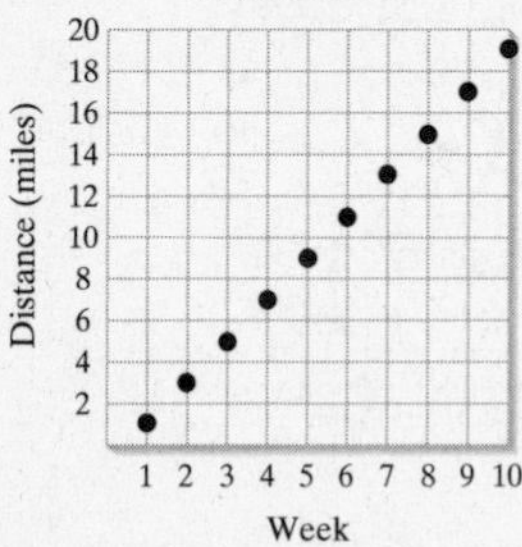

27. from 0 to 20 min and from 50 min to 70 min

Chapter 9 Test (below level)

1. Start with 8 and add 6 repeatedly; 32, 38, 44 **2.** Start with 96 and subtract 12 repeatedly; 48, 36, 24 **3.** Start with 1 and square the number of the term; 25, 36, 49 **4.** Start with 300 and divide by 2 repeatedly; 18.75, 9.375, 4.6875 **5.** arithmetic **6.** arithmetic **7.** neither **8.** geometric **9.** geometric **10.** the ninth week **11.** −10, −9, −6 **12.** 2, 5, 8 **13.** $n = 2xp - 3$ **14.** $n = \frac{t}{100} - 3$ **15.** $y = 4x + 1$ **16.** $y = -2x + 6$ **17.** $5,408 **18.** 15, 17, 19 **19.**

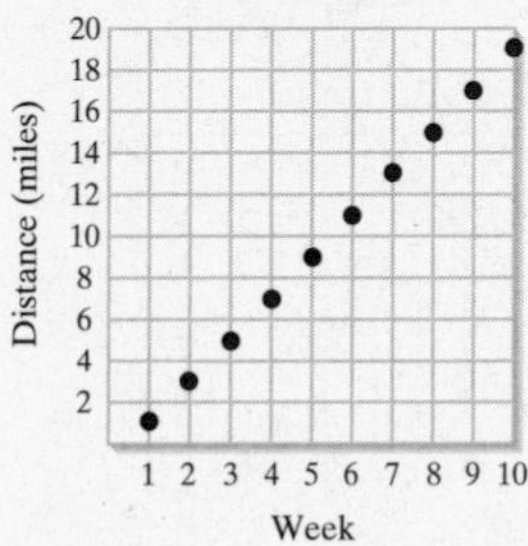

Chapter 9: Alternative Assessment

Exercise	Points	Explanation
1.	2	No pattern shown in data. While in some cases height is greater than spread, this is not always true OR other justified answer
	1	Response of no pattern without explanation
	0	Response of pattern OR no response
2.	2	Pattern considered likely and explanation given
	1	Pattern considered likely but no explanation given
	0	Pattern considered unlikely OR no response
3. a.	2	Correct function table given; labels shown. Table should resemble the following:
	1	Incorrect or incomplete function table
	0	No response
b.	2	Correct function table given; labels shown. Table should resemble the following:
	1	Incorrect OR incomplete function table
	0	No response
4.	2	Graph C chosen and explanation provided
	1	Graph C chosen without explanation OR Graph A or B chosen and explanation given
	0	No response OR other response
Excursion	5	Letter includes all seven needed items
	4	Letter covers five or six items, including measurements
	3	Letter covers three or four items, including measurements
	2	Letter covers at least three items, but does not include measurements
	1	Letter covers fewer than three items
	0	No response

Chapter 9 Cumulative Review

1. A **2.** J **3.** C **4.** J **5.** B **6.** H **7.** D **8.** F **9.** D **10.** H **11.** C **12.** F **13.** C **14.** J **15.** C **16.** J **17.** Sample answers: Students watch less TV on Tuesday, and more TV on Saturday. **18.** Justin's family

Chapter 10

Practice (regular) 10-1

1. L **2.** F **3.** D **4.** B **5.** I **6.** C **7.** (−5, 0) **8.** (2, 7) **9.** (−2, −7) **10.** (8, −8) **11.** (0, 7) **12.** (4, 2) **13.** II **14.** I **15.** IV **16.** III **17–21.** Check students' answers.

Guided Problem Solving 10-1

1. Explain how to tell in which quadrant an ordered pair is located. **2.** There are four quadrants; I, II, III, and IV. **3.** Both the x- and y-coordinates are positive. **4.** The x-coordinates are negative and the y-coordinates are positive. **5.** Both the x- and y-coordinates are negative. **6.** The x-coordinates are positive and the y-coordinates are negative. **7.** yes **8.** If you change the x-coordinate to −3, the point will be in Quadrant II. If you make both 3 and 5 negative, the point will be in Quadrant III. If you change the y-coordinate to −5, the point will be in Quadrant IV.

Practice (adapted) 10-1

1. L **2.** F **3.** D **4.** B **5.** (−5, 0) **6.** (2, 7) **7.** (−2, −7) **8.** (8, −8) **9.** II **10.** I **11.** III **12.** Check students' answers. **13.** Check students' answers. **14.** Check students' answers.

Chapters 9–12 Answers (continued)

Activity Lab 10-1

1–2. Check students' work. **3a.** no **3b.** A duplicate pair would mean that two people are sitting in the same seat. **4–9.** Check students' work. **10.** Sample answers: If each coordinate pair is the same, the quadrilaterals are the same. If the lengths of the sides and the shapes are the same, the quadrilaterals are the same.

Reteaching 10-1

1. A **2.** E **3.** C **4.** F **5.** R **6.** T **7.** $(2, -4)$ **8.** $(0, 6)$ **9.** $(-4, -7)$ **10.** $(0, -3)$ **11.** $(-8, 2)$ **12.** $(5, 3)$ **13.** III **14.** I **15.** IV **16.** II **17.** III **18.** II **19.** Check students' answers. **20.** Check students' answers.

Enrichment 10-1

1a. 2 **1b.** Two hundred feet from point A; 100 feet deep; 200 feet; 500 feet from A **1c.** postive; negative **1d.** $(200, -100)$ and $(500, -200)$ **2a.** 100 ft per unit

2b.

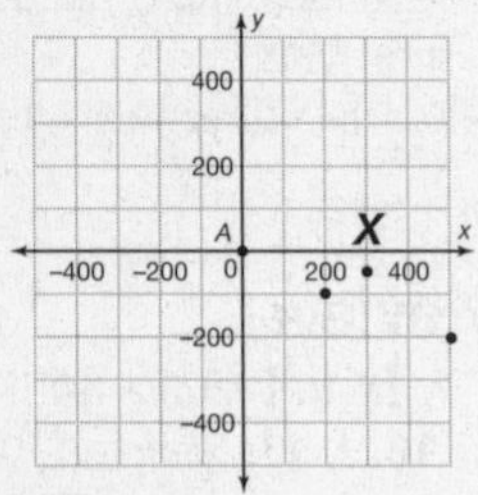

2c. Sample answer: Yes, if it would fit on the coordinate grid.
3. $X(300, -50)$

Puzzle 10-1

1. ABRAHAM LINCOLN **2.** TALLAHASSEE **3.** Check students' work.

Practice (regular) 10-2

1. yes **2.** no **3.** yes **4.** no **5.** Sample answers: $(0, 5)$, $(1, 6)$, $(2, 7)$ **6.** Sample answers: $(0, 7)$, $(1, 6)$, $(2, 5)$
7. Sample answers: $(0, -1)$, $(1, 1)$, $(2, 3)$

8.

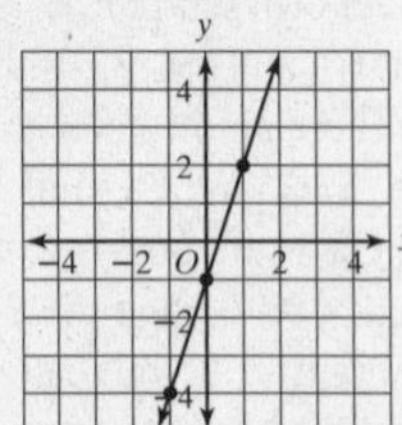

9.

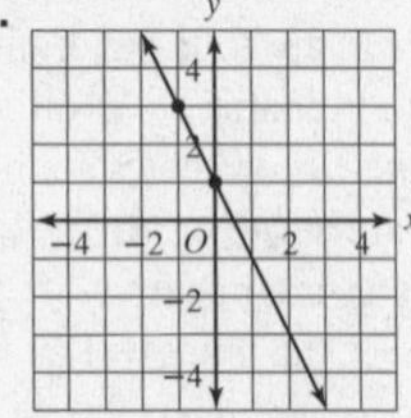

10.

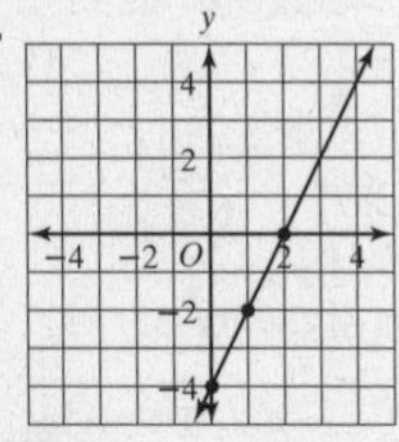

11. II and IV **12.** $(-1, 1)$

Guided Problem Solving 10-2

1. No, the question asks what error the student made, so the solution is wrong. **2.** $-3(-1) - 2$ **3.** $-3(-1) - 2 = 3 - 2 = 1$ **4.** yes; -5 **5.** Sample answer: The student probably multiplied $-3(-1)$ incorrectly and got -3 as an answer. **6.** Sample answer: $-5 = -3x - 2$; $x = 1$; the student may have lost track of the negative signs when dividing both sides by -3. **7.** Sample answer: The student simplified $4 - 5$ incorrectly, getting a value of -9 instead of -1.

Practice (adapted) 10-2

1. yes **2.** no **3.** yes **4.** Sample answers: $(0, 5)$, $(1, 6)$, $(2, 7)$
5. Sample answers: $(0, -1)$, $(1, 1)$, $(2, 3)$

6.

7.

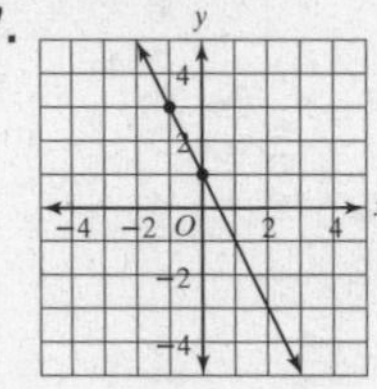

8. II and IV
9. $(-1, 1)$

Activity Lab 10-2

x	$x - 2$	y	(x, y)
0	0 − 2	−2	(0, −2)
1	1 − 2	−1	(1, −1)
2	2 − 2	0	(2, 0)
3	3 − 2	1	(3, 1)

1.

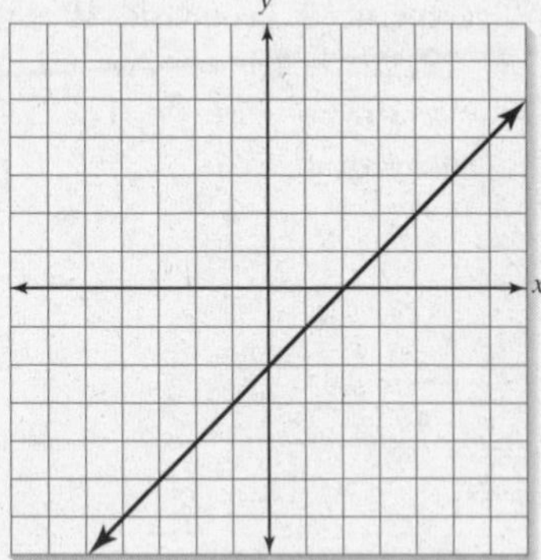

2. no **3.** $(6, 5)$ is not on the line $y = x - 2$. **4.** 4 **5.** yes **6.** yes
7. If a point (x, y) is on the line, then $y = x - 2$.

Reteaching 10-2

1.

x	$x - 4$	y	(x, y)
2	2 − 4	−2	(2, −2)
4	4 − 4	0	(4, 0)
6	6 − 4	2	(6, 2)

2.

x	$3x$	y	(x, y)
−1	3(−1)	−3	(−1, −3)
0	3(0)	0	(0, 0)
3	3(3)	9	(3, 9)

Name ______________________ Class ______________ Date ______________

Chapters 9–12 Answers (continued)

3.

x	−x + 1	y	(x, y)
0	0 + 1	1	(0, 1)
2	−2 + 1	−1	(2, −1)
−3	−(−3) + 1	4	(−3, 4)

4.

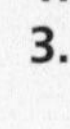

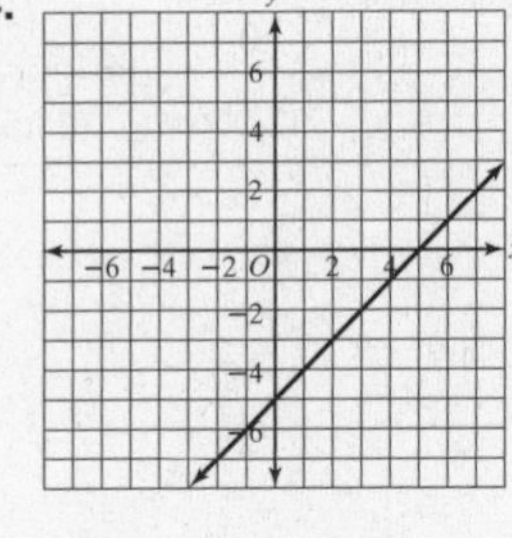

5.

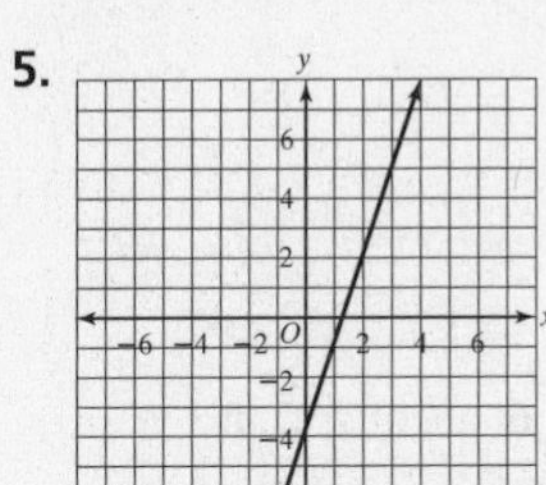

Enrichment 10-2

1. 8,400 beats/h **2.** 1 beat/h **3a.** $b = 140m$ **3b.** $b = \frac{m}{60}$

4a–b.

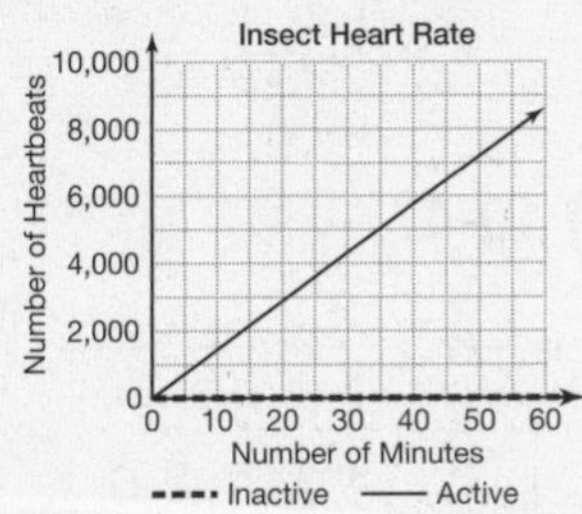

4a. Both have a positive slope. One is steep; The other is almost horizontal. **4b.** The graph with the smaller slope represents the lesser rate. **4c.** No, the equations show which is a lesser rate. **4d.** about 7,000; about 16,800 **5.** $r = 4{,}800 \frac{\text{beats}}{\text{h}}$; $r = 8{,}400 \frac{\text{beats}}{\text{h}}$; new baby's heart rate

Puzzle 10-2

1. A **2.** L **3.** G **4.** E **5.** B **6.** R **7.** A
ALGEBRA

Practice (regular) 10-3

1. 2 **2.** $-\frac{3}{4}$ **3.** $-\frac{1}{6}$ **4.** $\frac{3}{5}$ **5.** $\frac{1}{6}$ **6.** 2 **7.** $\frac{3}{2}$

8.

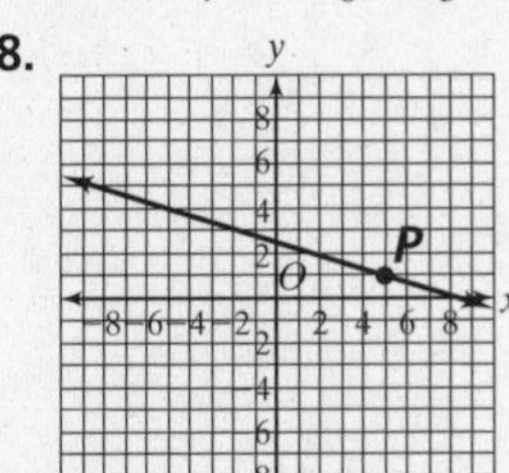

9.

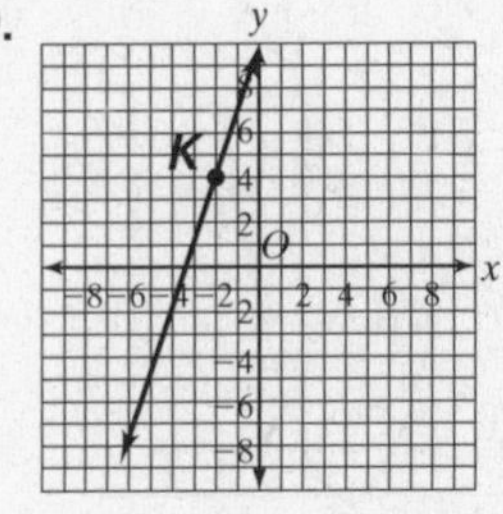

Guided Problem Solving 10-3

1. Explain why 3 is not the correct slope. **2.** Slope = rise/run

3.

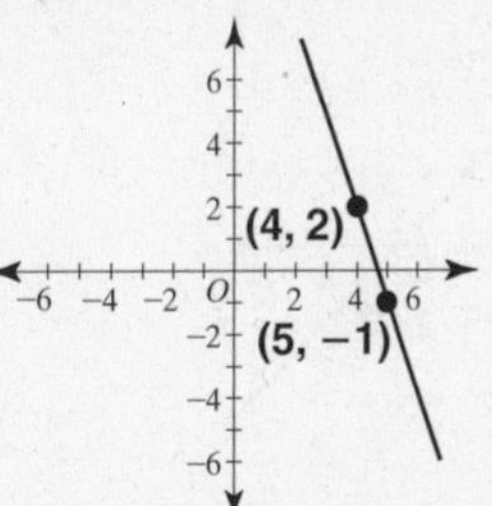

4. 1 **5.** −3 **6.** −3 **7.** 3 **8.** Sample answer: the student probably forgot to put the negative sign in front of the rise. **9.** rise = 3; run = −1 **10.** −3; yes **11.** The line slants up from left to right, so the slope should be positive 2.

Practice (adapted) 10-3

1. 2 **2.** $-\frac{3}{4}$ **3.** $-\frac{1}{6}$ **4.** $\frac{3}{5}$ **5.** $\frac{3}{2}$

6.

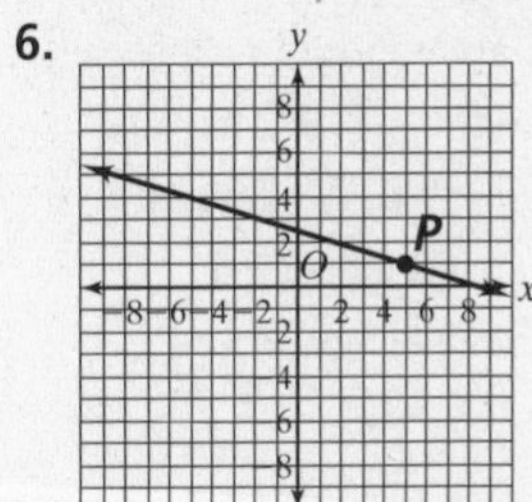

7.

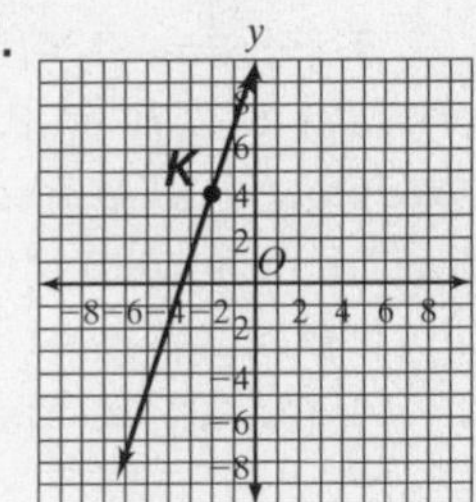

Activity Lab 10-3

1–3.

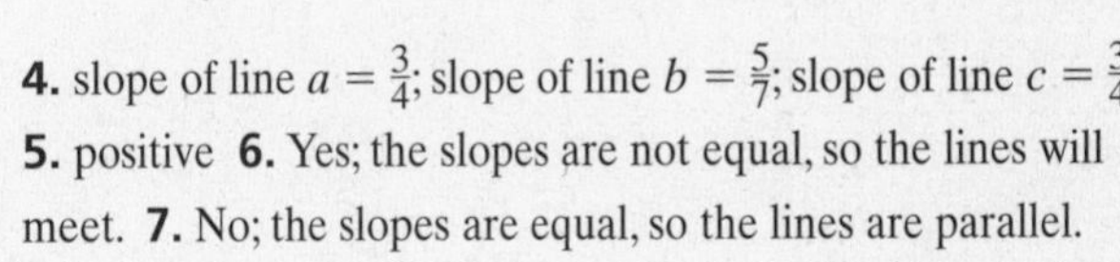

4. slope of line $a = \frac{3}{4}$; slope of line $b = \frac{5}{7}$; slope of line $c = \frac{3}{4}$ **5.** positive **6.** Yes; the slopes are not equal, so the lines will meet. **7.** No; the slopes are equal, so the lines are parallel.

Chapters 9–12 Answers (continued)

Reteaching 10-3

1. $\frac{3}{4}$ **2.** -1 **3.** 2

4. 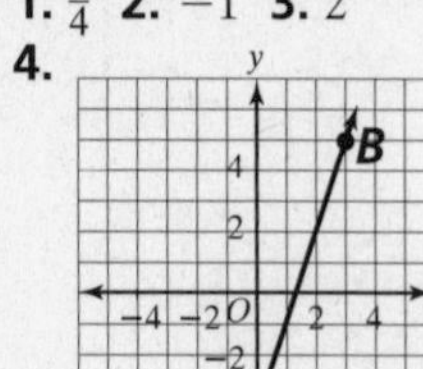

5. 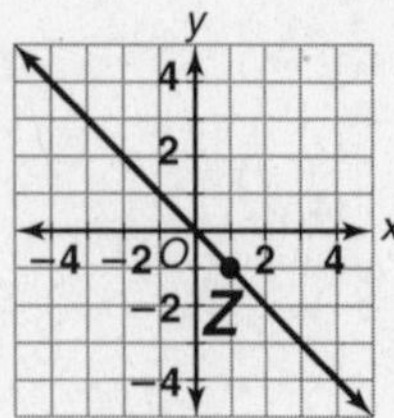

6. 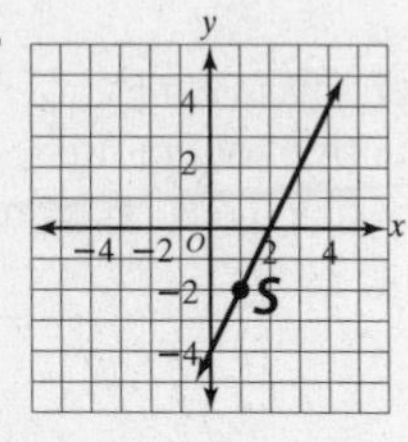

Enrichment 10-3

1. $\frac{3}{4}$ **2.** $-\frac{4}{3}$ **3.** $\frac{3}{4} \cdot -\frac{4}{3} = -1$ **4.** They are opposite reciprocals. **5.** perpendicular **6.** 2 **7.** $-\frac{1}{2}$ **8.** $2 \cdot -\frac{1}{2} = -1$ **9.** They are opposite reciprocals. **10.** perpendicular **11.** Two lines are perpendicular if the product of their slopes equals -1. **12.** Sample answer: $y = \frac{1}{3}x + 1$ **13.** Sample answer: $y = -\frac{5}{3}x - 10$ **14.** Sample answer: $y = 7x + 4$

Puzzle 10-3

1. 2 **2.** $-\frac{1}{2}$ **3.** -2 **4.** 0 **5.** $\frac{4}{3}$ **6.** $-\frac{1}{4}$ **7.** -5 **8.** $\frac{7}{4}$ **9.** $\frac{2}{3}$ **10.** 0 **11.** $\frac{7}{6}$ **12.** -1

RISE BY THE RUN

Practice (regular) 10-4

1. B **2.** F **3.** E **4.** C **5.** D **6.** A

7a.

x	−3	−2	−1	0	1	2	3
y	11	6	3	2	3	6	11

7b. 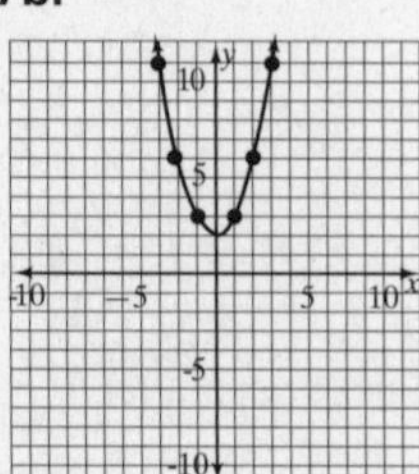

7c. Same shape, but its minimum *y*-value is 2 instead of 0.

Guided Problem Solving 10-4

1. time in seconds; height in feet above the ground **2.** parabola

3.

t	0	5	10	20
h	12,000	11,600	10,400	5,600

4. 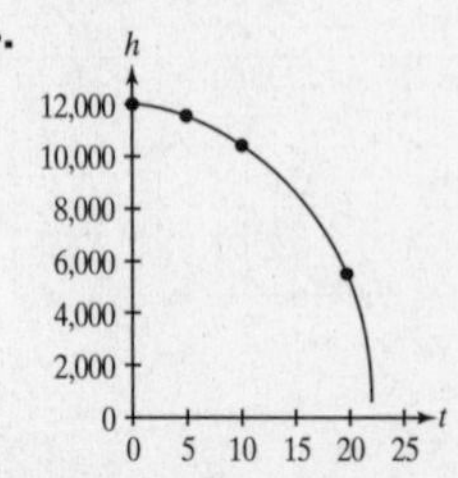

5. Estimates may vary; about 9,700 **6.** about 9,700 ft **7.** 9,696 ft; yes. **8.** about 130 feet

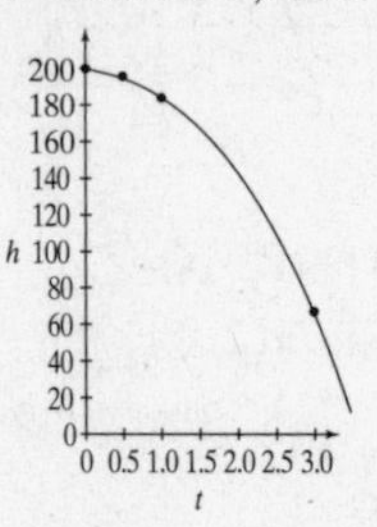

Practice (adapted) 10-4

1. A **2.** D **3.** B **4.** C

5a.

x	−3	−2	−1	0	1	2	3
y	11	6	3	2	3	6	11

5b. 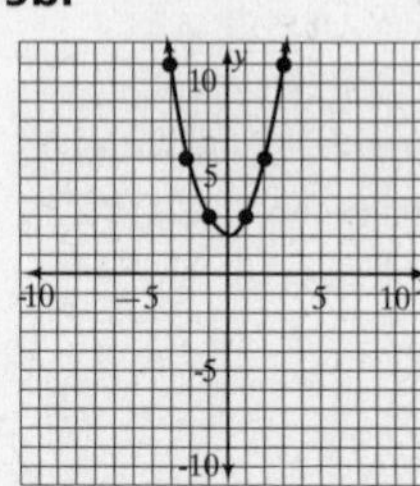

5c. Same shape, but its minimum value is 2 instead of 0.

Activity Lab 10-4

1a.

x	−4	−3	−2	−1	0	1	2
y	9	4	1	0	1	4	9

1b. 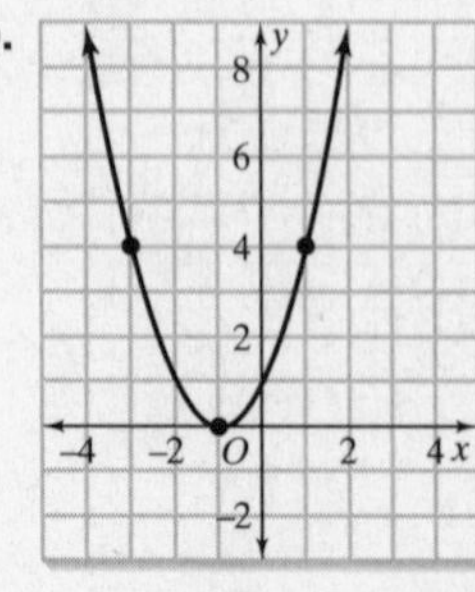

The graph is shifted 1 unit to the left.

Name ______________________ Class ______________ Date ______________

Chapters 9–12 Answers (continued)

2a.

x	−2	−1	0	1	2	3	4
y	9	4	1	0	1	4	9

2b.

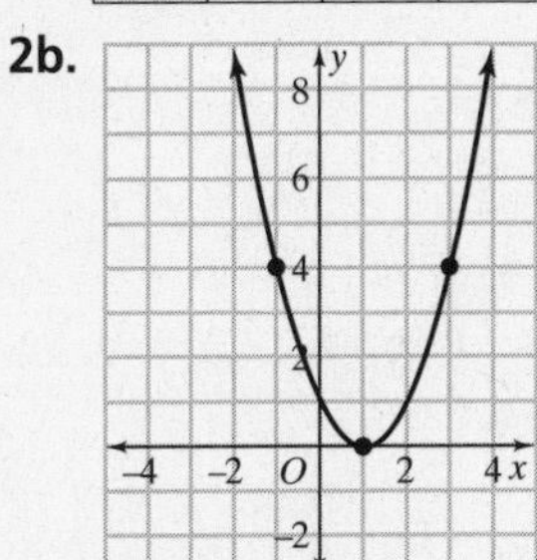

2c. The graph of $y = (x - 1)^2$ is the parabola $y = x^2$ shifted 1 unit to the right. **2d.** The graph is symmetric about the line $x = 1$. **3.** The graph of $y = (x - 4)^2$ is the parabola $y = x^2$ shifted 4 units to the right. The graph of $y = (x + 3)^2$ is the parabola $y = x^2$ shifted 3 units to the left.

Reteaching 10-4

1.

x	y
−2	2
−1	−1
0	−2
1	−1
2	2

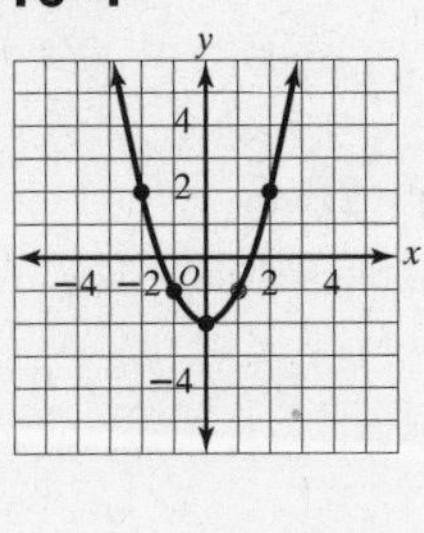

2.

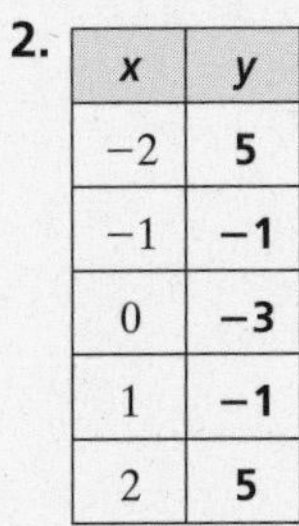

x	y
−2	5
−1	−1
0	−3
1	−1
2	5

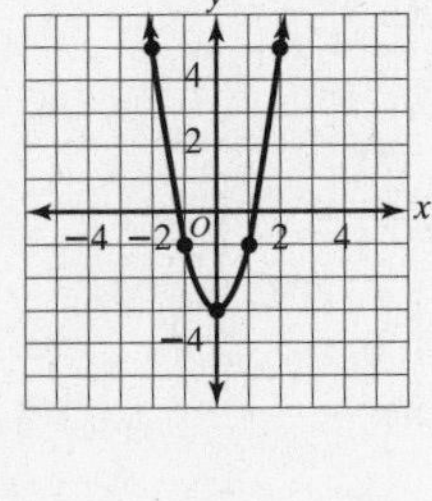

3.

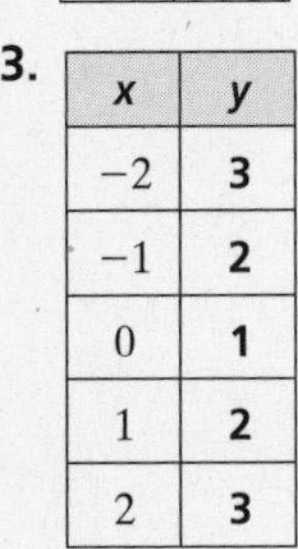

x	y
−2	3
−1	2
0	1
1	2
2	3

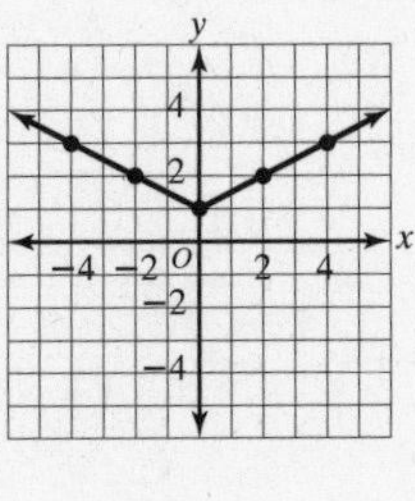

Enrichment 10-4

1a. Yes; different times correspond to the same height. **1b.** 0 s and 10 s **1c.** At 3 s and 7 s; the rocket is rising and falling back to Earth. **1d.** 0 m; the rocket has come back to Earth **1e.** It is assumed that the rocket does not penetrate the Earth. **2a.** At 1 s and 4 s; the object is rising and falling. **2b.** The object is at its highest point. **2c.** $43\frac{3}{4}$ or 43.75 ft **2d.** $4\frac{3}{8}$ or 4.375 ft

Puzzle 10-4

x	−3	−2	−1	0	1	2	3
y	9	4	1	0	1	4	9

MONTANA

Practice (regular) 10-5

1. (2, 2) **2.** (−4, −4) **3.** (1, 3)
4. A' (4, 1), B' (6, 5), C' (9, 4), D' (7, −1)

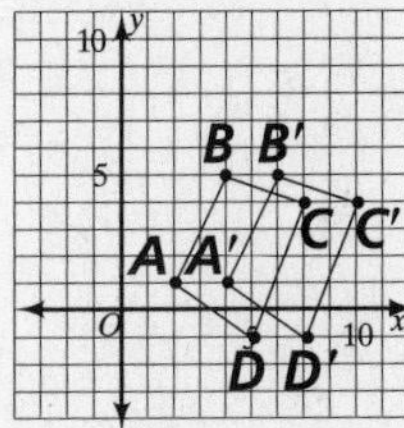

5. A' (0, 0), B' (2, 4), C' (5, 3), D' (3, −2)

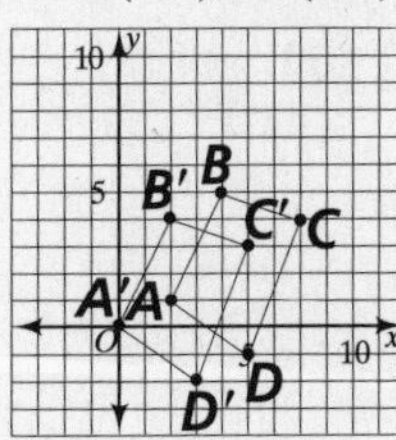

6. $(x, y) \rightarrow (x + 4, y - 4)$ **7.** $(x, y) \rightarrow (x - 4, y + 2)$

Guided Problem Solving 10-5

1. Find the new coordinates for the airplanes and write a rule to describe how the planes move. **2.** The change in the coordinates of airplane P will be the same for the other planes. **3.** (2, 4) **4.** 4 **5.** 3 **6.** (−1, 4) **7.** (2, 1) **8.** $(x, y) \rightarrow (x + 4, y + 3)$ **9.** Yes; all three planes move the same distance in the same direction, so their formation stays the same. **10.** R' (0, 0), S' (4, 0), $(x, y) \rightarrow (x + 2, y - 3)$

Practice (adapted) 10-5

1. (2, 2) **2.** (−4, −4) **3.** (1, 3)
4. A'(4, 1), B'(6, 5), C'(9, 4), D'(7, −1)

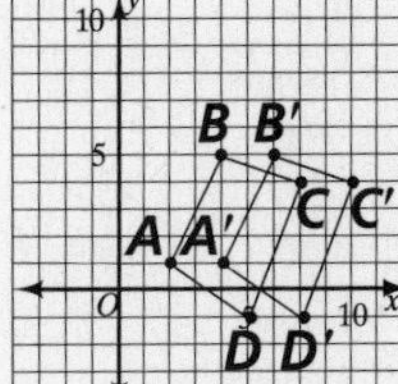

Name ______________________ Class ______________ Date ______________

Chapters 9–12 Answers (continued)

5. $A'(0, 0), B'(2, 4), C'(5, 3), D'(3, -2)$

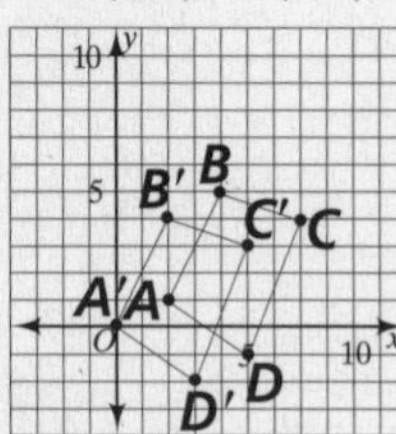

6. $(x, y) \rightarrow (x + 4, y - 4)$ **7.** $(x, y) \rightarrow (x - 4, y + 2)$

Activity Lab 10-5

1–2. Check students' work.
3. $A'(1, 4), B'(3, 6), C'(5, 4)$

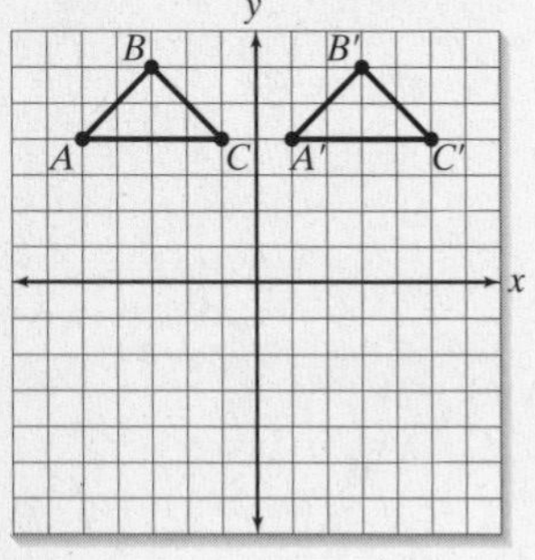

4. $D'(1, -3), E'(3, -1), F'(5, -3)$

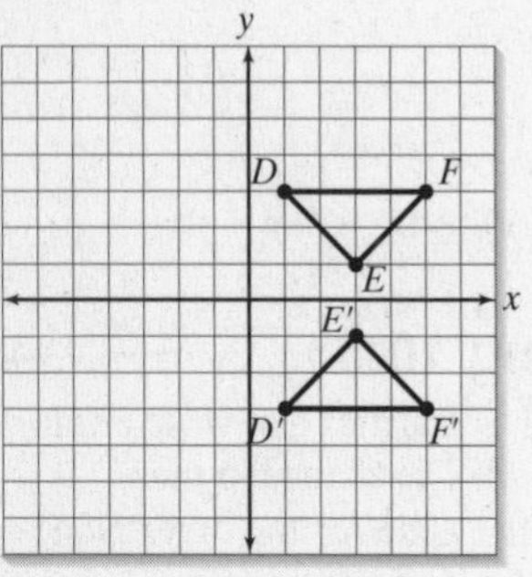

5. Check students' answers.

Reteaching 10-5

1. $-1, 4$ **2.** $3, 6$ **3.** $1, 3; 5, 2$

4.

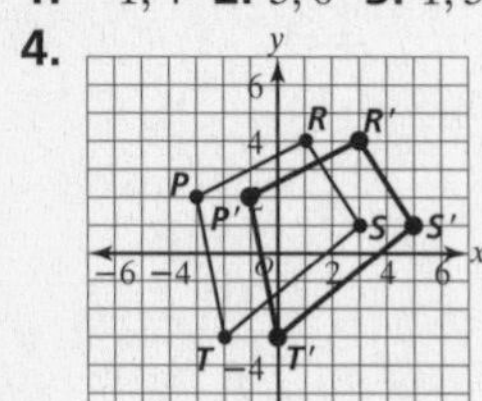

5.

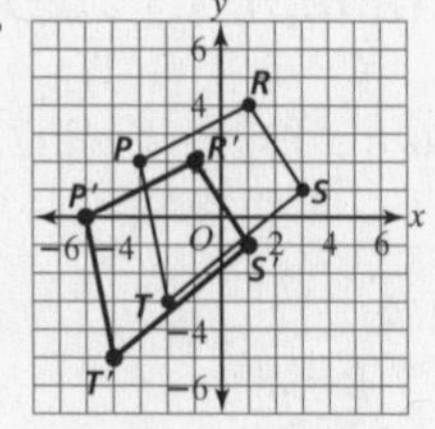

6.

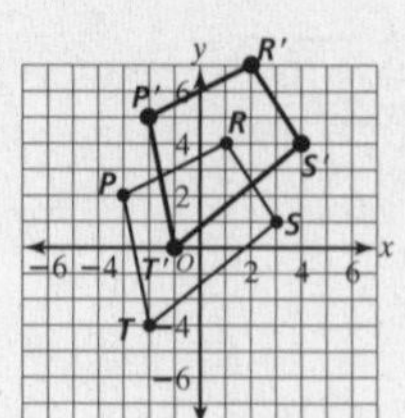

7. $(x + 3, y + 1)$ **8.** $(x - 4, y + 5)$ **9.** $(x - 1, y - 9)$
10. $(x, y) \rightarrow (x - 1, y - 3)$ **11.** $(x, y) \rightarrow (x + 1, y + 2)$
12. $(x, y) \rightarrow (x - 3, y + 2)$

Enrichment 10-5

1. Align the left edge of strip 3 along the right edge of strip 2. Translate strip 3 upward until the right part of the flower matches its left half on strip 2. **2.** Align the left edge of strip 4 along the right edge of strip 3. Translate strip 4 to the left until the right part of the pattern matches its left half on strip 3. Cut the strip vertically so that the pattern matches around the corner.

Puzzle 10-5

1. $R(9, 10); P(8, 7)$ **2.** $G(2, 6); Q(7, 5); N(6, 2)$

Practice (regular) 10-6

1. M, J **2.** K, N **3.** Sample answer: They are not the same distance from the y-axis.

4–6.

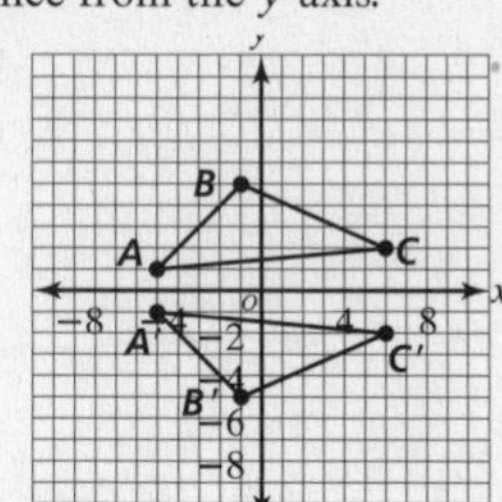

4. $(-5, -1)$ **5.** $(-1, -5)$ **6.** $(6, -2)$

7.

8. none

9.

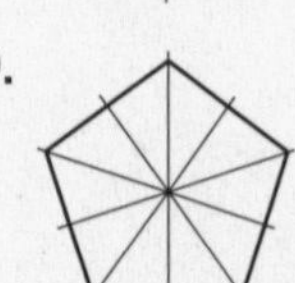

10.

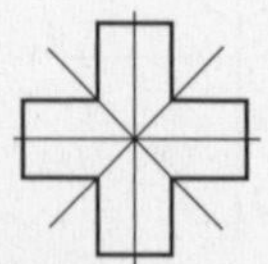

11–15.

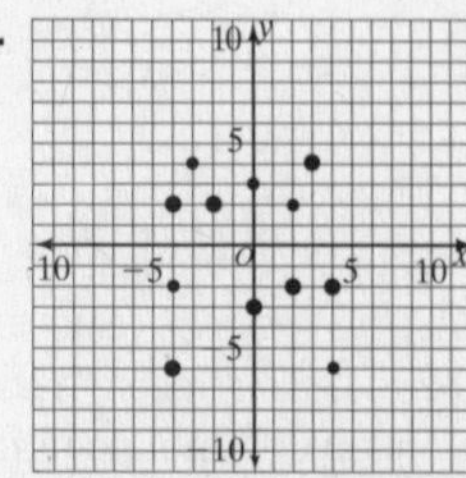

11. $(3, 4)$ **12.** $(-4, 2)$ **13.** $(2, -2)$ **14.** $(0, -3)$ **15.** $(-4, -6)$

Name ______________________ Class ______________ Date ______________

Chapters 9–12 Answers (continued)

Guided Problem Solving 10-6

1. Determine over which axis $\triangle WXY$ is reflected. **2.** Graph the two triangles on a coordinate plane. **3.**

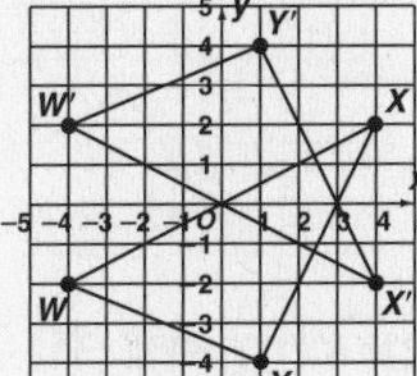

4. The x-coordinates of both triangles are the same. **5.** The y-coordinates of $\triangle WXY$ are opposite of the y-coordinates of $W'X'Y'$. **6.** x-axis **7.** x-axis **8.** yes **9.** y-axis; the x-coordinates were changed to their opposites.

Practice (adapted) 10-6

1. M, J **2.** K, N

3–5.

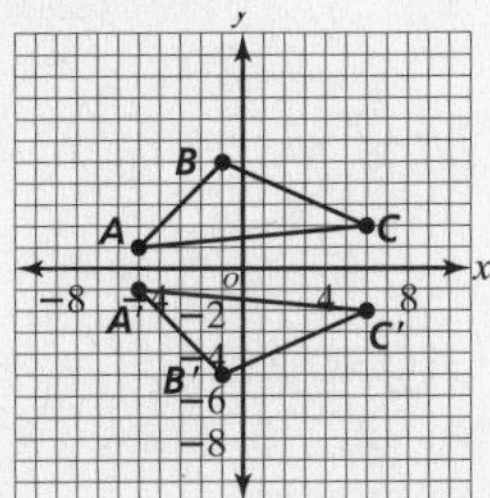

3. $(-5, -1)$ **4.** $(-1, -5)$ **5.** $(6, -2)$ **6.** none

7.

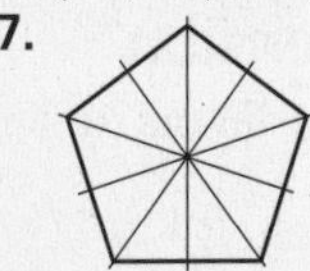

8.

9–11.

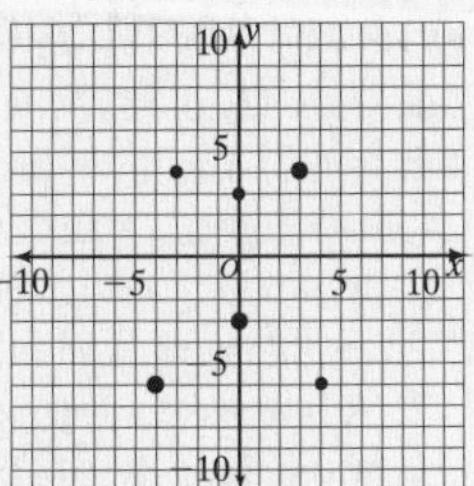

9. $(3, 4)$ **10.** $(0, -3)$ **11.** $(-4, -6)$

Activity Lab 10-6

1. 3 lines

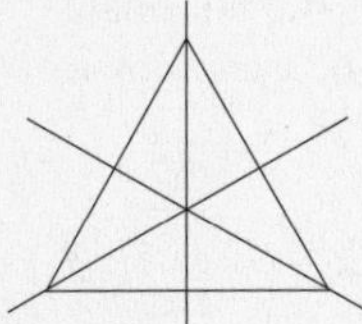

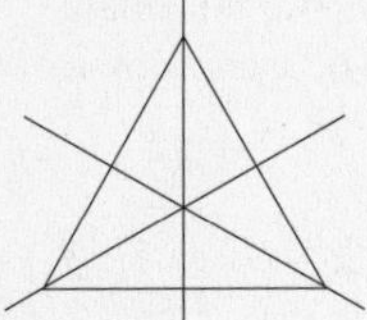

2. 4 lines

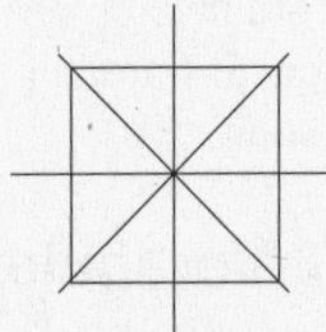

3. 5 lines

4. 6 lines

5. 7 lines

6. 8 lines

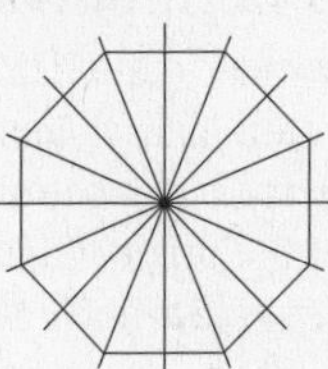

7. Sample answer: The number of lines of symmetry is the same as the number of sides. **8.** 12; 20; 100 **9.** Check students' work.

Reteaching 10-6

1.

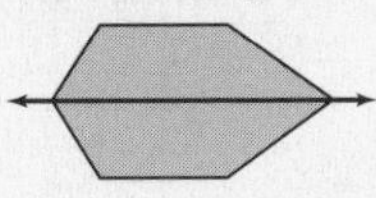

2. none **3.**

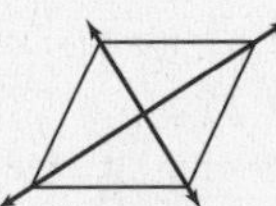

4. $(-4, -4)$; $(-2, 0)$; $(0, -2)$ **5.** $(4, 4)$; $(2, 0)$; $(0, 2)$

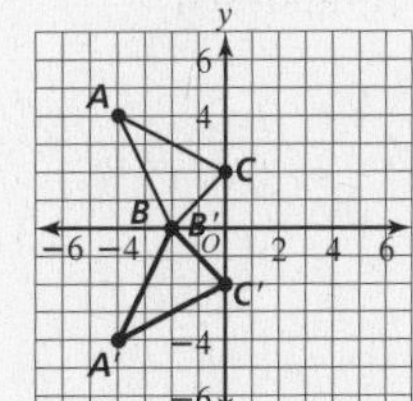

Enrichment 10-6

1a. $(7, 7)$ **1b.** $(5, 1)$ **1c.** $(2, 2)$ **2.** $(-7, 7)$, $(-5, 1)$, $(-2, 2)$; Sample answer: It is the image of the original figure reflected over the y-axis. **3.** Sample answer: It will be the image of the figure reflected over the x-axis. $(7, -7)$, $(5, -1)$, $(2, -2)$ **4.** $(-7, -7)$, $(-1, -5)$, $(-2, -2)$; Sample answer: Reflected the original figure over the line $y = -x$.

Puzzle 10-6

1. e **2.** d **3.** a **4.** f **5.** c **6.** b **7.** g

Practice (regular) 10-7

1–4. Check students' answers. **1.** yes **2.** yes **3.** no **4.** yes

5.

6.

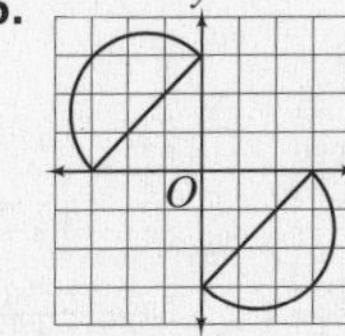

7.

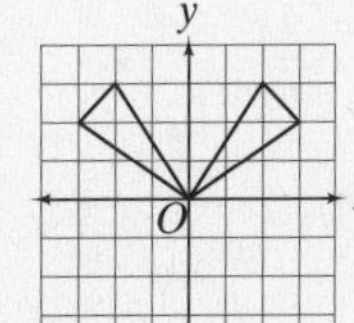

8.

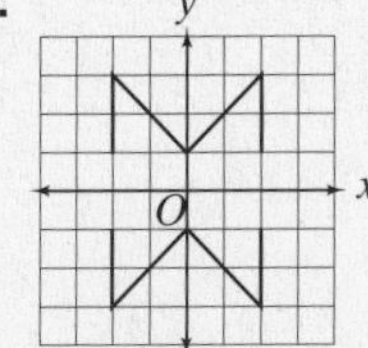

9. translation **10.** reflection or rotation **11.** reflection or rotation **12.** reflection or rotation

Name ______________________ Class ______________ Date ____________

Chapters 9–12 Answers (continued)

Guided Problem Solving 10-7

1. Determine by what rotation the points move and determine if the square has rotational symmetry. **2.** If a figure has rotational symmetry, it can be rotated less than 360° and fit exactly on top of the original figure. **3.** 90° **4.** 180° **5.** 270° **6.** yes **7.** yes **8.** yes **9a.** 180°; 180° **9b.** Yes; the figure can be rotated 180° and fit exactly on top of the original figure.

Practice (adapted) 10-7

1–3. Check students' answers. **1.** yes **2.** yes **3.** no

4.

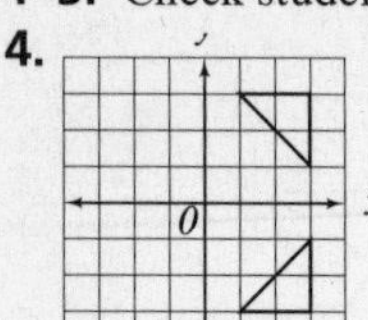

5.

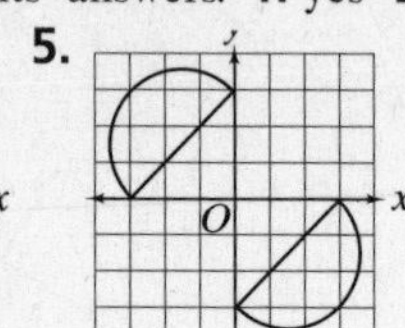

6.

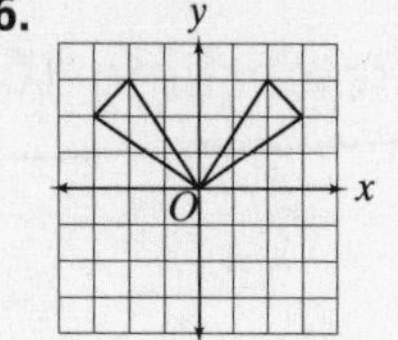

7. translation **8.** reflection or rotation **9.** reflection or rotation **10.** reflection or rotation

Activity Lab 10-7

1–3.

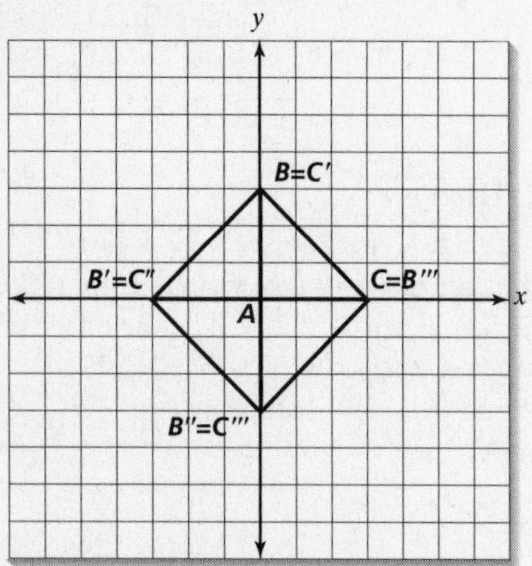

1. $A'(0,0), B'(-3,0), C'(0,3)$ **2.** $A''(0,0), B''(0,-3), C''(-3,0)$ **3.** $A'''(0,0), B'''(3,0), C'''(0,-3)$ **4.** yes **5.** square

Reteaching 10-7

1. yes **2.** no **3.** yes

4.

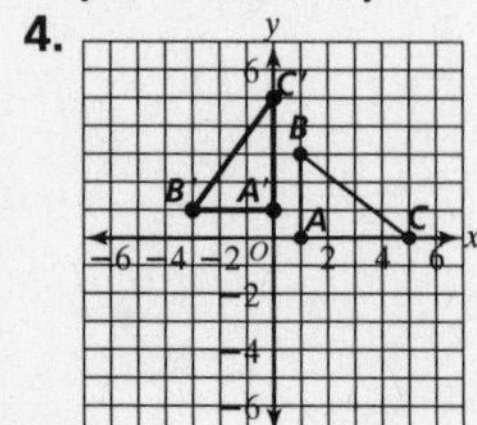

5.

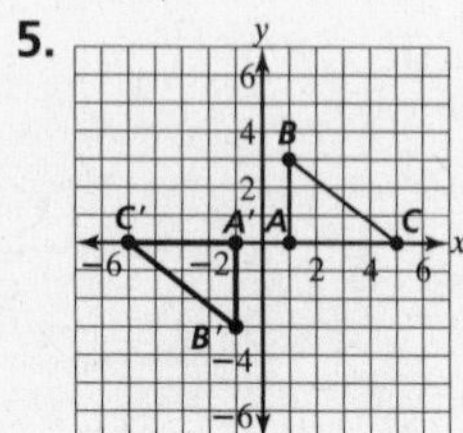

6.

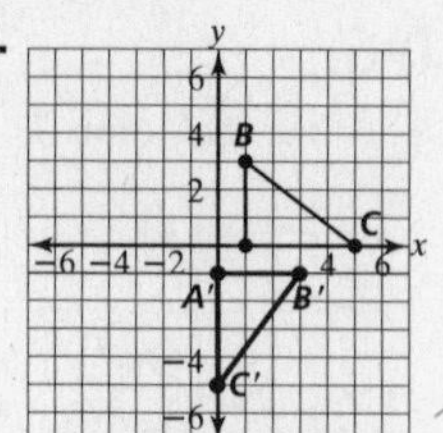

Enrichment 10-7

1. Sample answers: I: 90°; N: 90°; T: 180°; H: 90°; E: 90°; B: 270°; I: 90°; R: 180°; D: 90°; B: 90°; A: 90°; T: 270°; H: 90°
2. IN THE BIRD BATH

Puzzle 10-7

1. V **2.** I **3.** R **4.** G **5.** I **6.** N **7.** I **8.** A
VIRGINIA

Chapter 10A Graphic Organizer

1. Graphing in the Coordinate Plane **2.** 7 **3.** Answering the Question Asked **4.** Check students' diagrams

Chapter 10B Reading Comprehension

1. A6 or A7 **2.** H3 **3.** Des Moines **4.** San Antonio and Austin **5.** It has coordinates C3. **6.** 3 **7.** b

Chapter 10C Reading/Writing Math Symbols

1. The measure of angle A is 47 degrees. **2.** point M with coordinates $(-2, 0)$ **3.** y equals the sum of 4 and the product of 8 and x. **4.** Point P, located at $(3, 4)$ maps under a transformation to point P', located at $(5, 2)$. **5.** The point (x, y) is translated 2 units to the left and 1 unit up. **6.** The point (x, y) has both x- and y-coordinates greater than zero. **7.** A line passes through point C, located at $(1, 2)$, and has a slope of one half. **8.** $\overline{AD}$ and $\overline{AB}$ **9.** $\overline{AC}, \overline{CD}$, and $\overline{CE}$ **10.** $\overline{AD}$ **11.** $\angle ACE, \angle ECD$, and $\angle ACD$ **12.** $\overset{\frown}{ABD}$ and $\overset{\frown}{AED}$

Chapter 10D Visual Vocabulary Practice

1. origin **2.** y-coordinate **3.** linear equation **4.** coordinate plane **5.** reflection **6.** translation **7.** slope **8.** x-coordinate **9.** nonlinear equation

Chapter 10E Vocabulary Check

Check students' answers.

Chapter 10F Vocabulary Review

1. E **2.** B **3.** A **4.** C **5.** D **6.** G **7.** F **8.** L **9.** N **10.** M **11.** K **12.** J **13.** I **14.** H **15.** O

Chapter 10 Checkpoint Quiz 1

1. II **2.** IV **3.** III **4.** I

Name ______________________ Class ______________ Date ______________

Chapters 9–12 Answers (continued)

5a.

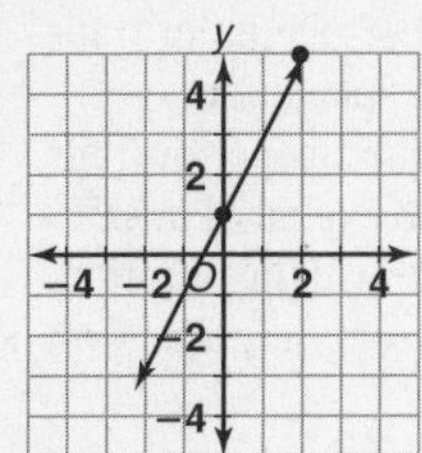

5b. 2 **6.**

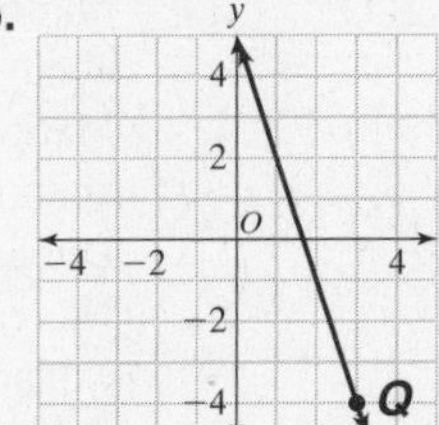

7.

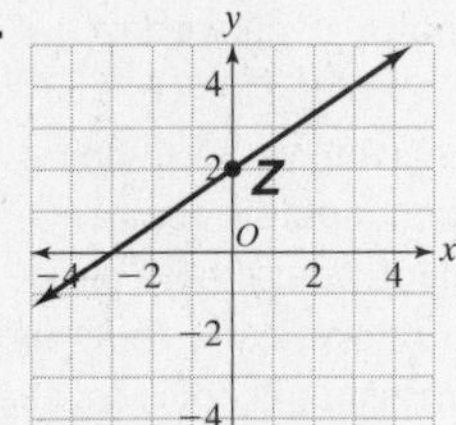

8.

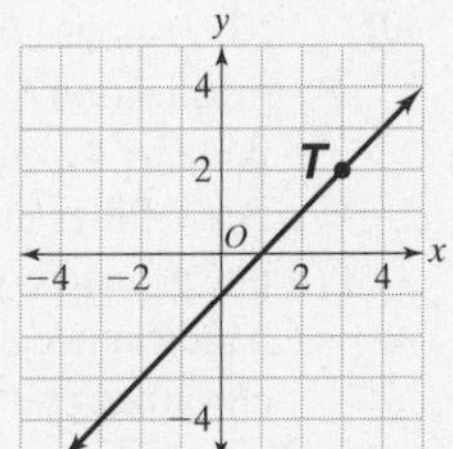

13. –1

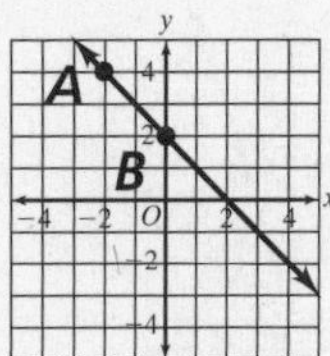

14. 3

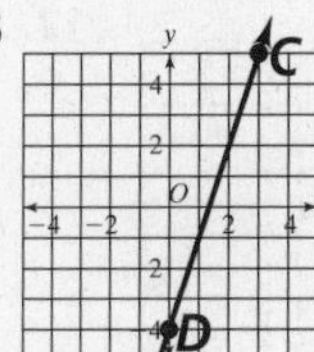

15.

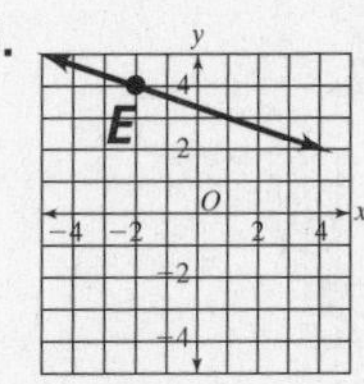

16.

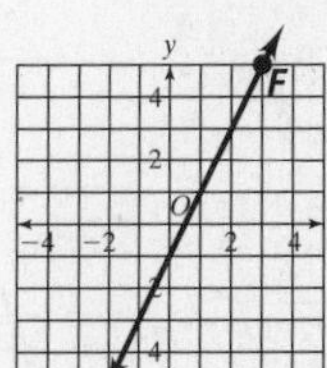

17.

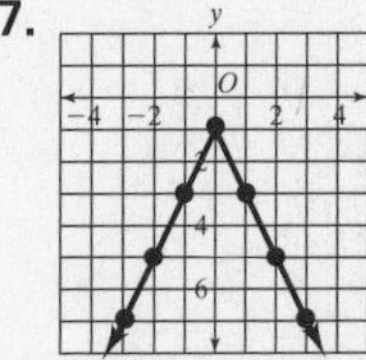

18.

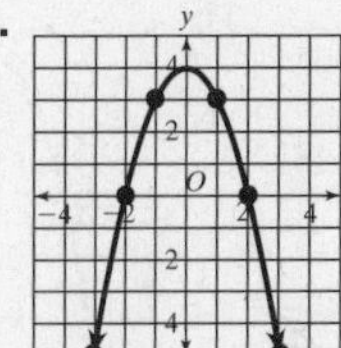

19.

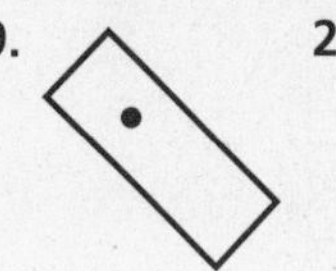

20.

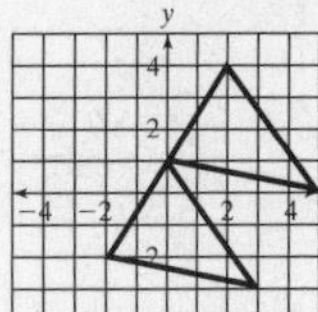

21.

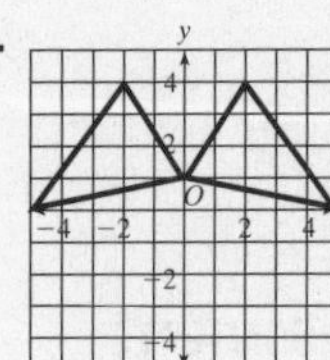

22.

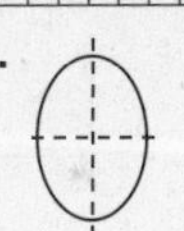

23.

24. none **25.**

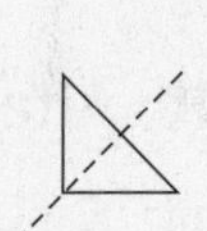

Course 2 Chapter 10 Checkpoint Quiz 2

1. **2.** **3.** **4.**

5. Sample answer: No, because $3(3^2) = 27$, not 12.
6. (0, –2) **7.** (–4, 2) **8.** (–1, 3) **9.** (4, –10)
10. $(x, y) \rightarrow (x + 7, y - 2)$ **11.**

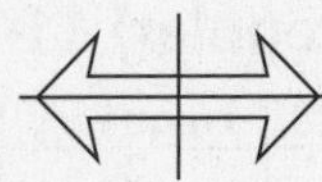

Chapter 10 Test (regular)

1–4.

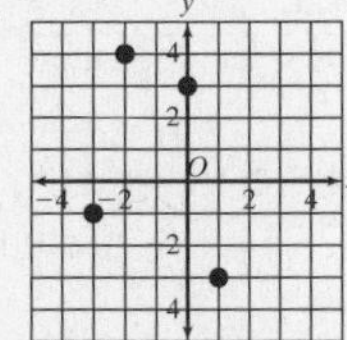

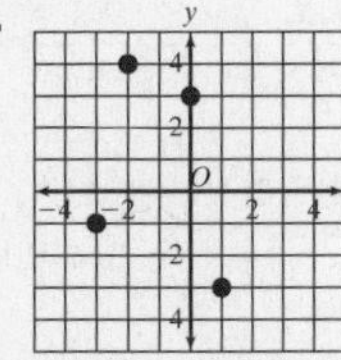

5–7. Check students' answers.

8. yes **9.** yes **10.** no

11.

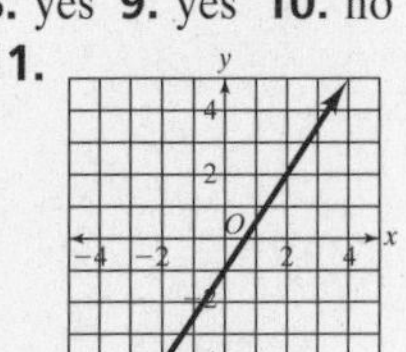

12.

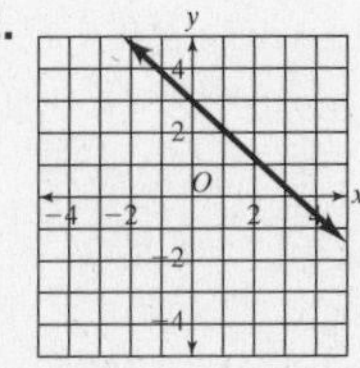

Chapter 10 Test (below level)

1–4.

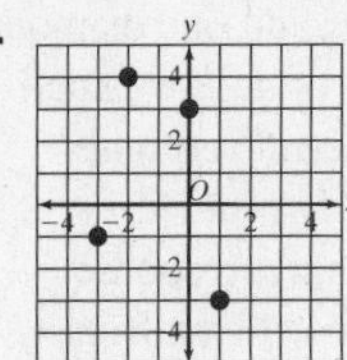

5–6. Check students' answers.

7. yes **8.** yes

9.

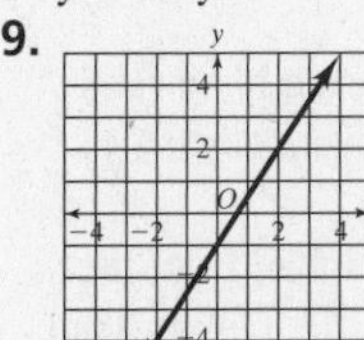

10.

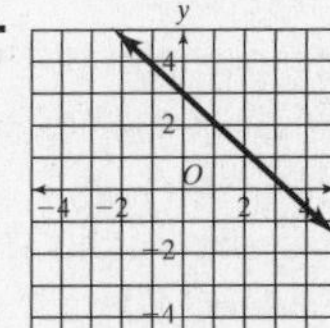

Chapters 9–12 Answers (continued)

11. –1

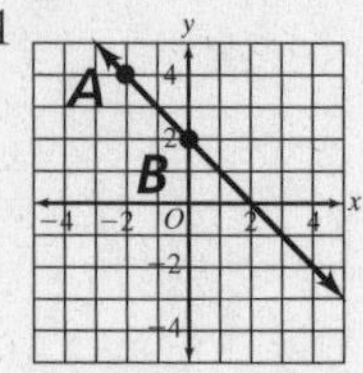

12. 3

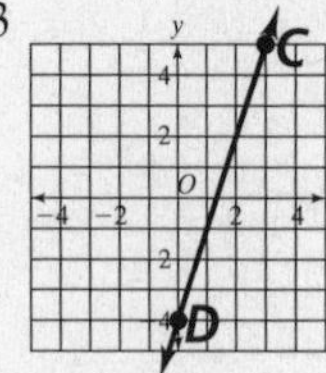

13.

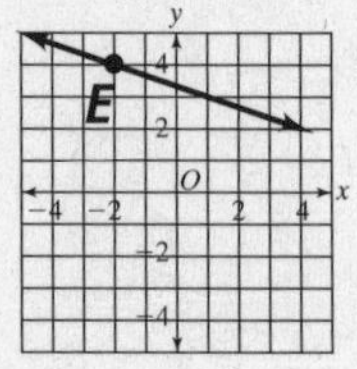

14.

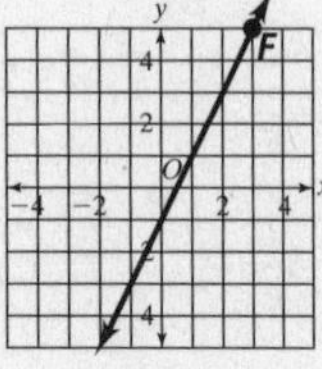

15.

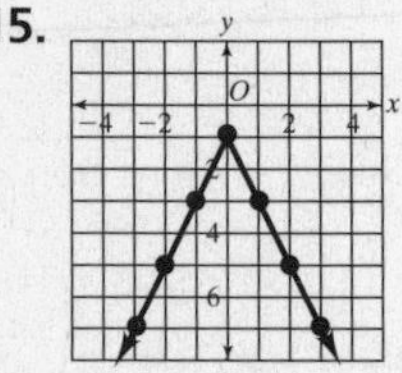

16.

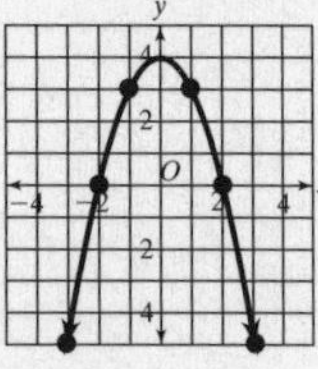

17.

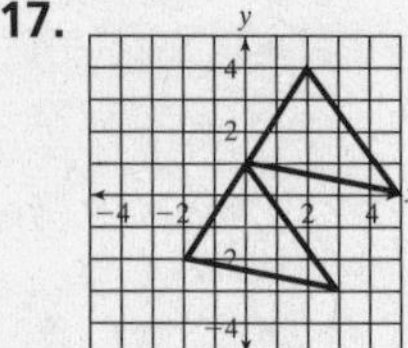

18.

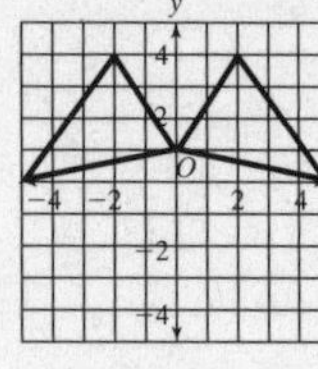

19.

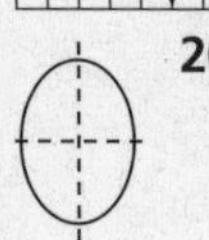

20. none **21.**

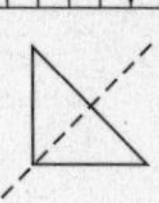

Chapter 10: Alternative Assessment

Exercise	Points	Explanation
1.	1	Mountain B looks steeper and therefore looks harder to climb.
	0	No response OR incorrect response
2.	1	One circle, one square, and one diamond trail circled; each appropriately named
	0	No response OR incorrect response
3.	1	Each slope is accurately profiled.
	0	No response OR incorrect response
4. a.	2	Any part of the Marlboro Trail from 1,900 to 2, 200; any part of the Dublin Trail from 2,000 to 2,400
	1	Steepest part of 1 trail correctly marked
	0	No response OR both trails incorrectly marked
b.	2	Any part of the Marlboro Trail from the road to 1,800; any part of the Dublin Trail from the road to 1,900
	1	Least steep part of 1 trail correctly marked
	0	No response OR both trails incorrectly marked
c.	2	Marlboro Trail a little steeper or trails about equal; good explanation
	1	Marlboro Trail a little steeper or trails about equal with no explanation OR Dublin Trail steeper with justification
	0	No response OR wrong response with no explanation
d.	1	Any justified answer
	0	No response OR choice given without justification
Excursion	5	At least 4 examples given, with ratings. Possibilities include mountains, roads, playground equipment, amusement parks, handicapped access ramps, stairs, roofs, hay elevators, and so on; justifed choice for the steepest slope
	4	4 examples given, but ratings, choice, or justification lacking
	3	At least 3 examples are given; some other elements missing
	2	At least 2 examples are given; some other elements missing
	1	One example given OR several examples but other elements missing
	0	No response

Chapter 10 Cumulative Review

1. C **2.** G **3.** D **4.** G **5.** A **6.** G **7.** D **8.** H **9.** B **10.** H **11.** D **12.** G **13.** A **14.** H **15.** B **16.** F **17.** 16 ft **18.** Sample answer: A negative times a negative equals a positive. Check students' sketches. **19.** Both scores are the same, since 32 out of 40 is $\frac{4}{5}$ and 24 out of 30 is also $\frac{4}{5}$.

Chapter 11

Practice (regular) 11-1

1.

Boxes Sold	Frequency
21	2
22	1
23	3
24	3
25	0
26	5
27	1

Boxes of Juice Sold

21	22	23	24	25	26	27
					✗	
					✗	
		✗	✗		✗	
✗		✗	✗		✗	
✗	✗	✗	✗		✗	✗

2. a student **3.** 3 students **4.** 13 students **5.** 80 and 85, 75 and 90 **6.** No; the interval includes 2–2.75 h. **7.** 10 students

Name ______________________ Class ______________ Date ______________

Chapters 9–12 Answers (continued)

8.

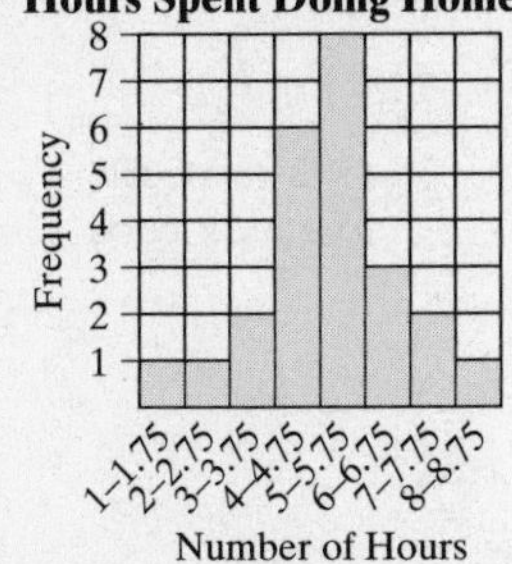

Guided Problem Solving 11-1

1. the number of books purchased **2.** the number of customers who bought a certain number of books **3.** columns 4, 5, and 6 **4.** 1 customer **5.** 1 customer **6.** 2 customers **7.** 4 customers **8.** The expression *more than* 3 does not include 3. **9.** 8 customers

Practice (adapted) 11-1

1.

Boxes Sold	Frequency
21	2
22	1
23	3
24	3
25	0
26	5
27	1

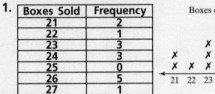

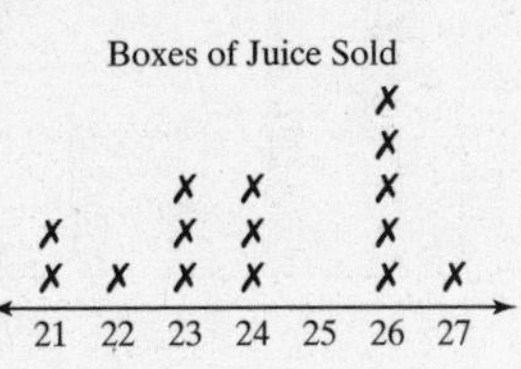

2. a student **3.** 3 students **4.** 13 students

5.

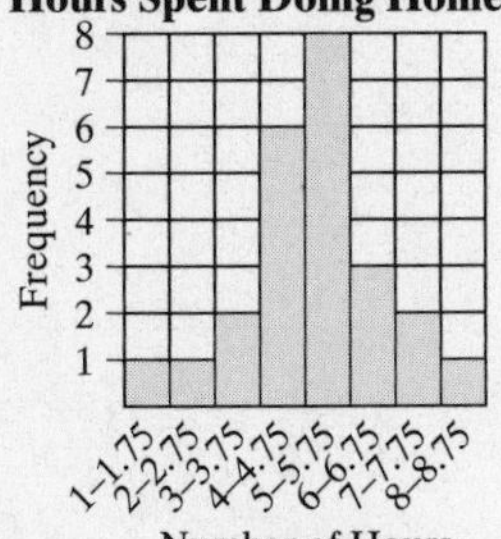

Activity Lab 11-1

Check students' work.

Reteaching 11-1

1.

Number of Rosebushes	1	2	3	4	5	6
Tally	|	||||	|||	~~||||~~ |	|	|
Frequency	1	4	3	6	1	1

2.

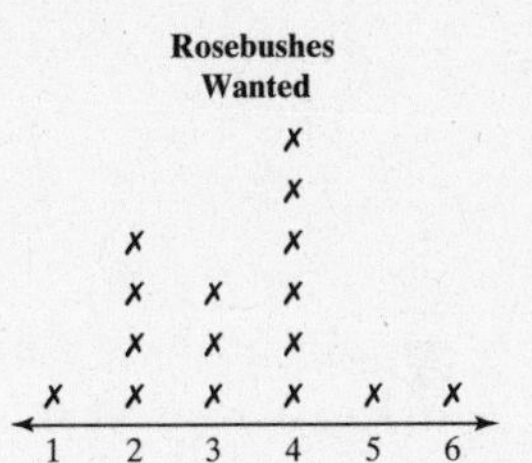

3.

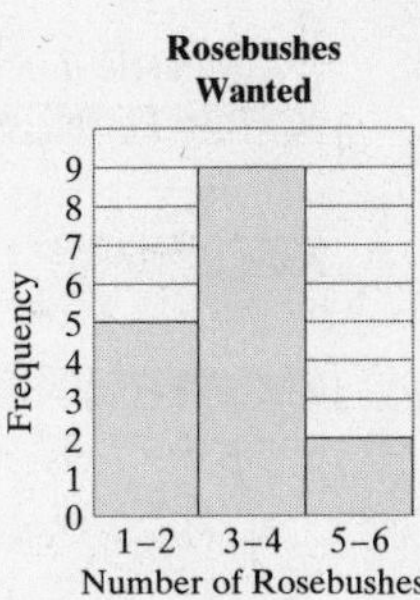

Enrichment 11-1

1. 10 **2.** 4

3.

Score	50–59	60–69	70–79	80–89	90–99
Students	1	5	11	4	7

4. No; it could be any number from 0 to 11. **5.** 28 **6.** Add new columns for the intervals 40 to 49 and 100 to 109.

7.

Score	40–49	50–59	60–69	70–79	80–89	90–99	100–109
Students	1	2	5	12	4	7	1

8. 7 **9.**

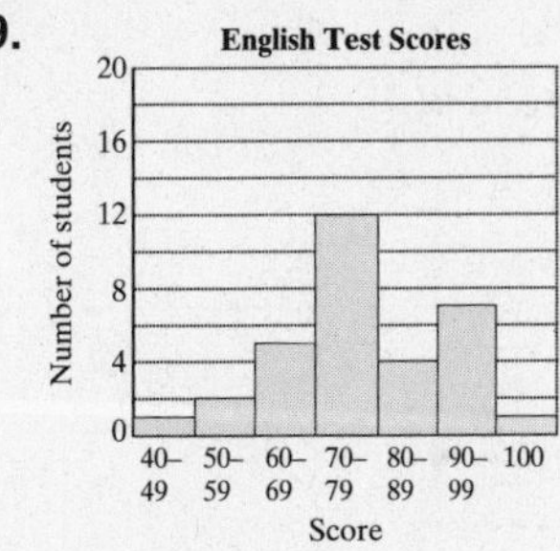

10. 25%

Puzzle 11-1

1. 1 **2.** 7 **3.** 18 **4.** 5 **5.** 1 **6.** 20 **7.** 22 **8.** 9 **9.** 5 **10.** 23
A GREAT VIEW

Practice (regular) 11-2

1. 125 **2.** C2 **3.** 51 tickets **4.** Friday had the greatest overall attendance, but Saturday had the greatest number of adults in attendance.

5. Students Taking a Foreign Language

Number of Students; Year ('03, '04, '05, '06); — girls; - - - boys

Name ______________ Class ______________ Date ______________

Chapters 9–12 Answers (continued)

6.

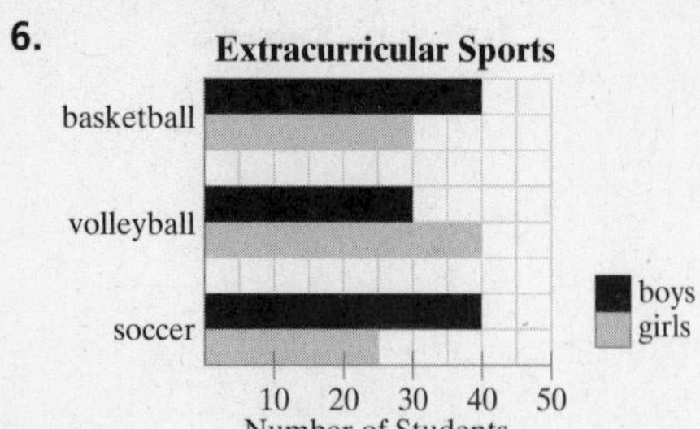

Guided Problem Solving 11-2

1. frequency tables, line plots, histograms, Venn diagrams, spreadsheets, bar graphs, double bar graphs, line graphs, and double line graphs **2.** spreadsheet, bar graph, line graph, double bar graph, and double line graph **3.** line graph **4.** Sample answer: increase of weight over time, increase of height over time **5.** Sample answer: weight in pounds, height in inches; days, weeks, months, years **6.** Check students' answers. **7.** Check students' answers. **8.** Check students' answers; A double bar graph would allow Olivia to compare preferences for each grade.

Practice (adapted) 11-2

1. 125 **2.** C2 **3.** 51 tickets

4.

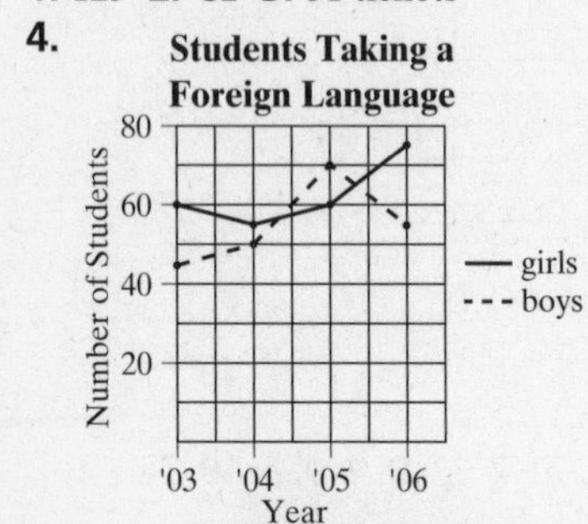

5.

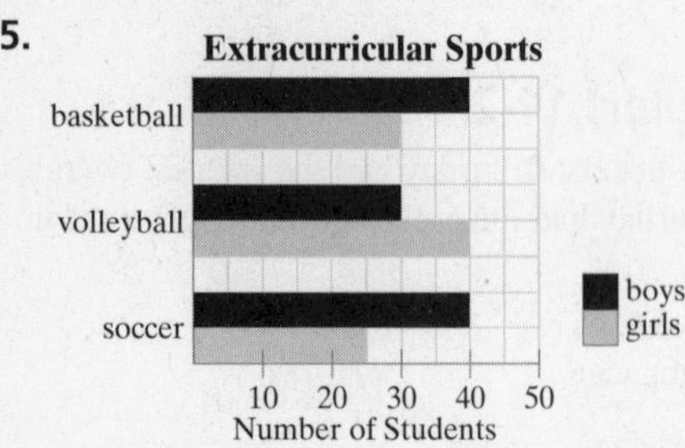

Activity Lab 11-2

1. 9 gold medals won by the U.S. **2.** 22 total medals won by Russia.

3.

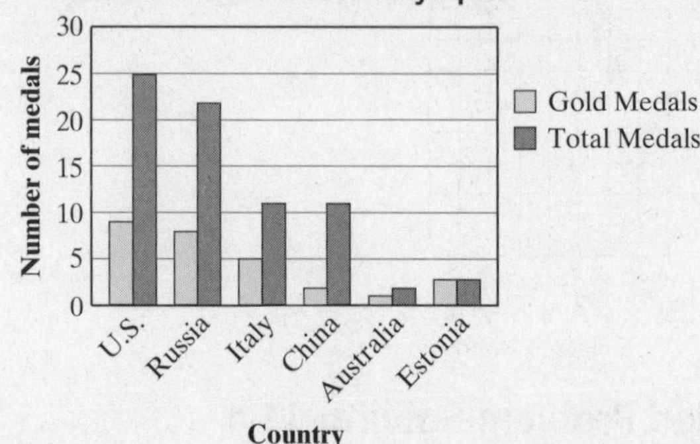

4. Sample answer: It shows both sets of data on one graph. **5.** The graph shows the number of medals for both countries. **6.** Add another row and enter data: cell A8: France; B8: 3; C8: 9

Medals in 2006 Winter Olympics

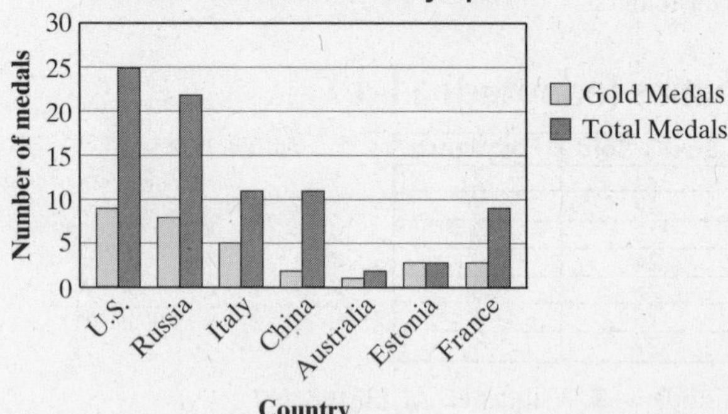

Reteaching 11-2

1. 78; 39 **2.** A5; A2

3.

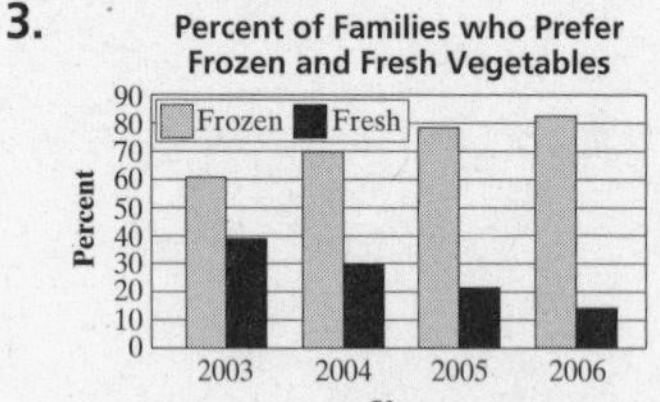

4.

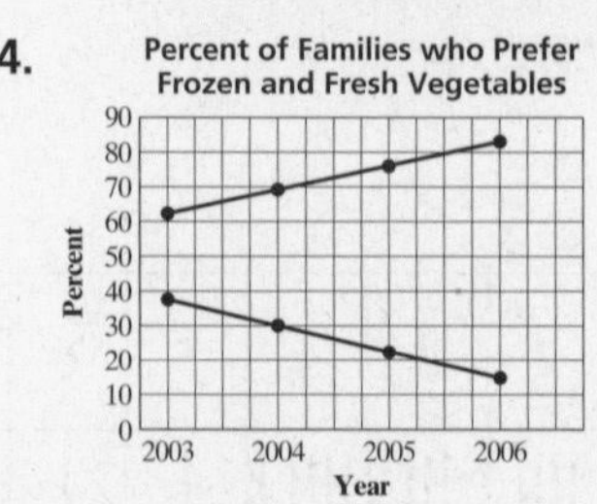

Enrichment 11-2

1. 36 points **2.** 41 points **3.** lose **4.** 11 times **5.** 11 games, because the line for points scored is above the line for points allowed for only 11 games. **6.** Since the lines meet at the same point, the game is a tie. **7.** Sample answer: 11 + 6 = 17 **8.** 3 games; 10/22, 12/31

Chapters 9–12 Answers (continued)

Puzzle 11-2

1. A **2.** C **3.** E **4.** L **5.** L
A CELL

Practice (regular) 11-3

1. 10 **2.** 52 **3.** 88 **4.** 6 games

5.

Stem	Leaves
6	0 8
7	3 8
8	3 5 5
9	2 5 9

6 | 0 means 60.

6. 85 **7.** 10 **8.** 81.8 **9.** The most effective data display choice is the double line graph because it shows that the number of DVDs bought is consistently greater than the number of video cassettes bought.

Guided Problem Solving 11-3

1. The heights of the female and male students. **2.** Determine how many males are 65 in. tall.

3., 6., 7.

Student Height (in.)

Female		Male
7 4 3 1 0 0	5	6 7
8 5 4 1 0	6	2 3 5 5 6 7 9
0	7	1 2 3 4 6

Key: 61 ← 1 | 6 | 3 → 63

4. ones place **5.** tens place **8.** 2 **9.** 56 in., 57 in., 62 in., 63 in., 65 in., 65 in., 66 in., 67 in., 69 in., 71 in., 72 in., 73 in., 74 in., 76 in.; two **10.** 4

Practice (adapted) 11-3

1. 10 **2.** 52 **3.** 6 games

4.

Stem	Leaves
6	0 8
7	3 8
8	3 5 5
9	2 5 9

6 | 0 means 60.

5. 85 **6** 81.8 **7.** The most effective data display choice is the double line graph because it shows that the number of DVDs bought is consistently greater than the number of video cassettes bought.

Activity Lab 11-3

1. whole miles; tenths of miles **2.** 4.2 miles **3.** 1.0 miles **4.** 2.3 miles **5.** 2.025 miles **6.** 3.2 miles **7.** Sample answer: Since the values are in order from least to greatest, it is easy to find the mode and range of the data set. **8.** Sample answer: She could create a double-bar graph with one bar representing running distance and one bar representing cycling distance for each day. This would allow her to compare distances for each day, and for each type of workout.

Reteaching 11-3

1.

Stem	Leaves
1	5 6
2	4 7
3	6 6 9
4	2 5
5	1 4 9
6	1 3 4

1 | 5 means **15.**

2. tens **3.** ones **4.** 64 **5.** 15

6.

Stem	Leaves
7	8 9
8	2 3 4 4 5 6 6 7 9
9	0 1 2

7 | 8 means 78.

Enrichment 11-3

1. 7, 6, 5, 4, and 3 tens **2a.** right **2b.** left **3a.** 42° **3b.** 71° **4.** 11 **5.** Sample answer: Portland's temperatures are higher in April than Boston's. **6.** Sample answer: There are more entries for the larger stems for Portland and more entries for the smaller stems for Boston, indicating higher temperatures for Portland in April.

Puzzle 11-3

Stem	Leaves
1	5 5 6
2	3 6 8
3	2 2 3 7
4	0 7
5	1 3 5 6

56,276 mi^2

Practice (regular) 11-4

1. random sample; The selected students represent the population. **2.** not a random sample; Students that use the vending machine may not represent all types of students. **3.** fair **4.** biased; Do you prefer hardwood floors in your home? **5.** fair **6.** biased; How many servings of fruits and vegetables do you eat? **7.** biased; Do you prefer thick carpeting? **8.** fair **9.** biased; Do you read the newspaper? **10.** biased; Does TV news portray life accurately?

Guided Problem Solving 11-4

1. In a random sample, each member of a population has an equal chance of being selected. **2.** Determine whether this sampling method is random. **3.** people who visit Yosemite National Park **4.** yes **5.** Yes; each person has an equal chance of being surveyed. **6.** Sample answer: Survey visitors as they leave the park. **7.** No, this is not a random sample. People who are not parents might also eat at the snack shack.

Practice (adapted) 11-4

1. random sample; The selected students represent the population. **2.** not a random sample; Students that use the vending machine may not represent all types of students. **3.** fair **4.** biased; Do you prefer hardwood floors in your home? **5.** fair **6.** biased; How many servings of fruits and vegetables do you eat? **7.** biased; Do you prefer thick carpeting?

Activity Lab 11-4

1. Carla's survey; because the sample size is larger, it is more likely to be an accurate representation of the whole population. **2.** Sample answers: Survey more students; make sure survey includes students from different grades, classes, and groups within the school. **3.** Sample answer: A combination of rock, country, and rhythm and blues since Carla's survey indicates a strong preference for each of these musical categories. **4.** Sample answer: about 29 country, 37 rock, 26 rhythm and blues, and 8 jazz.

Chapters 9–12 Answers (continued)

Reteaching 11-4

1. Answers will vary. Sample answer: a shopping mall **2.** biased **3.** fair **4.** No; you are more likely to interview homeowners. **5.** No; you are more likely to interview renters. **6.** Yes; you can't tell if people own or rent.

Enrichment 11-4

1. young people in Dallas, Texas **2.** The brochure will be more successful if the target population finds it interesting. **3.** No; the young people may have interests that differ from those of the target population. **4.** Sample answers: Most kids in the area love to attend the theatre. Do you? Which image motivates you more? A picture of the town's losing football team or a picture of the town's undefeated baseball team? **5.** Sample answers: Survey every fifth student entering a local downtown middle school; survey every other young person entering a downtown shopping mall. **6.** Sample answer: Estimate; exact data cannot be concluded from a survey because not every person in the population is questioned.

Puzzle 11-4

1787; 1836; 1959

Practice (regular) 11-5

1. 40 **2.** 1,968 **3.** 948 **4.** 4,410 **5.** 585 **6.** 158 **7.** 435 animals **8.** 625 animals **9.** 1,450 animals **10.** 1,260 animals **11.** 2,075 animals **12.** 4,033 animals **13.** 151 animals **14.** 2,357 animals **15.** 4,109 ducks **16.** 1,744 alligators

Guided Problem Solving 11-5

1. Find the error and make a correct estimate. **2.** $\frac{38}{x}$ **3.** 25 sharks; 8 sharks **4.** $\frac{8}{25}$ **5.** $\frac{8}{25} = \frac{38}{x}$ **6.** The 8 and 25 are reversed. **7.** about 119 sharks **8.** He captured 38 to begin with, so he knew there had to be more than 12 in the population. **9.** $\frac{32}{x} = \frac{4}{12}$; 96 jackrabbits; yes

Practice (adapted) 11-5

1. 40 **2.** 1,968 **3.** 948 **4.** 4,410 **5.** 585 **6.** 435 animals **7.** 625 animals **8.** 1,450 animals **9.** 1,260 animals **10.** 2,075 animals **11.** 4,033 animals **12.** 4,109 ducks **13.** 1,744 alligators

Activity Lab 11-5

1–4. Check students' work. **5.** Sample answer: the third prediction, because the sample is larger **6a–b.** Check students' work. **6c.** Sample answer: A larger sample is closer to the actual value, but it takes longer to count the beads.

Reteaching 11-5

1. 5; 15; 80; 240; 240 **2.** 45; 3; 20 · 45; 300; 300 **3.** about 472 sea lions **4.** about 9 owls **5.** about 54 rabbits

Enrichment 11-5

1. 30,000 16-year-old students **2.** about 4,732,646 people **3.** about 4,376,761 people **4.** about 248,709,873 people; about 318,569,598 people

Puzzle 11-5

1. 16 **2.** 20 **3.** 12 **4.** 18 **5.** 21 **6.** 15 **7.** 22 **8.** 24 **9.** 14 ECHOLOCATION

Practice (regular) 11-6

1.

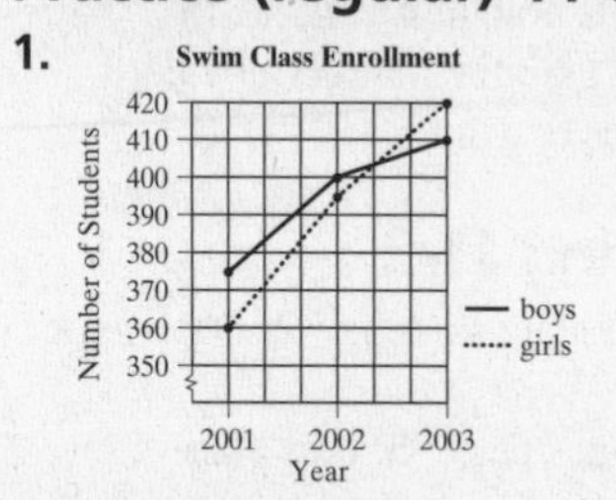

2.

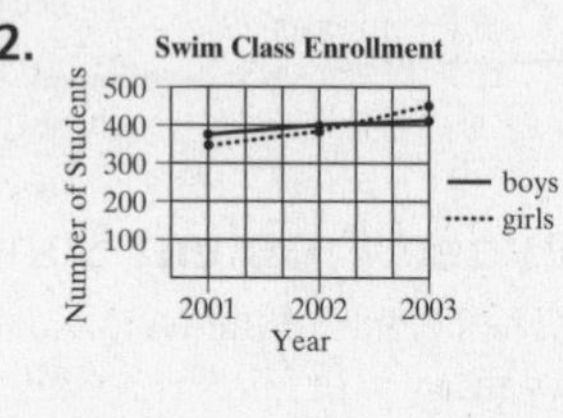

3. The first graph because it reinforces the need for additional time for swim class. **4.** mean: 88; median: 89, mode: 83 **5.** The median is the highest measure of his scores. **6.** The mode is the lowest measure of his scores.

Guided Problem Solving 11-6

1. 97% of its customers are satisfied. **2.** Determine whether this statement is misleading and then explain. **3.** 200 **4.** 100 **5.** no **6.** 100 **7.** Yes, because the statement implies that it represents *all* of the data. **8.** 48.5% **9.** The statement does not include those students who scored at the advanced level. It implies that only 30% of the students passed the test.

Practice (adapted) 11-6

1.

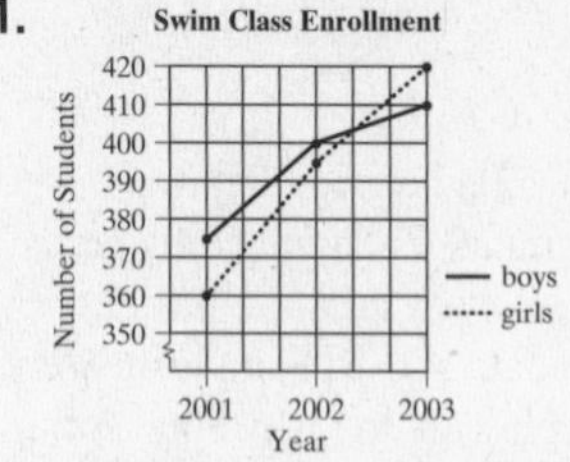

2.

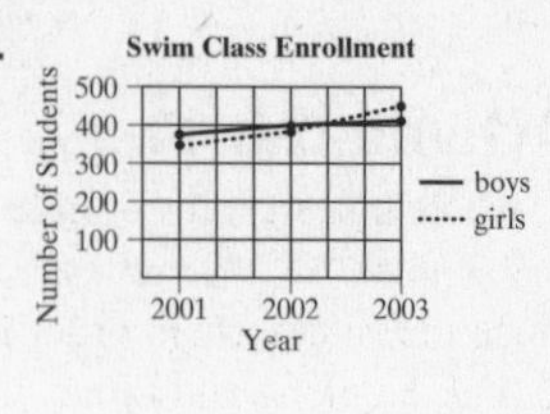

3. mean: 88; median: 89, mode: 83 **4.** The median is the highest measure of his scores.

Activity Lab 11-6

1–2. Check students' work. **3.** Sample answer: The second graph seems to show a more rapid increase in population because the vertical scale does not start at zero. This makes it look as though the population in 2000 was many times greater than the population in 1950, when, in fact, it was only about twice as great.

Name ____________________ Class ____________ Date ____________

Chapters 9–12 Answers (continued)

Reteaching 11-6

1a. It appears that Aretha Franklin had many more #1 singles than anyone else. **1b.** The vertical axis does not start at zero. **2a.** It appears that there has been a great amount of change in the civilian staff. **2b.** There is a break in the vertical axis.

Enrichment 11-6

1. She wants to encourage people to get flu shots. **2.** a slow gradual increase in the number of flu cases **3.** a sharp rise in the number of flu cases **4.** the second graph, because of the steepness of the line on the graph **5.** the second graph, because it appears that flu cases are dramatically increasing **6.** 40 **7.** Sample answer: Although both graphs use a break in the *y*-axis, the *y*-axis of the second graph has larger intervals than the *y*-intervals of the first graph. So when you plot the same set of data on the second graph, the points are spread farther apart vertically, causing a more dramatic effect.

Puzzle 11-6

1. C **2.** A **3.** D **4.** B

Practice (regular) 11-7

1. Positive trend; as a person grows taller, his or her foot gets larger. **2.** Positive trend; generally as a child gets older, his or her allowance increases. **3.** No trend; the distance one lives from school is not related to the length of the day. **4.** Negative trend; as a child grows older, he or she needs less sleep.
5. yes; positive trend

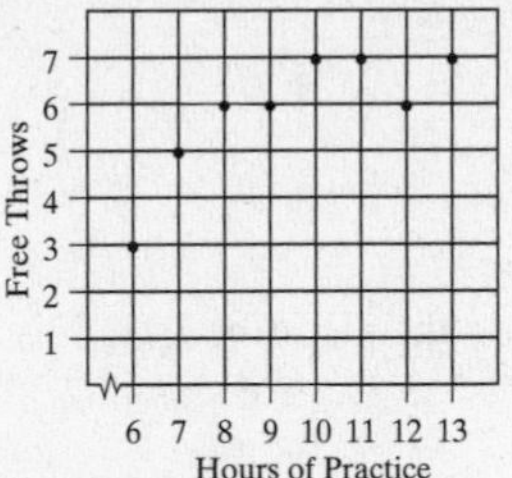

6. no trend **7.** negative **8.** positive

Guided Problem Solving 11-7

1. the number of people on the beach and the temperature **2.** Determine which scatter plot most likely represents Carmella's data. **3.** The hotter it gets, the fewer people go to the beach. **4.** It does not matter how hot it is. People go to the beach for various reasons. **5.** The hotter it gets, the more people go to the beach. **6.** choice C **7.** Sample answer: The most likely choice is C, because people like to go to the beach when its hot. **8.** Choice B, because whatever the temperature, people always go to the mall.

Practice (adapted) 11-7

1. Positive trend; as a person grows taller, his or her foot gets larger. **2.** Positive trend; generally as a child gets older, his or her allowance increases. **3.** Negative trend; as a child grows older, he or she needs less sleep.

4. yes; positive trend
5. no trend
6. positive

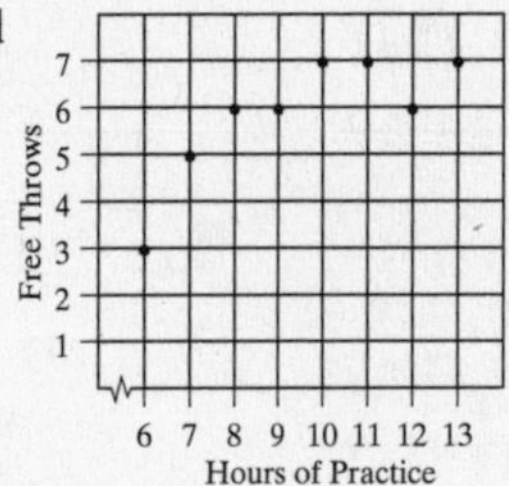

Activity Lab 11-7

1.

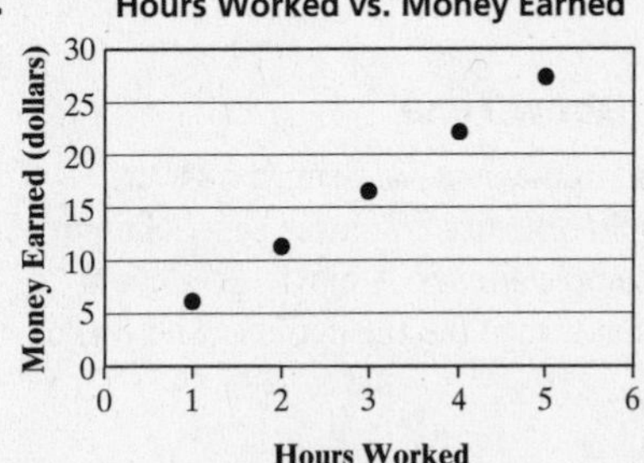

2. There is a positive trend.
3.

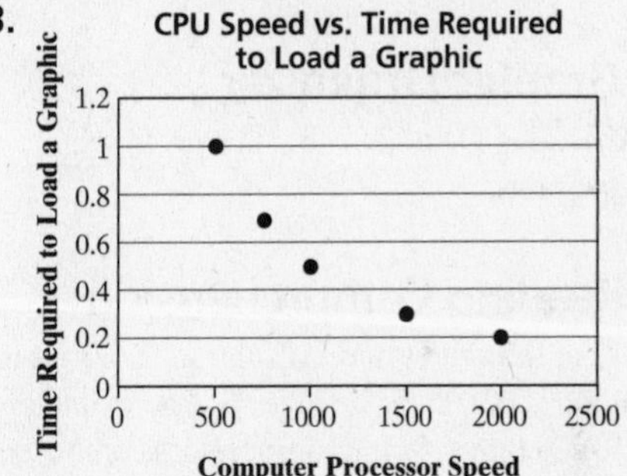

4. Sample answer: Yes; there is a negative trend; you would expect the time required to load a graphic to decrease as the speed of the computer processor increases. **5.** Sample answer: One would expect a heavier vehicle to have a lower fuel efficiency that a lighter vehicle. Scatter plot; A scatter plot will show if there is a trend between vehicle weight and fuel efficiency.

Reteaching 11-7

1.

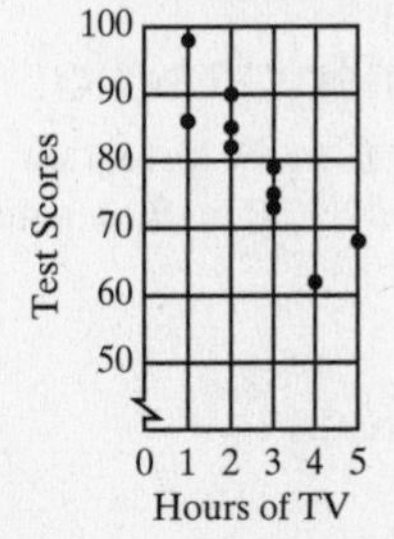

2. Negative; as one value goes up, the other goes down. **3.** The more TV students watch, the lower their test scores are.

Name ______________________ Class ______________ Date ______________

Chapters 9–12 Answers (continued)

Enrichment 11-7

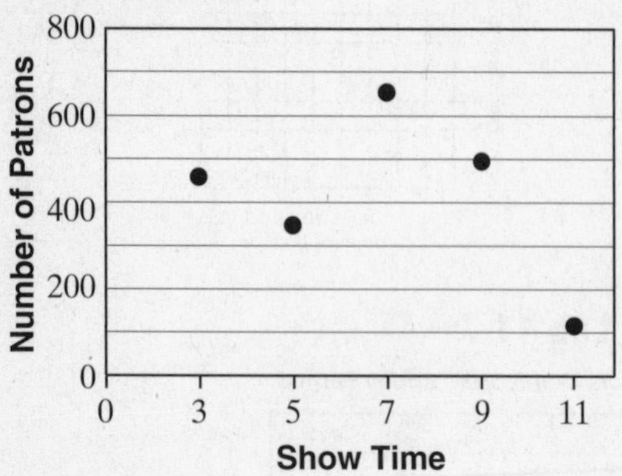

1. No; there is no trend in the data. **2.** Sample answer: A theater manager could optimize employee scheduling by observing trends. **3.** Sample answer: A movie-goer could observe trends and attend when the theater is least crowded.

Puzzle 11-7

1. no trend **2.** negative **3.** positive **4.** no trend

Chapter 11A Graphic Organizer

1. Displaying and Analyzing Data **2.** 7 **3.** Interpreting Data **4.** Check students' diagrams.

Chapter 11B Reading Comprehension

1. Electronic Numerical Integrator and Calculator **2.** about 62 years ago **3.** 5,000 **4.** 500,000,000 **5.** 1,800 ft^2 **6.** approximately 60,000 lb **7.** about 20,000 times **8.** microprocessors composed of transistors **9.** b

Chapter 11C Reading/Writing Math Symbols

1. The bar means the 3 repeats indefinitely. **2.** The bar means subtraction. **3.** The bar indicates a line segment. **4.** The bar means the 7 is negative. **5.** The bar is a fraction bar separating the numerator from the denominator; it means "divided by." **6.** equals **7.** is less than or equal to **8.** is congruent to **9.** are the two quantities equal? **10.** is not equal to **11.** absolute value **12.** parallel

Chapter 11D Visual Vocabulary Practice

1. no trend **2.** frequency table **3.** population **4.** histogram **5.** line plot **6.** double bar graph **7.** biased question **8.** negative trend **9.** sample

Chapter 11E Vocabulary Check

Check students' answers.

Chapter 11F Vocabulary Review

1. reflection **2.** x **3.** vertical **4.** line plot **5.** bar **6.** median **7.** range **8.** scatter plot **9.** arithmetic **10.** principal **11.** surface area **12.** circumference **13.** square root **14.** bisector

Chapter 11 Checkpoint Quiz 1

1. 55 **2.** 30 **3.** NY **4.** rows 2 and 5 (Colorado and New York)

5.

Number	Tally	Frequency
7	II	2
8	II	2
9	I	1
10	IIII	4
11	I	1
12	I	1

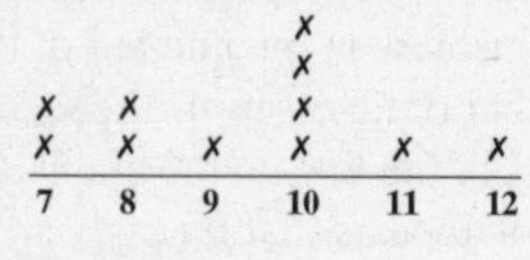

6.

1	6 7 8 8
2	1 2 3 3 5 6
3	1 2 5

1 | 6 means 16.

Chapter 11 Checkpoint Quiz 2

1. The graph is misleading because the intervals on the x-axis are irregular, which makes it seem like the book store's annual profit has steadily increased since it opened, which is not true.

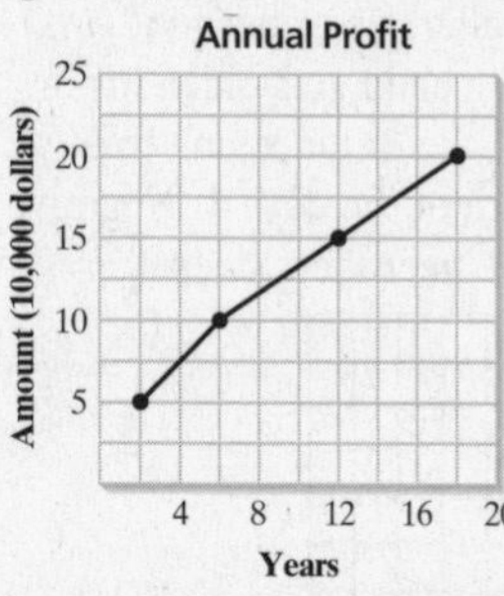

2. Sample answer: the mode, because it is the lowest. **3.** Check students' answers. **4.** about 2,300 whales

Chapter 11 Test (regular)

1. frequency table

Number of Hours	Tally	Frequency
0	I	1
1	III	3
1.5	I	1
2	I	1
2.5	II	2
3.5	III	3
4	II	2
5.5	I	1
6	I	1

2. line plot

	X				X			
	X			X	X	X		
X	X	X	X	X	X	X	X	X
0	1	1.5	2	2.5	3.5	4	5.5	6

3. histogram

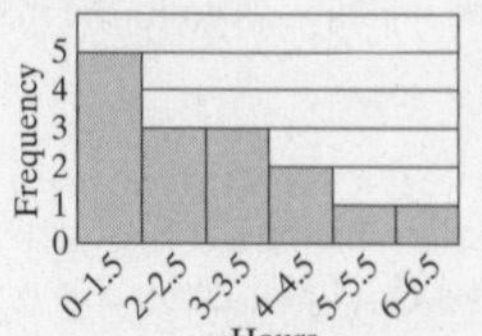

4. stem-and-leaf plot

Stem	Leaves
0	0
1	0 0 0 5
2	0 5 5
3	5 5 5
4	0 0
5	5
6	0

Key: 6 | 0 means 6.0

Name ______________________ Class ______________ Date ______________

Chapters 9–12 Answers (continued)

5a. Sample answer: the mean; the mean, 89.66, is higher than the median, 88.5, or the mode, 86. **5b.** Sample answer: the mean of 89.66 averages the actual scores. **6.** 27 **7.** D2 **8.** 11 **9.** B2 **10.** Biased, because the opinion is that Florida is nice and the Arctic is not. **11.** Fair, because there is no opinion given. **12.** week 1 **13.** week 4 **14.** 123 deer **15.** 760 birds

Chapter 11 Test (below level)

1. frequency table

Number of Hours	Tally	Frequency
0	I	1
1	III	3
1.5	I	1
2	I	1
2.5	II	2
3.5	III	3
4	II	2
5.5	I	1
6	I	1

2. line plot

	x				x			
	x			x	x	x		
x	x	x	x	x	x	x	x	x
0	1	1.5	2	2.5	3.5	4	5.5	6

3. histogram

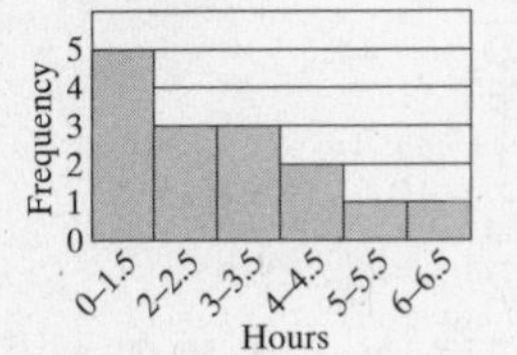

4. stem-and-leaf plot

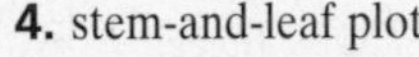

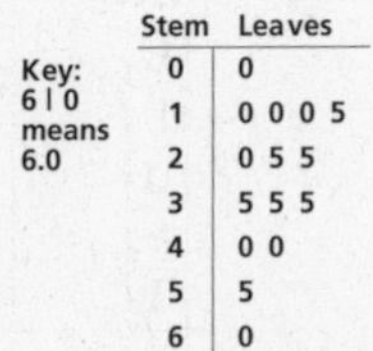

Stem	Leaves
0	0
1	0 0 0 5
2	0 5 5
3	5 5 5
4	0 0
5	5
6	0

Key: 6 | 0 means 6.0

5. Sample answer: the mean; the mean, 89.66, is higher than the median, 88.5, or the mode, 86. **6.** 27 **7.** D2 **8.** Biased, because the opinion is that Florida is nice and the Arctic is not. **9.** week 1 **10.** week 4 **11.** 123 deer

Chapter 11: Alternative Assessment

Exercise	Points	Explanation
1.	2	Accurate and labeled graph
	1	Graph partially correct
	0	No response
2.	4	Time schedule with one person identified as the cashier and the correct number of servers for each hour. (No person may work fewer than two or more than four hours.)
	3	One or two errors
	2	Three or four errors
	1	Five or six errors
	0	Seven or more errors
3.	1	Yes or no with good explanation
	0	No justified response
4.	2	Shows the total sales for different numbers of customers; about $2; the points would all be in a straight line
	1	Shows the total sales for different numbers of customers; incorrect amount per customer due to computational error(s); no valid conclusion
	0	Incorrect response OR no response
Excursion	5	Complete description of realistic job, job duties, schedule, and amount earned in an hour, a week, and a month
	4	Complete description of above; incorrect weekly or monthly salary due to computational error(s)
	3	Complete description of above; unrealistic hourly wage for the job; correct process for weekly and monthly wage
	2	Partial description of above; unrealistic or no wages or incorrect process
	1	Partial description of the job
	0	No response

Chapter 11 Cumulative Review

1. B **2.** G **3.** B **4.** J **5.** A **6.** G **7.** B **8.** J **9.** C **10.** F **11.** C **12.** H **13.** A **14.** J **15.** C **16.** G **17.** A **18.** J **19.** 58,500 rock CDs. $\frac{5}{3} = \frac{x}{35,100}$; $x = 58,500$ **20.** 15 ft

Chapter 12

Practice (regular) 12-1

1. $\frac{1}{10}$; 0.1; 10% **2.** $\frac{1}{2}$; 0.5; 50% **3.** 1; 1.0; 100% **4.** $\frac{1}{5}$; 0.2; 20% **5.** $\frac{8}{23}$ or 34.8% **6.** $\frac{6}{23}$ or 26.1% **7.** Add a marble that is not blue. **8.** $\frac{1}{2}$ **9.** $\frac{1}{4}$ **10.** $\frac{1}{4}$ **11.** $\frac{3}{4}$ **12.** $\frac{3}{4}$ **13.** $\frac{1}{2}$ **14.** $\frac{1}{2}$ **15.** $\frac{3}{4}$ **16.** $\frac{3}{4}$ **17.** $\frac{2}{7}$ **18.** $\frac{1}{7}$

Guided Problem Solving 12-1

1. E is the complement of not E. **2.** 1 **3.** Part a gives the probability of E as a decimal. Part b gives the probability of not E as a percent. **4.** $0.3 + P(\text{not } E) = 1$ **5.** $P(\text{not } E) = 0.7$ **6.** 0.65 **7.** $P(E) + 0.65 = 1$ **8.** $P(E) = 0.35$ **9.** For Part a, add 0.3 and 0.7 to make sure the answer is 1. For Part b, add 0.35 and 0.65 to make sure the answer is 1. **10.** $\frac{1}{5}$

Practice (adapted) 12-1

1. $\frac{1}{10}$; 0.1; 10% **2.** $\frac{1}{2}$; 0.5; 50% **3.** 1; 1.0; 100% **4.** $\frac{8}{23}$ or 34.8% **5.** $\frac{6}{23}$ or 26.1% **6.** $\frac{1}{2}$ **7.** $\frac{1}{4}$ **8.** $\frac{1}{4}$ **9.** $\frac{3}{4}$ **10.** $\frac{3}{4}$ **11.** $\frac{1}{2}$ **12.** $\frac{2}{7}$ **13.** $\frac{1}{7}$

Activity Lab 12-1

1. 2 probability puzzles, 7 geometry puzzles, 1 algebra puzzle **2.** 4 probability puzzles, 4 geometry puzzles, 2 algebra puzzles **3.** 6 probability puzzles, 1 geometry puzzle, 3 algebra puzzles **4a.** basketball: 3 : 2; baseball: 1 : 4; football: 2 : 13; volleyball: 1 : 14 **4b.** basketball, because the odds are highest **5.** Check students' work.

Name ______________________ Class ______________ Date ______________

Chapters 9–12 Answers (continued)

Reteaching 12-1

1. 1; 0.2; 20% **2.** 5; 0.4; 40% **3.** $\frac{1}{2}$; 0.5; 50% **4.** $\frac{3}{10}$; 0.3; 30% **5.** $\frac{9}{10}$; 0.9; 90% **6.** $\frac{2}{3}$ **7.** $\frac{8}{9}$ **8.** $\frac{1}{5}$ **9.** $\frac{3}{25}$

Enrichment 12-1

1. 2 probability tasks, 1 algebra task, 7 geometry tasks
2. 4 probability tasks, 2 algebra tasks, 4 geometry tasks
3. 6 probability tasks, 3 algebra tasks, 1 geometry task
4. 9 : 6 or 3 : 2; 3 : 12 or 1 : 4; 2 : 13; 1 : 14 **5.** Basketball, since 9 chances out of 15 is more likely to happen than 3 out of 15, 2 out of 15, or 1 out of 15.

Puzzle 12-1

I. $\frac{1}{2}$ **T.** $\frac{3}{5}$ **A.** $\frac{3}{10}$ **C.** $\frac{7}{10}$ **E.** $\frac{2}{5}$ **N.** $\frac{1}{10}$ **R.** $\frac{1}{5}$
CERTAIN

Practice (regular) 12-2

1. $\frac{3}{5}$ **2.** $\frac{1}{20}$ **3.** $\frac{3}{20}$ **4.** $\frac{1}{5}$ **5.** 0 **6.** $\frac{1}{4}$ **7.** 32% **8.** 8% **9.** 12% **10.** 20% **11.** 68% **12.** 36% **13.** Check students' answers. **14.** 60% **15.** about 75 boys **16a.** 8.7% **16b.** 457 answers **16c.** 52 sweaters

Guided Problem Solving 12-2

1. It means a person cannot see certain colors. **2.** Find how many males out of 1,000 will be colorblind. **3.** 80 **4.** 80 males **5.** Sample answer: Not necessarily; the 8% colorblind is based on experimental results. The results of other experiments may differ. **6.** Sample answer: Use a proportion; $\frac{x}{1{,}000} = \frac{8}{100}$ **7.** 55 people

Practice (adapted) 12-2

1. $\frac{3}{5}$ **2.** $\frac{1}{20}$ **3.** $\frac{3}{20}$ **4.** $\frac{1}{5}$ **5.** 0 **6.** $\frac{1}{4}$ **7.** 32% **8.** 8% **9.** 12% **10.** 68% **11.** Check students' answers. **12.** 60% **13.** about 75 **14a.** 8.7% **14b.** 457 sweaters

Activity Lab 12-2

1–5. Check students' work.

6.

Outcome	1	2	3	4	5	6
Tally	20	20	20	20	20	20
Percent	$16\frac{2}{3}$%	$16\frac{2}{3}$%	$16\frac{2}{3}$%	$16\frac{2}{3}$%	$16\frac{2}{3}$%	$16\frac{2}{3}$%

7–8. Check students' work.

Reteaching 12-2

1. 5; $\frac{1}{4}$ **2.** $\frac{7}{20}$; 35% **3.** $\frac{2}{5}$ **4.** $\frac{4}{15}$ **5.** $\frac{1}{3}$ **6.** Sample answer: Flip a coin 20 times. **7.** Sample answer: Spin a spinner divided into six equal sections.

Enrichment 12-2

1. $\frac{12}{25}$ = 48% = 0.48 **2.** $\frac{8}{25}$ = 32% = 0.32 **3.** $\frac{1}{5}$ = 20% = 0.2 **4.** $\frac{1}{25}$ = 4% = 0.04 **5.** $\frac{4}{5}$ = 80% = 0.80 **6.** $\frac{13}{25}$ = 52% = 0.52 **7.** $\frac{9}{125}$ = 7.2% = 0.072 **8.** ≈ 6.75% = 0.0675 **9.** $\frac{7}{100}$ = 7% = 0.07 **10.** 92.8% = 0.928 **11.** 86.25% = 0.8625 **12.** 79.05% = 0.7905

13. 100%

Puzzle 12-2

0.030; 0.025; 0.020; 0.035

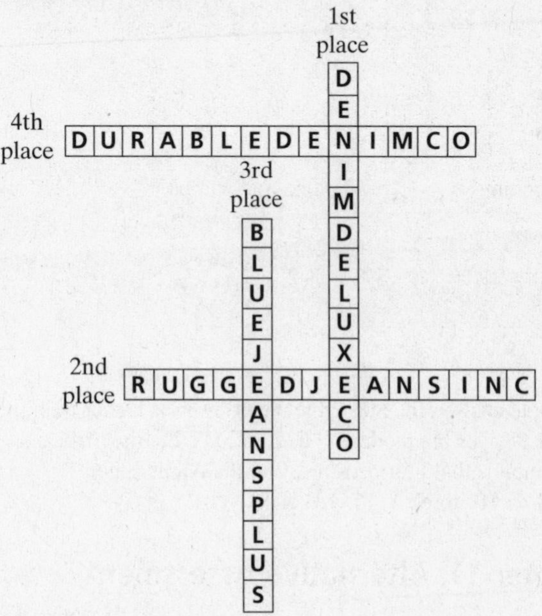

Practice (regular) 12-3

1. $\frac{1}{10}$ or 10%

	1	2	3	4	5	6	7	8	9	10
A	A1	A2	A3	A4	A5	A6	A7	A8	A9	A10
B	B1	B2	B3	B4	B5	B6	B7	B8	B9	B10
C	C1	C2	C3	C4	C5	C6	C7	C8	C9	C10
D	D1	D2	D3	D4	D5	D6	D7	D8	D9	D10
E	E1	E2	E3	E4	E5	E6	E7	E8	E9	E10
F	F1	F2	F3	F4	F5	F6	F7	F8	F9	F10
G	G1	G2	G3	G4	G5	G6	G7	G8	G9	G10
H	H1	H2	H3	H4	H5	H6	H7	H8	H9	H10

2a.

H < H < H, T ; T < H, T
T < H < H, T ; T < H, T

2b. $\frac{1}{8}$ **3.** 12 kinds **4.** 9 **5.** $\frac{17}{27}$ **6.** $\frac{1}{27}$ **7.** $\frac{1}{3}$ **8.** $\frac{1}{27}$

Guided Problem Solving 12-3

1. Four suit jackets; four dress shirts **2.** Divide the number of outcomes wanted by the total number of possible outcomes. **3.** 4 **4.** 4 **5.** 16 **6.** 4 **7.** 12 **8.** $\frac{12}{16}$ or $\frac{3}{4}$ **9.** Use a tree diagram. **10a.** 12 **10b.** $\frac{3}{12}$ or $\frac{1}{4}$

Name ______________________ Class ______________ Date ______________

Chapters 9–12 Answers (continued)

Practice (adapted) 12-3

1. $\frac{1}{10}$

	1	2	3	4	5	6	7	8	9	10
A	A1	A2	A3	A4	A5	A6	A7	A8	A9	A10
B	B1	B2	B3	B4	B5	B6	B7	B8	B9	B10
C	C1	C2	C3	C4	C5	C6	C7	C8	C9	C10
D	D1	D2	D3	D4	D5	D6	D7	D8	D9	D10
E	E1	E2	E3	E4	E5	E6	E7	E8	E9	E10
F	F1	F2	F3	F4	F5	F6	F7	F8	F9	F10
G	G1	G2	G3	G4	G5	G6	G7	G8	G9	G10
H	H1	H2	H3	H4	H5	H6	H7	H8	H9	H10

2a.
H — H — H, T
H — T — H, T
T — H — H, T
T — T — H, T

3. 15 kinds **4.** 9 **5.** $\frac{17}{27}$ **6.** $\frac{1}{27}$

Activity Lab 12-3

1. 24 **2.** Black ink on a black shirt is not a practical choice because you will not be able to see the design. **3.** 20 **4.** 120 shirts **5.** 6 **6.** 48 **7.** 12

Reteaching 12-3

1. 12; $\frac{1}{12}$

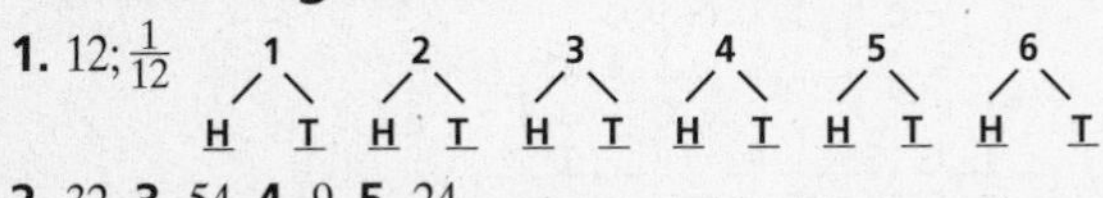

2. 32 **3.** 54 **4.** 9 **5.** 24

Enrichment 12-3

1.

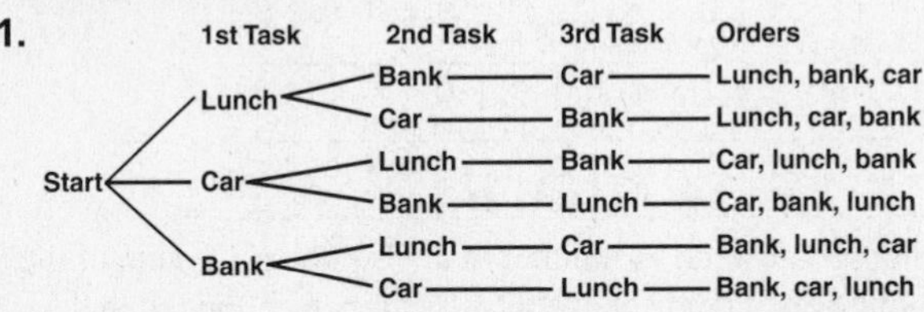

2. 6 orders **3.** Lunch, since it is 10:00 A.M. **4.** Bank, since it closes at 11:30 A.M. **5.** Sample answer: Go to bank, meet friend for lunch, and wash car. **6a.** 24 orders **6b.** Sample answers: Go to bank first, then to the library either before or after lunch to get the errands done before washing the car.

Puzzle 12-3

$g = 11; a = 9; c = 1; y = 5; d = 12; x = 4; f = 10; b = 8$

Practice (regular) 12-4

1. $\frac{16}{169}$ **2.** $\frac{12}{156} = \frac{1}{13}$ **3.** $\frac{1}{36}$ **4.** $\frac{1}{36}$ **5.** $\frac{1}{216}$ **6.** 0 **7.** $\frac{14}{33}$ **8.** $\frac{1}{11}$ **9.** $\frac{8}{33}$ **10.** $\frac{8}{33}$ **11.** $\frac{1}{100}$ **12.** $\frac{1}{4}$ **13.** $\frac{1}{20}$ **14.** 0 **15.** $\frac{1}{5}$ **16.** $\frac{1}{5}$

Guided Problem Solving 12-4

1. Disjoint events have no outcomes in common. **2.** Find the probability of selecting an even *or* prime number between 21 and 30. **3.** because there are no even prime numbers besides 2 **4.** 10 **5.** 22, 24, 26, 28, 30; 5 **6.** $\frac{5}{10} = \frac{1}{2}$ **7.** 23, 29; 2 **8.** $\frac{2}{10} = \frac{1}{5}$ **9.** $\frac{7}{10}$ **10.** $\frac{7}{10}$; 0.7; 70% **11.** $\frac{2}{3}$

Practice (adapted) 12-4

1. $\frac{16}{169}$ **2.** $\frac{12}{156} = \frac{1}{13}$ **3.** $\frac{1}{36}$ **4.** $\frac{1}{36}$ **5.** $\frac{1}{216}$ **6.** 0 **7.** $\frac{14}{33}$ **8.** $\frac{1}{11}$ **9.** $\frac{1}{100}$ **10.** $\frac{1}{4}$ **11.** $\frac{1}{20}$ **12.** 0

Activity Lab 12-4

1. $P(\text{red}) = \frac{3}{5}$; $P(\text{blue}) = \frac{2}{5}$ **2.** independent; $\frac{9}{25}$ **3.** dependent; $\frac{1}{3}$ **4–7.** Check students' work.

Reteaching 12-4

1. $\frac{6}{25}$ **2.** $\frac{9}{25}$ **3.** $\frac{4}{25}$ **4.** $\frac{4}{15}$ **5.** $\frac{1}{3}$ **6.** $\frac{2}{15}$ **7.** $\frac{1}{28}$ **8.** $\frac{1}{32}$

Enrichment 12-4

1. 4 sides **2.** no **3.** 4 outcomes **4.** 1 way **5a.** $\frac{1}{4}$ **5b.** $\frac{1}{4}$ **6.** Multiply the probabilities. **7.** independent **8.** $\frac{1}{4} \times \frac{1}{4} = \frac{1}{16}$ **9.** The probability of the second outcome does not depend on the result of the first outcome. **10.** $\frac{1}{16}$

Puzzle 12-4

I. $\frac{1}{12}$ **D.** $\frac{7}{20}$ **T.** 0 **E.** $\frac{1}{16}$ **N.** $\frac{4}{9}$ **S.** $\frac{1}{21}$ **I.** $\frac{48}{95}$ **W.** $\frac{18}{25}$
WINDIEST

Practice (regular) 12-5

1. 120 **2.** 720 **3.** 40,320 **4.** 5!; 120 **5.** 4!; 24 **6.** 6!; 720 **7.** 24 **8.** 60 **9.** 120 **10.** 362,880 **11.** 5,040 **12.** 720 **13.** 336 ways **14.** 45 outfits **15.** 6 arrangements **16.** 12 ways

Guided Problem Solving 12-5

1. 15 employees; three different jobs **2.** Find the number of ways that the jobs can be assigned. **3.** A permutation is an arrangement of objects in a particular order. **4.** 15 people **5.** 14 people **6.** 13 people **7.** 2,730 **8.** There are not 15 jobs for 15 people; there are only 3 jobs for 15 people. **9.** 73,440 ways

Practice (adapted) 12-5

1. 120 **2.** 720 **3.** 40,320 **4.** 5!; 120 **5.** 4!; 24 **6.** 24 **7.** 60 **8.** 5,040 **9.** 720 **10.** 336 ways **11.** 45 outfits **12.** 6 arrangements

Activity Lab 12-5

1. Check students' work.

Name ______________________ Class ______________ Date ______________

Chapters 9–12 Answers (continued)

2–6.

Number of Letters	Number of Ways to Arrange the Letters
1	1
2	**2**
3	**6**
4	**24**
5	**120**
6	**720**

5b. $n(n-1)(n-2) \times \ldots \times 2 \times 1 = n!$

Reteaching 12-5

1. 3; 2; 24 **2.** 10; 9; 8; 720 **3.** 24 **4.** 20 **5.** 720 **6.** 60 **7** 6 **8.** 12 **9.** 30 **10.** 42 **11.** 6 **12.** 60 **13.** 24 **14.** 120

Enrichment 12-5

1. 3 **2.** tape-deck, CD player, laser disk, equalizer, and surround-sound stereo **3.** number of ways **4a.** 5! **4b.** 3! **4c.** 2! **5.** $5 \cdot 4 \cdot 3 = 60$ ways **6.** $\frac{5 \cdot 4 \cdot 3}{3 \cdot 2 \cdot 1} = 10$ ways **7.** TCL;TCE; TCS; TLE; TLS; TES; CLE; CLS; CES; LES **8.** 5 ways **9.** 10 ways

Puzzle 12-5

Letters	Number permutations of all letters	Number of two-letter permutations	Number of three-letter permutations
F, O, X	6	6	6
B, E, A, R	24	12	24
S, N, A, K, E	120	20	60
M, O, N, K, E, Y	720	30	120
L, E, O, P, A, R, D	5,040	42	210
W, I, L, D, B, O, A, R	40,320	56	336

TIGER

Practice (regular) 12-6

1. 4 **2.** 15 **3.** 8,10; 8,12; 8,20; 10,12; 10,20; 12,20 **4.** 3, 5, 15 **5.** 8, 3; 8, 5; 8, 15; 10, 3; 10, 5; 10, 15; 12, 3; 12, 5; 12, 15; 20, 3; 20, 5; 20, 15 **6.** 3, 5; 3, 8; 3, 10; 3, 12; 3, 15; 3, 20; 5, 8; 5, 10; 5, 12; 5, 15; 5, 20; 8, 10; 8, 12; 8, 15; 8, 20; 10, 12; 10, 15; 10, 20; 12, 15; 12, 20; 15, 20 **7.** 10 ways **8.** 6 races **9.** combinations **10.** 4 combinations of eight graders **11.** 1 combination of seventh graders

Guided Problem Solving 12-6

1. 5 different CDs; 3 CDs **2.** Find the number of different CD combinations for your CD player. **3.** A combination is a grouping of objects in which the order of the objects does not matter. **4.** combinations = total number of permutations ÷ number of permutations of selected group **5.** 60 permutations **6.** 6 permutations **7.** 10 combinations **8.** 10 combinations **9.** 50 **10.** 28 combinations

Practice (adapted) 12-6

1. 6 **2.** 15 **3.** 8,10; 8,12; 8,20; 10,12; 10,20; 12,20 **4.** 3, 5, 15 **5.** 8, 3; 8, 5; 8, 15; 10, 3; 10, 5; 10, 15; 12, 3; 12, 5; 12, 15; 20, 3; 20, 5; 20, 15 **6.** 10 ways **7.** 6 races **8.** combinations **9.** 4 combinations of eight graders

Activity Lab 12-6

1. ${}_5C_2 = 10$ **2.** ${}_7P_4 = 840$ **3.** ${}_6P_3 = 120$

Reteaching 12-6

1. 3 combinations; EO, EU, OU **2.** 10 combinations; CMP, CMT, CMR, MPT, MPR, PTR, PTC, TRC, TRM, CRP **3.** 20 combinations **4.** 276 ways **5.** 10 ways **6.** 120 sets

Enrichment 12-6

1 and 3.

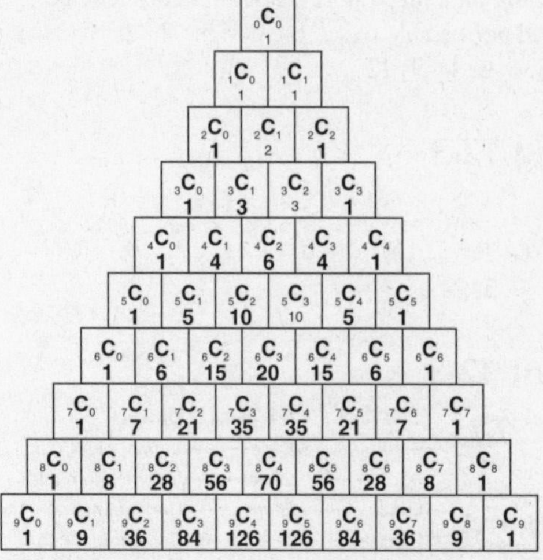

2. Sample answers: A number in any square is the sum of the two numbers directly above it. All numbers in the left and right squares on the drawing are 1s.

Puzzle 12-6

Jamal won a free pizza. ${}_{15}C_3 = 455$

Chapter 12A Graphic Organizer

1. Using Probability **2.** 6 **3.** Eliminating Answers **4.** Check students' diagrams

Chapter 12B Reading Comprehension

1. July 26 (evening)–August 2 **2.** July 26 **3.** 24°F **4.** 20%, or $\frac{1}{5}$ **5.** July 27 and July 29 **6.** 1 to 4 **7.** 3 to 2 **8.** a

Chapter 12C Reading/Writing Math Symbols

1. the probability of event *A* occurring **2.** the probability of event *A* not occurring **3.** the probability of event *A* occurring and then event *B* occurring **4.** 5 factorial, or $5 \times 4 \times 3 \times 2 \times 1$

Name ______________________ Class ______________ Date ______________

Chapters 9–12 Answers (continued)

5. n factorial, or $n \times (n-1) \times (n-2) \times \ldots \times 1$ **6.** the number of ways n items can be selected r at a time, where order matters **7.** the number of ways n items can be selected r at a time, where order does not matter **8.** the number of ways 9 items can be selected 4 at a time, where order does not matter **9.** $P(C)$ **10.** $P(\text{odd})$ **11.** $P(D, \text{ then } E)$ **12.** 7! **13.** ${}_{10}C_5$ **14.** ${}_6P_3$

Chapter 12D Visual Vocabulary Practice

1. factorial **2.** combinations **3.** sample space **4.** independent events **5.** outcome **6.** counting principle **7.** permutations **8.** dependent events **9.** complement

Chapter 12E Vocabulary Check

Check students' answers.

Chapter 12F Vocabulary Review Puzzle

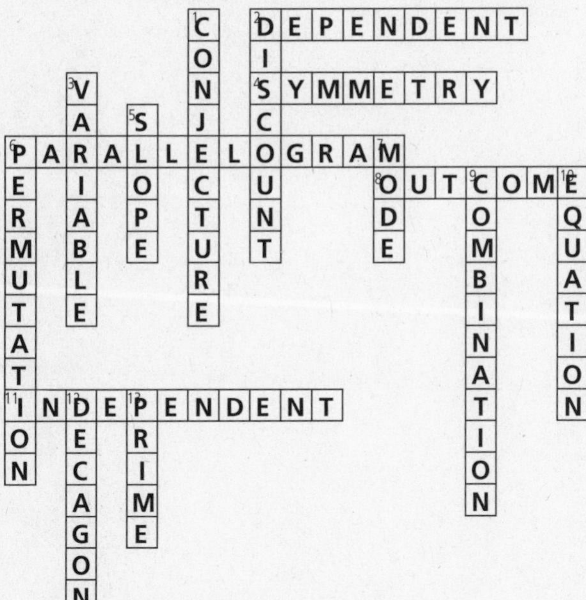

Chapter 12 Checkpoint Quiz 1

1. $\frac{2}{5}$; 0.40; 40% **2.** $\frac{4}{5}$; 0.80; 80% **3.** $\frac{3}{5}$; 0.60; 60% **4.** 8 choices **5.** (H, H) (H, T) (T, H) (T, T) **6.** $\frac{1}{4}$ **7.** $\frac{1}{4}$ **8.** $\frac{1}{2}$

Chapter 12 Checkpoint Quiz 2

1. $\frac{1}{22}$ **2.** $\frac{5}{44}$ **3.** $\frac{5}{33}$ **4.** 20; 10 **5.** 60; 10 **6.** 12; 6 **7.** 120 arrangements **8.** permutation; 2,184 **9.** combination; 120

Chapter 12 Test (regular)

1. $\frac{2}{3}$; $0.\overline{6}$; $66\frac{2}{3}$% **2.** $\frac{1}{3}$; $0.\overline{3}$; $33\frac{1}{3}$% **3.** 12% **4.** 240 T-shirts **5.** $\frac{3}{8}$ **6.** $\frac{3}{8}$ **7.** $\frac{1}{4}$ **8.** $\frac{3}{4}$ **9.** $\frac{5}{8}$ **10.** $\frac{1}{4}$ **11.** $\frac{3}{10}$ **12.** $\frac{2}{5}$ **13.** $\frac{4}{5}$ **14.** $\frac{7}{10}$ **15.** $\frac{1}{45}$ **16.** $\frac{2}{5}$ **17.** $\frac{1}{32}$ **18.** $\frac{1}{64}$ **19.** HHH, HTH, HTT, THH, TTH, THT, TTT, HHT **20.** $\frac{3}{8}$ **21.** $\frac{1}{2}$ **22.** 20 permutations **23.** 60 permutations **24.** 36 **25.** 36

Chapter 12 Test (below level)

1. $\frac{2}{3}$; $0.\overline{6}$; $66\frac{2}{3}$% **2.** $\frac{1}{3}$; $0.\overline{3}$; $33\frac{1}{3}$% **3.** 12% **4.** 240 T-shirts **5.** $\frac{3}{8}$ **6.** $\frac{3}{8}$ **7.** $\frac{1}{4}$ **8.** $\frac{3}{4}$ **9.** $\frac{3}{10}$ **10.** $\frac{2}{5}$ **11.** $\frac{4}{5}$ **12.** $\frac{7}{10}$ **13.** $\frac{1}{32}$ **14.** $\frac{1}{64}$ **15.** HHH, HTH, HTT, THH, TTH, THT, TTT, HHT **16.** $\frac{3}{8}$ **17.** $\frac{1}{2}$ **18.** 20 permutations **19.** 36 **20.** 36

Chapter 12: Alternative Assessment

Exercise	Points	Explanation
1.	1	Correct observation that the popular boys' names change less OR that the order of the boys' names changes but most of the names remain on the list OR that girls' names change more permanently, etc.
	0	No response OR incorrect observation
2.	1	Boy's name chosen as easier to predict; explanation given
	0	No response OR response that lacks explanation
3. a–b.	1	26 because there are 26 letters in the English alphabet
	0	No response OR incorrect response OR no justification
4.	1	Correct partial diagram with some branching indicating a first initial can be paired with 26 possible last initials
	0	No response OR incorrect diagram
5.	2	676 possibilities; method and explanation given
	1	Correct method and explanation but computational error
	0	No response OR incorrect method
6.	1	Reasonable choice of initials with explanation
	0	No response OR response without explanation
Excursion	5	Clear rules; correct calculation based on given rules; reasonable assessment of future needs
	4	Clear rules; minor calculation error OR weak assessment
	3	Rules given; weak calculation no assessment
	2	Rules unclear OR calculation and assessment missing
	1	Rules unclear; no calculation and assessment OR no rules
	0	No response

Chapter 12 Cumulative Review

1. B **2.** G **3.** C **4.** H **5.** B **6.** J **7.** A **8.** J **9.** D **10.** H **11.** B **12.** G **13.** C **14.** H **15.** C **16.** J **17.** D **18.** F **19.** D **20.** Slope = 2; the slope is the same as the rate of savings.